THE
AIR FORCE

THE AIR FORCE

General James P. McCarthy, USAF (Ret)
Editor-in-Chief

Colonel Drue L. DeBerry, USAF (Ret)
Managing Editor

BARNES & NOBLE BOOKS
NEW YORK

AIR FORCE HISTORICAL FOUNDATION

Air Force Historical Foundation

The Air Force Historical Foundation, established in 1953, is an independent, 501 (c)(3) non-profit organization dedicated to the preservation, perpetuation and publication of the history and traditions of American military aviation. The Foundation emphasizes the history and traditions of the United States Air Force, its predecessor organizations dating to the Aeronautical Division of the United States Army Signal Corps in 1907, and the men and women whose lives and dreams were devoted to flight.

Past Presidents of the Foundation read like a Who's Who of air power pioneers and leaders and include General Carl A. Spaatz, General Hoyt S. Vandenberg, Major General Benjamin D. Foulois, General Curtis E. LeMay, and General Bernard A. Schriever. The logo of the Foundation, a Wright aircraft designated Signal Corps No. 1, was the first aircraft accepted by the United States Army in 1909.

A McGuire Air Force Base, New Jersey, KC-10A Extender taxis down the flightline to an anxiously waiting crowd of family members and reservists. About fifty Air Force reservists returned to McGuire on 19 October 2001 after spending a month overseas in support of Operation Enduring Freedom. (USAF)

The Foundation's activities include the quarterly air power journal *Air Power History*; a series of biographies of aviation greats; an annual awards program to recognize outstanding United States Air Force Academy and Air Force Reserve Officers Training Corps cadets, active duty USAF and Royal Air Force officers; and biennial symposia on diverse aspects of aerospace power of special historical interest and significance.

Individuals may learn more about the Air Force Historical Foundation and become a Foundation member at www.afhistoricalfoundation.com.

The Air Force Historical Foundation
1535 Command Drive, Suite A-122
Andrews AFB, Maryland 20762
www.afhistoricalfoundation.com
e-mail: afhf@earthlink.net

This edition published by Barnes & Noble, Inc., by arrangement with Hugh Lauter Levin Associates, Inc. 2005 Barnes & Noble Books

M 10 9 8 7 6 5 4 3 2 1
ISBN 0-7607-7115-4
Printed in China

Design: Lori S. Malkin
Project Editor: James O. Muschett
Illustration Editor: Guy Aceto

All photography and illustrations courtesy U.S. Air Force unless otherwise credited.

The opinions expressed in this book do not represent an official opinion of the Federal Government or the U.S. Air Force.

Contents

Foreword

The Air Force Historical Foundation is proud to present this book to commemorate the fifty-fifth birthday of the United States Air Force in 2002 and, in 2003, the one-hundredth anniversary of man's first powered flight. In *The Air Force*, we not only highlight the contributions of the Air Force and its predecessor organizations to the defense of the nation, we also describe the accomplishments of its people, the systems capabilities and the operations concepts of today, and we offer a glimpse at the Air Force of the future.

As you explore this book, notice the emphasis on people. While many of the images are of equipment that the Air Force operates, people build it, fly it or launch it, maintain it, and support it. Air Force men and women assume their most visible roles in times of war. Their commitment, dedication, and sacrifices at other times are less well known. A major purpose of the Foundation is to highlight the human dimension of the Air Force.

People are the Air Force's most important resource and you can see that every day as individuals shoulder responsibility for their unit's success or failure. You can see it in the trust that exists between a crew chief and a pilot; the genuine smile of greeting by the security force at our installations' gates; and the count of cadence as units march on our training bases. You also see it on the faces of squadron mates when one of their own fails to return from a mission—or when their unit is recognized for outstanding performance. The demands of alert, temporary duty, combat, or support of daily operations bring Air Force people together in what can best be described as a family.

This book attempts to capture this spirit and dedication in vignettes where authors describe their own personal experiences or those of individuals who have gone before. I hope that in each of these vignettes, you will see the human qualities that make the Air Force a family and the greatest military organization in the world. The Air Force family includes members of all ranks, the civilian members of the Air Force team, the National Guard and Reserve forces that contribute so much in every national crisis or conflict; and all of the families who share the personal sacrifices that their loved ones make. Our expanded family also includes the defense contractors that provide the equipment that gives the Air Force its superior technical advantage. This book is dedicated to the people of the Air Force family.

General W. Y. Smith USAF (Ret)
President, Air Force Historical Foundation

Editor-in-Chief's Comments

The major challenge for the editorial team in planning and organizing this book was to describe the rich heritage and dynamic future of the Air Force within necessary limits of format and page count. We recognize that the size and diversity of the Air Force precludes us from including many stories that deserve to be told. I take full responsibility for those that you find missing.

The heart and soul of the Air Force is its people, their resourcefulness, and their dedication. We have attempted to capture this Air Force spirit by using representative vignettes illustrating how individual airmen made a difference. Thousands more deserve to have their story told.

The events of 11 September 2001 occurred after much of this book was written. Although several vignettes highlight Air Force contributions to the resulting War on Terrorism, the full story of that effort must await future publications.

I would like to express my appreciation to each chapter and vignette author. Their professionalism and cooperation made this book happen. The quality and accuracy of our publication is directly attributable to the Managing Editor, Colonel Drue DeBerry, USAF, Retired. His perspective, historical knowledge of the Air Force, attention to detail, and personal dedication have earned my lasting gratitude.

All of us who contributed to this book love the Air Force. I hope that we have conveyed the spirit and character of the Air Force in these pages.

General James P. McCarthy, USAF (Ret)
Editor-in-Chief

General John P. Jumper, Air Force chief of staff, visits the men and women of Whiteman Air Force Base, Missouri, on 20 September 2001. "When the nation is in crisis," Jumper said, "it turns to its people in uniform— people like you who are charged with doing the nation's business." (USAF)

The bedrock foundation of our airpower is the commitment and dedication of the men and women who serve the nation in the United States Air Force. (USAF)

"Wings Through Time," Robert E. Bell, United States Air Force Art Collection

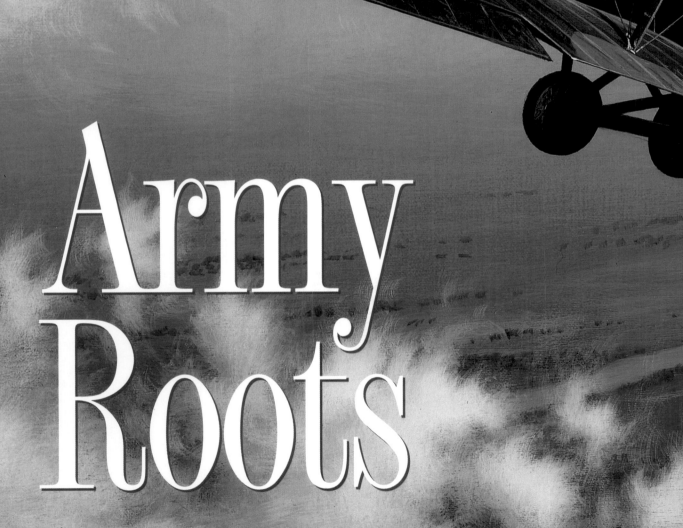

Army
Roots

Army Roots

David R. Mets, Ph.D.

From the very dawn of powered flight, the Wright brothers predicted the utility of aviation to armies and navies. However, the epic flights by Orville and Wilbur Wright over sandy North Carolina beaches on 17 December 1903 stirred little interest in the United States military. The Army had employed aerial reconnaissance well before the Wrights invented the airplane. During the American Civil War and the Spanish-American conflict, the Army used balloons to observe enemy forces and direct artillery fire. The Wright brothers encountered skepticism and delay in America, but initial sales of their aircraft to army organizations in Europe confirmed the Wrights' early expectations. Finally, in 1908, the U.S. Army bought a Wright Flyer and proceeded with a modest air effort—very modest compared to the European powers.

Above, left: Lieutenant Henry H. Arnold in flight training with the Wright brothers at Dayton, Ohio, in 1911. (USAF photo)

Above: Lieutenant Carl A. Spatz (spelled Spaatz from 1937) in flight training at North Island near San Diego, California, circa 1916. Spatz went on to serve with the 1st Aero Squadron on the initial Army air deployment into combat with the Pershing Punitive Expedition to Mexico in 1916. He ultimately became the last Commanding General of the U.S. Army Air Forces and the first Chief of Staff of the U.S. Air Force. (USAF)

Beginnings

The contract for the first Wright Flyer required that the Wrights provide flight instruction for two Army officers. Subsequently the Army established pilot training at College Park, Maryland; Augusta, Georgia; and later at North Island near San Diego, California. Army leaders expected military aviation merely to do what cavalry had always done and what observation balloons had recently accomplished—reconnaissance and artillery spotting. Aviators believed the airplane could do more. They quickly demonstrated that men could perform the liaison function better from airplanes than from horseback. Then they turned to more ambitious goals. In 1911 at College Park an Army officer fired a machine gun from a Wright Flyer, and before World War I, American pilots began experimenting with aerial bombing.

Smiles on the faces of Lieutenant Benjamin D. Foulois and Orville Wright on 30 July 1909 confirm the successful conclusion of Army acceptance tests of the Wright brothers' flying machine. Foulois accompanied Wright as navigator-observer on the final test, a five-mile cross-country flight from Fort Myer to Alexandria, Virginia, and back. (National Archives)

Air technology was then on the steep part of the development curve, especially in Europe. Both engine and aerodynamic sciences advanced rapidly. Even in America, by 1915, a closed fuselage was common and airplane builders had adopted the more efficient tractor format with the engine and propeller up front rather than the pusher configuration of the Wright Flyer. Between 1903 and 1919, engine power advanced from about twelve to four-hundred horsepower.

In the first decade of the century, the Signal Corps was among the more technologically oriented parts of the Army. The air arm therefore was organized under the Signal Corps and was a part of that organization on the eve of the World War. That was a natural scheme as long as reconnaissance, artillery spotting, and liaison constituted the main tasks of Army aviation.

In their first combat employment, Army airplanes did not perform their expected functions very well. On 9 March 1916, Mexican revolutionary Pancho Villa invaded United States territory and killed nineteen Americans at Columbus, New Mexico. By 15 March, President Woodrow Wilson ordered Brigadier General John J. Pershing to lead a punitive expedition against Villa, who had fled back across the border. The First Aero Squadron commanded by Captain Benjamin D. Foulois was ordered to join Pershing.

The deployment turned out to be a fiasco, and nothing much was achieved beyond the ferrying of Pershing's Christmas cards back to the United States for posting. Foulois's airplanes were Martin tractors—primitive compared to the French Nieuports and German Fokkers employed

over the Western Front at that very moment. Still, Foulois's effort paid off because it motivated legislators to do something about American weakness in the air. In March 1916, Congress approved an emergency appropriation of $500,000 for the Army air arm.

The Army had further to go than did the Navy. Although starting a little later than the Army, Navy aviation got into combat at Vera Cruz in 1914, and naval warfare had already been undergoing a technological revolution for some years. In contrast, the Army was hardly beyond its Indian fighting days. In August 1916 with an election approaching, Congress yielded to growing demands for preparedness and appropriated another $13 million for Army aviation.

From that point things moved quickly for the aviators of the Signal Corps. Carl Spatz graduated from West Point in 1914 and served with Foulois in Mexico. By the end of 1916, Spatz was ordered to San Antonio to take command of a newly formed squadron, one of many. By mid-1917, just three years out of the Military Academy, Major Spatz commanded a squadron en route to the battlefields of France.

World War

Major William "Billy" Mitchell was already in France. He had completed a private flying training program in the fall of 1916 and was sent to Europe as a military observer in the spring of 1917. When the United States entered the war, Mitchell was the senior American airman in Europe, though other American pilots—volunteers who flew for France and Great Britain—had been in combat more than a year.

In 1916, partly as a public relations move, France had authorized the formation of an all-American squadron, the *Lafayette Escadrille*. Under the command of a French officer, the *Lafayette Escadrille* entered combat on the Verdun front in May. In February 1918, the Army invited most of the pilots in the *Lafayette Escadrille* to join the Army Air Service, forming the 103rd Aero Squadron.

General John J. Pershing, selected to command the American Expeditionary Forces (AEF), arrived in France in June 1917. The bulk of his force was not deployed and ready for combat until the early summer of 1918. Although the American contribution to victory probably was decisive—at least in financial and moral terms—the United States Army

Top, left: *Before the United States entered the war, 180 Americans flew for France as members of the Lafayette Escadrille, the aviation division of the French Foreign Legion. This photo shows several members of the squadron and their mascots, including two lion cubs, Whiskey and Soda. Soda is the small one. (USAF)*

Top, right: *Lieutenant Eddie Rickenbacker and members of the 94th Aero Squadron stand beside a French Spad aircraft sporting the famous "Hat-in-the-Ring" emblem of the 94th. Several members of the squadron, including Major Raoul Lufbery, had previously flown with the Lafayette Escadrille. (USAF)*

Built by Glenn Curtis, the JN-4 Jenny was one of the few American World War I aircraft purchased by other nations. (USAF)

To identify their nationality, Americans serving in the Lafayette Escadrille adopted the drawing of an American Indian in feathered headdress as the emblem of their squadron. (USAF)

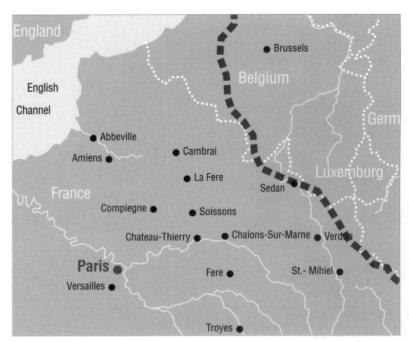

entered battle only in the last year of the war when the rest of the combatants were thoroughly weary.

The AEF did not adjust easily to the coming of aviation. Pershing chose to organize his fliers as the Air Service of the AEF, thus removing aviation from Signal Corps control. Still the word "Service" was an annoyance for the airmen. To them, it implied that they were not equal to the combat branches—infantry, artillery, and cavalry—but rather were only a service, like supply, that was auxiliary to the combatant arms.

The flying training program in the United States was not up to task at that point, and airmen arrived in Europe unready for combat. They required additional training to catch up with the fast-changing aviation technology, most of which was developed by the British and the French. Pilots completed tactical training in combat aircraft in Europe because no first-line combat aircraft were available in the United States. The AEF established several huge training centers in France and Great Britain where the Americans completed their preparation for the fighting.

No American-designed aircraft reached the front with the Army. Even the British-designed, American-built DH-4 only arrived in relatively small numbers very near the end of the conflict. The one successful part of the U.S. production program was the design and manufacture of the Liberty engine. Thousands were built, and they served well in the World War and for many years thereafter.

Practically all of the roles and missions in modern United States Air Force doctrine have precedents in World War I. The doctrinal tension that later developed to vicious levels between ground and air officers was already in its infancy in 1918. Some airmen thought of airpower as an independent or autonomous force capable of achieving decisive results on its own. Most ground officers saw aviation as a supporting force, one that could only achieve results by enhancing the power of the "Queen of Battle"—the infantry.

The rub came with talk of strategic bombing—attacks on targets not directly related to the battle on the ground. Germany made such attacks

on the British homeland, including London itself, first with airships and later with airplanes. Near the end of the war, the British organized an independent air force under General Hugh Trenchard to retaliate by bombing Germany. Pershing would have none of it, believing instead that the proper role of aviation was "to drive off hostile airplanes and procure for the infantry and artillery information concerning the enemy's movements."

Personal rivalries and the administrative incompetence of the airmen added to the tension. Mitchell, in Europe first and now a lieutenant colonel, deemed that he had squatter's rights to lead the American air war by virtue of his early arrival. Brigadier General Benjamin Foulois, senior to Mitchell in both rank and experience, arrived later with a complete staff to take command. The personal rivalry—even animosity—between these two so confused affairs that Pershing had to step in to organize things for a few good men running around in circles.

Pershing sent Mitchell to the front to lead the force in combat and kept Foulois in Paris to organize the rear areas. Pershing further recruited his West Point classmate, Major General Mason Patrick—a non-flier—to take charge of the Air Service and bring order out of chaos, which Patrick did.

By September 1918, Mitchell was at the front commanding the largest air force employed in that war—the greater part of which was French. The Americans fought the Battle of St. Mihiel that month, and Mitchell's airmen acquitted themselves well. The Meuse-Argonne battle soon followed, then the war was over. The redeployment and demobilization of the AEF was about as confused as the preparation for combat. Military leaders vowed never to repeat the experience. It was as unsatisfactory for the Air Service as for any other part of the Army.

Student pilots learn to fly the Curtiss JN-4 Jenny at Kelly AFB, Texas, one of the twenty-seven Army flying fields used for training pilots during World War I. Canada, Great Britain, and the United States ordered JN-4s for pilot training. The Canadian-built JN-4 Canuck and the American-built Jenny remained the standard trainer in these two countries through the mid-1920s. (USAF)

Brigadier General William Mitchell emerging from his Thomas Morse Scout, Selfridge Field, Michigan. At the time, Mitchell, in an Army Air Service numbering about 10,000 men, was fighting for an independent air force. (USAF)

Aerial Combat in the Great War

Major Michael R. Terry, USAF (Ret)

"Military aviation is apparently the most dangerous sport man has discovered since the contests of the gladiators." —Anonymous Pilot

The 20th Aero, a pursuit squadron flying American-built DH-4 aircraft with Liberty engines, joined the 1st Day Bombardment Group at Amanty aerodrome on 7 September 1918. One week later, the squadron mission changed from pursuit to bombardment. Overnight, squadron aircraft were transformed into bombers and ordered into combat the following day. Armorers worked through the night converting aircraft and loading bombs trucked to Amanty from another aerodrome. The 20th flew its first mission on 14 September. Most of the squadron pilots and observers had never flown across the trench lines of the Western Front—a few had never flown in DH-4 Liberty aircraft—none of them had ever dropped a bomb. On takeoff for the first mission, one pilot stalled his aircraft and died in the ensuing crash. Despite this inauspicious beginning, the squadron flew eight missions in its first three days of combat.

In the afternoon of 16 September 1918, Lieutenant A. F. Seaver ran up the 410 horsepower Liberty engine on his De Haviland DH-4. The heavily laden bi-winged aircraft labored across the sodden airdrome and lifted into the air with 185 pounds of bombs. Seaver then joined formation with other DH-4s from the 20th Aero Squadron for the squadron's eighth bombing mission, a strike against the marshalling yards at Etain. Improving weather gave the unit a clear shot at attacking this major rail junction and interdicting German lines of communication, a target the Germans defended ably with Fokker D-7s and anti-aircraft artillery.

Of six DH-4s dispatched by the 20th Aero against Etain on 16 September, only Lieutenant Seaver crossed the front lines. The other five aircraft turned back after experiencing mechanical difficulties, a persistent problem that the squadron had encountered for its first three days of combat and one that had earlier plagued Seaver. Lieutenant John Y. Stokes, observer and bombardier, accompanied Seaver on the mission. After the other aircraft of the 20th squadron turned back, Seaver joined a formation of five DH-4s from the 11th squadron, also based at Amanty. As this amalgamated formation of six DH-4s neared Etain, accurate anti-aircraft fire hit Seaver's aircraft, throwing it out of control. The engine began missing and lost power, forcing Seaver to drop out of formation. With a crippled aircraft and a sputtering engine, Seaver and Stokes nevertheless elected to bomb the target.

Approaching Etain, the DH-4 engine quit.

Seaver glided across the target while Stokes dropped the bombs, then Seaver pointed the DH-4 toward friendly territory as a German Fokker maneuvered to attack. While Seaver dove away from the enemy aircraft and frantically tried to restart the Liberty engine, Stokes maintained fierce defensive fire

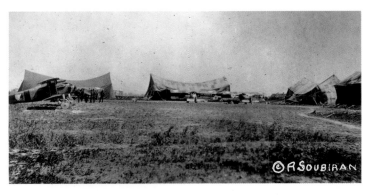

Aircraft of the 103rd Pursuit Squadron are parked beside tent hangers in Flanders. The 103rd, formed with American pilots who previously flew with the French, adopted the Indian head logo made famous by the Lafayette Escadrille. (USAF)

with his twin machine guns, preventing a successful German attack.

Seaver maneuvered his stricken aircraft in its glide across the lines. At the end of a long, powerless descent, Seaver crashed the DH-4 in the treetops of a forest. Miraculously, Seaver and Stokes survived. For gallantry under fire while accomplishing their mission, they were both recommended for the Distinguished Service Cross. A special courier returned Stokes recommendation to the 20th squadron with the suggestion that his action

probably qualified him for the Medal of Honor. Eventually, both men received the Distinguished Service Cross.

In the course of four days, 1,481 aircraft, the largest aggregation of air forces to engage in a single operation during World War I, engaged German aircraft for air superiority while observing and bombing German ground forces. The First Army Air Service, consisting of 29 squadrons, made 3,300 flights, destroying 12 enemy balloons and more than 60 enemy planes. Along with the 185 pounds of bombs courageously dropped by Seaver and Stokes, the 20th Aero Squadron dropped more than eight tons of explosives during the Battle of St. Mihiel.

Above: This photo, taken at an American bombing school, shows the rudimentary techniques employed by airmen during World War I. (Corbis-Bettmann)

Left: The De Havilland DH-4, of British design, was the only U.S.-manufactured aircraft to get into combat with the AEF Air Service before the armistice in 1918. Equipped with a U.S.-designed and built Liberty Engine, the DH-4 aircraft soldiered on in the Air Service and the Air Corps for many years after World War I. (USAF)

Brigadier General Billy Mitchell standing beside his personal aircraft. Note the one star designating his rank on the side of the plane. (USAF)

Brigadier General Billy Mitchell, aggressive advocate of centralized control of all American aviation—military, naval, and commercial— was banished from Washington, D.C., to San Antonio, Texas, in 1925. When he continued to criticize military and political leaders, President Calvin Coolidge ordered him court-martialed for conduct prejudicial to good order and military discipline. (USAF)

Brigadier General Billy Mitchell returned to the United States aboard the SS *Aquitania* fully expecting to take over the Army's air arm. He treated one of his fellow passengers, Navy Captain Jerome Hunsaker, to a full description of his vision for the future of airpower. In 1919, Mitchell was not particularly taken with the prospect of strategic bombing. Rather, then and for a long time afterward, the main plank of his platform was that America must organize all her airpower into a single, independent service. For a long time, he even wanted to include civilian aviation as a part of his scheme. Hunsaker quickly relayed the message to the General Board of the Navy where it rang the fire bells, and Mitchell soon testified to the admirals along the same line.

Mitchell and Airpower in the 1920s

Immediately after World War I, Congress introduced numerous bills proposing a separate air force—complete with its own academy. All failed. The National Defense Act of 1920 adopted the name "Air Service" and gave the air arm legal status equal to the other combat arms of the Army—though the "Service" word remained a rub for the airmen.

The draw down after the war was radical and, as usual in such circumstances, led to vicious inter-service squabbling. Mitchell tried to make his case for independence at the expense of the Navy. He argued that the surface fleet was obsolete and that airplanes could sink any battleship afloat. He demanded a battleship to serve as a target so he could prove his point. Finally, his agitation led to bombing tests in the summer of 1921. Those tests included attacks on various ships by both Navy and Army aircraft.

Each service attempted to stack the deck in its own favor. The most important target vessel was the former German battleship, *Ostfriesland*, a ship of relatively recent design acquired as part of the war settlement. Mitchell's bombers managed to sink her by concussion with 2,000-pound bombs dropped in the water alongside. Although undefended, stationary, and easy to find near the coast, these conditions did not matter much to the media for the sinking was the thing. The airmen scored a public relations coup of the first order.

Mitchell's success unintentionally strengthened the hand of aviators within the Navy and eased the way for naval arms limitations later in the

The Martin MB-2 bomber was designed for World War I, but not delivered to the Air Service in time to see combat. The aircraft in this photo were part of the First Provisional Air Brigade that sank the German battleship Ostfriesland *in 1921 bombing tests. (USAF photo)*

decade. A host of military, executive department, and congressional committees convened to ponder the future of military aviation. Through it all and without any visible benefit to the Air Service, Mitchell became ever more strident in his arguments. After his term as the Assistant Chief of the Air Service expired in the spring of 1925, he reverted to his permanent rank. Colonel Mitchell, posted to San Antonio, Texas, was banished from Washington but not from the controversy over an independent air force.

Soon after Mitchell arrived in San Antonio, the Navy airship *Shenandoah* went down with the loss of fourteen lives. That and the loss of a Navy flying boat in the first attempt to fly from the West Coast to Hawaii set off another Mitchell explosion. In a deliberate, written comment to the press, he accused the highest leadership of both services of incompetence and "almost treasonable" behavior in the development of U.S. airpower. For these comments, Mitchell faced a court-martial in late

Two airmen demonstrate the use of communication equipment in a DH-4. Intercoms were not used extensively for crew communications until the late 1920s. (USAF)

Above: *Captain Frank "Monk" Hunter at Selfridge Field Michigan in 1922. Hunter, a fighter pilot in France during World War I, rose to lead the Eighth Air Force Fighter Command during the darkest hours of the Combined Bomber Offensive in World War II. (USAF)*

Left: *In tests off Cape Hatteras, North Carolina, in September 1921, Air Service bombers sank the confiscated German battleship* Ostfriesland *in an escalating dispute with the Navy over the vulnerability of ships to attack by aircraft. (USAF)*

Douglas World Cruiser Chicago, *one of a flight of four commanded by Major Frederick L. Martin, embarked on a round-the-world flight in 1924. Martin crashed en route, but two of the Air Service aircraft completed the 175-day, 26,000-mile odyssey. (USAF)*

American entertainer Will Rogers (left) with Brigadier General William Mitchell, circa 1925. (USAF)

1925 in which he was convicted of conduct prejudicial to good order and discipline—a verdict that has never been reversed. Mitchell, scion of a wealthy railroad family, resigned from the Army rather than accept the sentence of five years suspension at half pay.

During the 1920s, Air Service Chief Major General Mason Patrick shared most of Mitchell's ideas but was not much inclined to confrontational methods. He did manage to gain General Staff approval for the division of the air arm into "air service" and "air force" units. The former would support Army units in the field and be subordinate to their ground commanders. The latter, concentrated under Patrick's General Headquarters, would conduct independent operations. Patrick, like Mitchell, wanted a separate air force, but Patrick was more willing to wait. In the interim, he advocated an Air Corps with a status in the Army similar to that of the Marine Corps within the Navy. The Air Corps Act of 1926 did not go that far, but it did give the Air Service a new name and promised more money.

The Navy was not alone in trying to gather headlines with spectacular flights like those of the *Shenandoah* and the flying boat on the Hawaii trip. In 1924, the Air Service launched the first round-the-world flight with four Douglas Cruisers under the command of Major Frederick L. Martin. The trip had its mishaps, and Martin himself crashed, but the Army fliers enjoyed wide support, even from the Navy. Two of the original

Left: Major Carl A. Spatz in front of a sporty sedan and the Fokker Tri-Motor C-3 he commanded for the endurance tests of 1929. Note the catwalks around the engines installed for in-flight maintenance—and flight engineer, Sergeant Roy Hooe, did indeed get out on them during the flight. (USAF)

four planes actually arrived back in the United States after an around-the-world odyssey of 175 days.

In 1929, the Air Corps sought another spectacular record with the *Question Mark* flight commanded by Major Carl Spatz. Spatz remained aloft for almost seven days by means of aerial refueling. The techniques were crude and dangerous, but the achievements of the Question Mark crew pointed the way to future capabilities. Three of the five crew members—Spatz, Ira Eaker, and Elwood Quesada—ultimately became general officers and commanded combat organizations during World War II.

Almost simultaneously with the Mitchell court-martial, President Calvin Coolidge convened an aviation review board led by his Amherst classmate, Dwight Morrow. The Morrow Board included a number of the most distinguished aviation and political authorities in America, and it

The Question Mark refuels over southern California in 1929. A similar air-refueling concept was used later by Strategic Air Command's B-50D bomber force. (USAF)

Above: The Curtis PW-8 was the principal pursuit model of the mid-1920s. The offspring of a successful racer, the PW-8 had a top speed of 178 miles per hour.

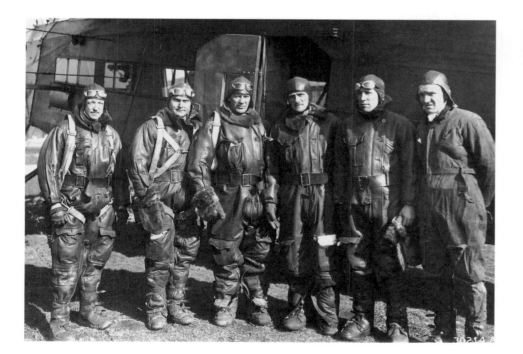

Left: In January 1929, the crew of the Question Mark set a new endurance record. From the left, Captain Ross Hoyt, pilot of the refueling plane; Captain Ira Eaker; Air Corps chief, Major General James C. Fechet; Major Carl Spatz; Lieutenant Elwood Quesada; and Master Sergeant Roy Hooe. Spatz, Eaker, Quesada, Lieutenant Harry Halverson (not shown), and Hooe remained aloft for nearly seven days. (USAF)

Above: *Captain George C. Kenney, U.S. Army Air Corps, flew combat missions in Europe during World War I. While assigned to the Air Corps Tactical School between 1926 and 1929, Kenney taught the attack course (tactical air). He later rose to command Allied Air Forces in the Southwest Pacific. (USAF)*

Claire Lee Chennault, pictured here as a lieutenant, taught the pursuit course at the Air Corps Tactical school in the 1930s. Retired from active service in 1937 due to physical disability, Chennault went to China where he taught pursuit tactics to the Chinese Air Force. He subsequently organized and led the American Volunteer Group—the Flying Tigers—in combat against the Japanese. (USAF)

The Curtiss A-12 Shrike was an early low-wing monoplane fighter that entered service with the Air Corps in the early 1930s. Although relegated to second-line units by 1939, nine A-12s remained in service in Hawaii in December 1941. (USAF)

generally decided that Mitchell's arguments were alarmist. The board concluded that for the foreseeable future America faced no serious air threat. Congress enacted the Morrow Board recommendations in 1926 and promised the air arm, renamed the Air Corps in the legislation, a substantial building program. Those promises were subsequently swept away by the Great Depression.

Immediately after World War I, the Air Service established a Field Officers Course at Langley Field, Virginia. Filled with Mitchell cronies, many destined to lead the U.S. Army Air Forces in World War II, the Field Officers Course soon evolved into the Air Corps Tactical School and relocated from Langley to Maxwell Field, Alabama. Like Mitchell, the school was not particularly focused on strategic bombing before the famous court-martial.

In the 1920s, both the Air Service and the Tactical School called for a balanced air force with emphasis on pursuit. The envisioned air force also included bombers, ground attack aircraft, and observation airplanes. This search for balance resulted in the organization of the Air Corps into three specialized groups in the United States, one for bombing, one for pursuit, and one for attack. In consequence, the Air Corps developed specialized aircraft to serve each one of these functions. Two composite groups formed overseas, one in the Panama Canal Zone and one in the Philippines.

After the court-martial, Mitchell became more dedicated to the idea of strategic bombing. The notion was not altogether new to him, for precursors to these views appeared in his lectures to the Army War College in the early 1920s. Likewise, the Air Corps Tactical School increasingly emphasized the "air force" or strategic bombing part of its curriculum. As the 1930s wore on, though, the Tactical School never dropped the courses on attack, observation, and pursuit. Although instructors at the school refined Mitchell's ideas into a rather elaborate theory before World War II, the Army General Staff was far from accepting that theory as doctrine.

While the conceptual framework emerging from the Air Corps Tactical School resembled the ideas of Giulio Douhet, the Italian air

theorist, the Tactical School approach differed in significant ways. Both the School and Douhet assumed that war was inevitable, that airpower was necessarily offensive, and that the enemy would be an advanced industrial power. Both thought aerial attack on vital targets in an enemy's homeland could drive him to his knees, avoiding bloody battles like those fought in World War I by merely flying over enemy armies and navies to bomb those vital targets. Both thought suffering from bombing would be awful, but that bombing would end the war so rapidly that the total human agony would be less.

Douhet believed that this result would be achieved best by first knocking out the enemy air force on the ground, then bombing cities to crush the morale of the civilian population, causing it to rise up and force the government to capitulate.

The Air Corps Tactical School concept argued differently, aiming to undermine enemy capability rather than will. The school likened the enemy economy to a spider web with certain nodal points. If those nodal points were destroyed, the entire web would collapse. Attacking a limited number of nodes would accomplish the task quickly without need of a huge army as required in World War I. The attack would require precision bombing, and that in turn demanded attack in daylight. This was practical because the bombers would fly at such high altitudes and speeds that enemy interceptors would never reach them in time to prevent the attack. The Norden bombsight, developed for the Navy in the 1920s and later modified for Air Corps use, would enable the needed precision even from those high altitudes.

Above: *The Boeing P-26 Peashooter, the world's first monoplane, all-metal fighter, entered service in 1932. Some P-26s actually got into combat for the Philippine air force against the Japanese in December 1941. (USAF)*

Opposite, top: *Colonel Billy Mitchell faced court-martial charges in 1925 and was convicted. He resigned from the Army rather than accept the five-year suspension imposed by the court. (AP/Wide World Photos)*

Three "old timers" meeting in 1945: (left to right) General Henry H. Arnold, Commanding General of the Army Air Forces; Captain Eddie Rickenbacker, America's highest scoring ace in World War I and later the President of Eastern Air Lines; and Major General Howard Davidson who was with Pershing in Mexico in 1916 and rose to lead the Tenth Air Force during World War II. (USAF)

Three colorful Boeing P-12s from the 43rd Pursuit Squadron fly from Kelly Field, Texas, in the early 1930s—one trailing straw from the tail skid. The artist, Keith Ferris, knew the P-12 well. His father was an instructor pilot in the 43rd. ("Boeing P-12," Keith Ferris)

The U.S. Army Air Corps in the 1930s

Theory gave way to more practical concerns in the spring of 1934 when the Roosevelt Administration canceled airmail contracts with the airlines and assigned airmail responsibility to the Air Corps. General Foulois hastily committed his organization to the task. The Air Corps was neither trained nor equipped to fly through the weather encountered on airmail routes. Between 19 February and 7 May, the Air Corps delivered nearly 800,000 pounds of mail, but experienced sixty-six crashes. Eleven officer-pilots and one enlisted man lost their lives.

The resulting public relations disaster stimulated additional boards and commissions to investigate the Air Corps. Former Secretary of War Newton Baker led one investigation and Atlanta editor Clark Howell chaired another. The collective result of the Baker Board and the Howell Committee added impetus for reform, including additional funding to improve Air Corps instrument flying capabilities and the removal of bureaucratic obstacles to reorganization that would permit more centralized control of air force assets.

In 1935, the combat power of the air arm was concentrated under the command of GHQ Air Force led by Major General Frank M. Andrews. The training and equipping part of the work remained under the direction of Air Corps Chief, Major General Oscar Westover. Some airmen thought the reorganization a mere sop thrown their way, but many felt it was an important step on the path to an autonomous air force.

Mitchell's desired independent air force remained but a distant dream. Through it all, he advocated a balanced air force that would include not only bombers, but also pursuit, ground attack aircraft, and

U.S. Army Chief of Staff, Major General Malin Craig, and Assistant Chief of the Air Corps, Brigadier General Henry H. Arnold, circa 1935. (USAF)

Army Air Corps and the Air Mail

Colonel Drue L. DeBerry, USAF (Ret)

At four a.m. on 21 February 1934, Air Corps airmail pilot Lieutenant Durward O. Lowry departed a rainy, overcast Chicago with a load of mail for Cleveland. With snow squalls forecast en route, Lowry, an experienced pilot, expected a cold, miserable flight in his Curtiss O-39 biplane. He was not disappointed. As the clouds lowered, Lowry descended, trying to follow familiar landmarks. Then he encountered dense fog that swallowed every ground reference. The fog persisted. Low on fuel, Lowry dropped his mail sacks over the side moments before his engine quit. Lowry died in the crash. The mail was recovered.

Earlier that month, charging contract improprieties, the Roosevelt Administration had cancelled airmail agreements with commercial airlines and called on the Army Air Corps to deliver the mail until new contracts were written. Major General Benjamin D. Foulois, Air Corps chief, had ten days to prepare his men and their equipment for this new responsibility. Despite requests for funding, the Air Corps lacked the flight instruments and radios of commercial aircraft, and Army pilots were untrained in instrument procedures. Depression austerity had severely restricted average Army pilot flight time to less than 100 hours a year, hardly any of that time at night or in weather. Most commercial airmail flights were scheduled at night and few were cancelled due to weather. Foulois and the Air Corps tried to maintain those schedules.

During the 11 weeks that the Air Corps flew the airmail, 12 fliers died in aircraft accidents. Banner headlines dramatized the deaths and accidents, and in so doing, drew public and congressional attention to the ill-equipped and under-trained state of the Army Air Corps. The Administration released $7.5 million for new equipment and training, and promised more for succeeding years, thus beginning the transformation of Army aviation into the modern force that would be tested in combat all too soon.

Above: Once mail sacks were loaded aboard a Douglas O-38 observation biplane, the pilot received his itinerary. The mail was carried in a plywood box built into the rear cockpit for that purpose. (USAF)

Bottom, left: Crewmen load mail sacks aboard a Keystone B-4 bomber. The normal mail load for this open-cockpit aircraft was approximately 1,100 pounds. (USAF)

Bottom, right: Armed ground crewmen at Reno, Nevada, load mail aboard a Douglas B-7. The Air Corps possessed six of these gull-wing monoplanes in 1934. Four of them crashed flying the airmail. (USAF)

The Boeing Y1B-9 first flew on 14 July 1932. This aircraft featured four open cockpits—one forward for a bomb aimer or gunner followed by a pilot's cockpit over the leading edge of the wing, a copilot's cockpit aft of the wing, and another cockpit farther back on the fuselage for another gunner. Boeing was disappointed when the Air Corps chose the Martin B-10 over the Y1B-9, but turned their attention to designing a four-engine bomber that became the B-17. (USAF)

Major General Oscar Westover, chief of the Army Air Corps in his Northrop A-17. He was killed at the controls while attempting to land in California in 1938. (USAF)

observation planes. After the court-martial and the Morrow Board, though, he became ever more committed to strategic bombing and to ideas resembling those of Douhet. But Mitchell's influence was much diminished. He died in New York City on 19 February 1936, his dream still unfulfilled, but not forgotten.

During the infancy of the GHQ Air Force in the 1930s, America was in the very depths of the Depression. Passage of the Neutrality Acts reflected congressional isolationism. But Japanese aggression in China, the Spanish Civil War, and Hitler's belligerence created tensions that demanded action. Immediately after Prime Minister Neville Chamberlain's appeasement of Hitler at Munich in 1938, President Franklin Roosevelt moved American foreign policy toward meeting these challenges. He credited much of Hitler's success in cowing all of Europe to the German air force. The President therefore emphasized the building up of U.S. airpower in preparation for a war that seemed on the horizon.

Arnold, Technology, and Preparation for War

Major General Henry Arnold succeeded Westover as Chief of the Air Corps in 1938 when Westover died in the crash of his Northrop A-17 in California. Arnold noted in his memoirs, *Global Mission*, that with the call for Air Corps expansion, problems changed overnight from a lack of money to a

lack of time. The American aircraft industry languished, decimated by the draw down of the 1920s. Rebuilding contracts promised by the Air Corps Act of 1926 had never materialized. In the 1930s, money was simply too short to maintain the aviation industry. To accommodate Air Corps expansion in anticipation of another world war, industry needed to rebuild practically from the ground up. Similarly, the training of aircrew and maintainers lagged, and a huge rebuilding was required in that realm as well.

Fortunately, a research-and-development base had evolved before Munich. In the early 1930s, General Foulois established Air Corps requirements for new bombers. The Martin B-10, the first bomber with retractable landing gear and all-metal construction, entered service in 1932. The B-17 Flying Fortress, destined to become the workhorse heavy bomber of World War II, first flew in 1935. The Army Air Corps possessed fewer than three dozen of these aircraft when war broke out in Europe in 1939. The B-17's harness mate, the Consolidated B-24 Liberator, first flew in December 1939. Clearly, the United States led the world in heavy bomber technologies, radial engines, and fuels—a result, no doubt, of the emphasis placed on the bombing mission by the Air Corps Tactical School.

For a time, too, America also led in fighter development. In 1932, the Air Corps introduced the first all-metal, monoplane fighter, the Boeing P-26. The Air Corps also led the way with closed cockpits and retractable landing gear for fighters with the P-35 and P-36, both first

A dramatically advanced concept for a bomber aircraft, the Martin B-10 was the fastest bomber in the world when it entered service. Even before aircraft began rolling off the production line in June 1934, fifteen YB-10 test models were rushed into service to carry the airmail. (USAF)

Major General Henry H. Arnold became chief of the Air Corps on 29 September 1938 and commanded the U.S. Army Air Forces during World War II. In December 1945, Arnold was promoted to General of the Army—the only Army Air Forces or United States Air Force officer to ever wear five stars. (USAF)

Opposite, top: This Seversky P-35 all-metal closed-cockpit fighter with retractable landing gear began entering service in 1937 when the Luftwaffe and the RAF were still flying biplanes with fixed landing gear. However, by the onset of war four years later, both of those air forces had pulled ahead of the Air Corps in fighter design. (USAF)

Right: Impressed with the performance of the Curtiss P-36 during service trials in 1937, the Army Air Corps placed an order for 210 of these new fighters—the largest peacetime order of fighters to date. By 1941, though still in service, the P-36 was obsolete due to very rapid technological change. In December of that year, Americans flew P-36s in defense of Pearl Harbor and the Philippines. (USAF)

Bottom, left: The Boeing Model 299 shown here first flew in July 1935. In October of that year, the Air Corps ordered thirteen of these aircraft, designated the YB-17, and began testing them. Early in World War II, this revolutionary aircraft became a stalwart of the strategic bombing campaign against Germany and in Pacific campaigns before the advent of the B-29. Boeing and partner companies built about 12,000 B-17s before World War II ended. (USAF)

Bottom, right: A late model Northrop A-17 with retractable landing gear. Notwithstanding charges that the Air Corps neglected ground attack aviation, this airplane came on line in 1936, a year before the Luftwaffe deployed its famous JU-87 Stuka with fixed landing gear to Spain. (USAF)

flying in 1935. By 1937, however, Great Britain and Germany, each facing much more dangerous air defense problems, surpassed U.S. fighter technology with their Spitfire, Hurricane, and Me-109. Meanwhile, in the Far East, the Japanese produced a superior Zero fighter in 1940.

Although later accused of ignoring tactical air requirements, the Air Corps actually brought out a string of attack aircraft during the 1930s, culminating in the Douglas A-20, thousands of which were produced throughout the coming war. The attack course also remained in the curriculum at the Air Corps Tactical School throughout the 1930s, and George Kenney, destined to become perhaps the foremost tactical airpower expert in the Southwest Pacific, taught the course.

As the lights went out again in Europe, the Air Corps certainly was not as ready as it might have been. Atop all the poverty of the interwar period and the pain of interservice rivalry, the Air Corps had to compete after 1939 with European demands for the products of American factories. But the Air Corps was in better shape than the Army air arm had been in 1917. At least it had a small team of senior leaders who were well

experienced in aviation. Many had World War I combat experience. George Kenney and Carl Spaatz, for example, were but two who had shot down enemy aircraft and commanded air units in that conflict. Most of these leaders had been through the Air Corps Tactical School and benefited not only from the instruction in organization and employment, but also from firm personal friendships established with others who would also lead in World War II. Many, like Spaatz and Hoyt Vandenberg, completed the Army Command and General Staff School at Fort Leavenworth where they formed close relationships with the ground officers with whom they would work in offensives against the Axis.

The organization of the air arm also had progressed. Still not autonomous as demanded by Billy Mitchell, the Air Corps took another large step in that direction when the Army reorganized just before Pearl Harbor. Achieving equality with Army Service Forces and Army Ground Forces, the Army Air Forces now stood one level above the infantry, artillery, and armor branches.

When the twenty-year peace ended, much had been accomplished. By 1941, Army aviation incorporated well-developed doctrinal ideas, an organization capable of rapid expansion, and leaders prepared to conduct worldwide operations against strategic targets deep in an enemy's home-land. It had a research-and-development base plus the support of a grow-ing aircraft industry. Well that it did because the greatest airpower cam-paigns in American history lay ahead—campaigns that would be fought not by an independent air force, but by the United States Army Air Forces.

In 1937, Lieutenant Curtis LeMay aspired to fly one of the few B-17s in the Air Corps. Although assigned to the B-17 equipped Second Bomb Group, LeMay was far down the list of pilots—mostly captains—scheduled to checkout in the new aircraft. Nevertheless, as an accomplished long-range navigator, a rare skill in 1937, LeMay flew many missions on the aircraft, including leading the successful intercept of the Italian liner Rex 776 miles out in the Atlantic Ocean in May 1938. (USAF)

Forging an Air Force

Forging an Air Force

Dik Alan Daso, Ph.D.

In April 1941, at the suggestion of Captain Claire L. Chennault, a retired U.S. Air Corps officer, the Chinese government agreed to form several fighter squadrons manned by American volunteers. By December 1941, about 100 pilots and 200 ground staff had joined the American Volunteer Group, and Chennault had two operational squadrons in Kunming, China, and one in Rangoon, Burma, to protect that seaport and the Burma Road. After America entered the war, Chennault's command was absorbed into the U.S. Army Air Forces. This print shows P-40 Tomahawks of the American Volunteer Group—the Flying Tigers—engaging Japanese Nakajima fighters over southern China. ("The Flying Tigers," Robert Taylor)

In the 1930s, the world was fraught with dangerous conflicts. Global depression, upheaval, and political realignments rocked nations from China to Germany. The United States, better off than most but still suffering from a banking industry collapse, stood alone in splendid isolation. Rather than foreign policy issues, many Americans pondered topics like economic chaos, the hope for recovery, and the threat of domestic violence. Other Americans like Air Corps Major Generals Benjamin D. Foulois, Oscar Westover, and Frank M. Andrews struggled to train and equip the relatively small Army air arm—numbering only about 20,000 men and 1,600 aircraft of all types—despite depression-era budgets.

Japan attacked China in June 1937 in what would later be called the first battle of the Second World War. American military leaders recognized the danger on the horizon. Remembering the dismal state of readiness when America entered the First World War, they concentrated on planning for the inevitable. Those in the Air Corps had the furthest to go. Through the 1930s, Air Corps leaders called for improved military aircraft, the aircraft industry built new models, and the government purchased them in small numbers. The industry languished but established a foundation for expansion. Air Corps pilot training also lagged. Through the decade, on average, only two hundred new pilots annually completed training.

While Air Force leaders prepared for the expected conflict, a tragic accident on 21 September 1938 forced a change in leadership. Air Corps chief Oscar M. Westover died in California in the crash of his Northrop A-17A aircraft. The following week, President Franklin Delano Roosevelt selected Major General Henry H. "Hap" Arnold as the new Air Boss.

Arnold Takes Command

When Arnold took command of the Air Corps, a number of critical aviation issues were under consideration at Wright Field, Ohio, and at the National Advisory Committee for Aeronautics (NACA) facility at Langley,

The YB-15, developed by Boeing, first flew in 1937. Underpowered, it never entered production, but design features introduced in this aircraft became important in subsequent Boeing aircraft, including the B-17 and the B-29. (USAF)

Page 30—31: Betty Boop, The Pistal Packin' Mama *of the 390th Bomb Group approaches the white cliffs of Dover after another mission over Germany. ("When Prayers are Answered," William S. Phillips)*

Major General Oscar Westover, named chief of the Air Corps in December 1935, devoted considerable effort toward increasing pilot training and aircraft production. He was killed in an aircraft crash on 21 September 1938 near the Lockheed plant in Burbank, California. (USAF)

Jimmy Doolittle stands beside his Shellightning, the only metal Lockheed Orion ever built. As a pilot, Doolittle advocated the development of more powerful engines for both commercial and military aircraft. As an engineer with an earned Ph.D. from MIT, he urged Shell Oil Company to develop the high-octane fuel required for those more powerful engines. (USAF)

In the 1930s, Jimmy Doolittle (in civilian hat) toured Europe to promote aviation for Shell Oil Company and Curtiss-Wright. He also gathered useful business and military information on aviation developments in Europe. Captain John K. "Joe" Cannon (flight helmet and goggles) accompanied Doolittle on the trip. (USAF)

Students at the Air Corps Tactical School at Maxwell Field in the 1930s solve a map problem. Among both students and instructors, the school environment at Maxwell fostered healthy debates that influenced the evolution of air planning and strategy. (USAF)

Virginia. Many projects were related to the new B-17 bomber, a major advancement in aviation technology. Arnold called a distinguished group of academics to a meeting at the National Academy of Sciences to address problems confronting the Air Corps and to accelerate Air Corps research and development efforts. His first message as Army Air Corps chief emphasized his priorities. "Until quite recently," he wrote, "we have had marked superiority in airplanes, engines, and accessories. That superiority is now definitely challenged by recent developments abroad [in Germany]. This means that our experimental development programs must be speeded up."

At Arnold's invitation, several major engineering universities, including the California Institute of Technology and the Massachusetts Institute of Technology, sent representatives to Washington to discuss methods to accelerate U.S. aeronautical development. This meeting began Arnold's push to make science and technology an integral part of the Air Corps.

Several men influenced Arnold's thoughts about the state of American aviation technology. While touring Europe in late 1938, Charles Lindbergh wrote Arnold expressing concern over U.S. lethargy in airplane development. "It seems to me," Lindbergh observed, "that we should be developing prototypes with a top speed in the vicinity of 500 mph at altitude . . . the trend over here seems to be toward very high speed." Aircraft manufacturer Larry Bell and Shell Oil executive and legendary aviator James H. Doolittle, also visiting Germany during the 1930s, reported similar aeronautical advances. These revelations worried the new chief of the Air Corps.

Arnold's public statements reflected these worries. In January 1939, while speaking to the Society of Automotive Engineers in Detroit, he explained that America was falling behind in military aircraft development and attributed this failing to an inadequate program of scientific research. "All of us in the Army Air Corps realize that America owes its present prestige and standing in the air world in large measure to the money, time, and effort expended in aeronautical experimentation and research. We know that our future supremacy in the air depends on the brains and efforts of our engineers." Arnold's dedication to continuous research, experimentation, and development was focused and defined, and he carried that message across the country.

Preparations for War

The prospect of war in Europe prompted a growing concern for military readiness in the United States, and in January 1939, Congress authorized the purchase of more than 3,000 military aircraft. American aircraft production accelerated. Army Air Corps leaders realized they needed every airplane that American factories could produce just to equip U.S. fighting forces with aircraft of existing designs.

In March 1939, Arnold established a special air board to study the problems raised by Lindbergh, Doolittle, and Bell. The following month Arnold convinced Lindbergh to accept an active duty commission as a member of the study group. This group, known as the Kilner Board, produced a five-year plan for research and development within the Air Corps. The report was shortsighted in many respects—jet propulsion and missiles, for example, were not even considered—but it did represent the immediate needs of the air arm. Arnold believed that expending effort on building futuristic weapons to win here and now wars was as ridiculous as trying to win future wars with yesterday's weapons and doctrines. Steady improvement in production models was important but could not stand in the way of building the requisite numbers of aircraft. Accordingly, from September 1939 until the spring of 1944, most research and development efforts focused on improving existing aviation technologies.

After Germany invaded Poland in September 1939, much of American production was diverted to Great Britain and France. On 16 May 1940, President Roosevelt called for a five-fold increase in aircraft production. His challenge to produce 50,000 planes each year seemed a tall order to everyone but Arnold who had recommended double that number to the President. The buildup of American air forces had begun.

As Chief of the Army Air Corps Arnold held a seat on the National Advisory Committee for Aeronautics (third from right). Other notables in this November 1939 NACA panel photo included Charles Lindbergh (fifth from left), Orville Wright (sixth from left), Jerome Hunsaker (seventh from left), and Vannevar Bush (head of table). (Robert Arnold Collection)

Arnold visits with Henry Ford on the auto assembly line. During World War II, Ford's company built the durable B-24 heavy bomber for the Army Air Forces. (Robert Arnold Collection)

Lieutenant General Henry H. "Hap" Arnold (left), commanding general of the Army Air Forces, and Army Chief of Staff General George C. Marshall. Despite occasional differences of opinion, General Arnold found Marshall an ardent supporter of the Army Air Forces and, with war's end, Marshall favored an autonomous air force. (USAF)

Above: *Trainees, bound for service as pilots in the Army Air Forces, line up for final instructions before their first flight in August 1942. Stewart Field, in Newburgh, New York, served as a center for Army Air Forces flight training during World War II. (USAF)*

Right: *Workers at a North American plant assemble B-25 Mitchell bombers. The Army Air Forces used this twin-engine attack bomber widely. Armed with a 75-mm cannon and six machine guns, it proved particularly effective against Japanese shipping. (USAF)*

Supporting Roosevelt's dictum, Arnold began a campaign of personal encouragement in aircraft factories. The spirit behind his enthusiasm resulted directly from the lessons he had learned in 1917 and 1918. "I can remember the last World War when in the beginning the American aircraft industry had a capacity of less than 100 planes a year. I saw one factory sign a contract eighteen months later to deliver 100 planes a day . . . The American aircraft industry today is incomparably superior in every regard to the state it had reached even at the close of the last war . . . So, make no mistake about it, we shall train the mechanics, we shall train the flyers, and we shall build the planes." While American industry organized to increase the production of airplanes, Arnold and his commanders forged the administrative structure to handle a massive personnel expansion. Arranging training courses for new pilots, negotiating locations for new bases, and haggling over congressional legislation consumed his days in Washington. In the months prior to Pearl Harbor and in the early years of American involvement in World War II, Arnold continued touring factories and encouraging factory workers because he believed they were vital to the creation of real American air supremacy. He also feared that aircraft production was well behind schedule.

Nevertheless, American production accelerated. After formalizing aid to the Allies by passing the Lend-Lease Act in March 1941, America sent aircraft by the thousands to Russia and Britain in an effort to slow the German aerial juggernaut.

Before Pearl Harbor, Lend-Lease was more than just a transfer of supplies to the embattled British and others—it was a political demonstration of support to those under attack by the Axis powers. Strategically, supplies sent to the Soviet Union helped keep open a third combat front, one that tied up vital Axis resources while the Allies' war machines built up production momentum. American technicians who assisted in the maintenance of Lend-Lease aircraft also provided intelligence reports on the air war. By 1942, and throughout the remainder of the war, reverse Lend-Lease between local British industry and deployed

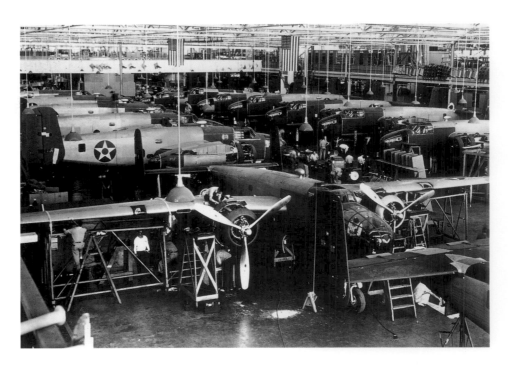

Army Air Forces units worked to ease American supply requirements while lessening the total Lend-Lease bill.

Arnold clearly understood both the politics and the strategy of Lend-Lease. Despite the impact that the program had upon the expansion of American airpower, he convinced Air Chief Marshal Sir Charles "Peter" Portal, Arnold's Royal Air Force counterpart, that the agreement had teeth.

Portal was both relieved and enthused by Arnold's personal visit to England shortly after the Lend-Lease Act passed. "You have impressed us deeply," he wrote to Arnold, "by your sympathy and understanding of our problems and by your evident readiness to bear sacrifices in the equipment of your own service in order that ours may have what it requires."

Oscar Westover (left) and Henry H. "Hap" Arnold (right) circa 1934. In January 1936, Brigadier General Arnold was transferred back to Washington from his southern California headquarters. Major General Westover, Chief of the Air Corps, had convinced General Malin Craig, Army Chief of Staff, that he needed Arnold as his assistant. (Robert Arnold Collection)

Above: General Arnold presenting wings to new WASP pilots at Avenger Field, Sweetwater, Texas, in December 1944. Jacqueline Cochran (left) organized and led the Women Air Service Pilots during the war. Women also contributed in the factories assembling aircraft. (Robert Arnold Collection)

Left: During World War II, women factory workers filled many positions on assembly lines, women pilots ferried thousands of aircraft from production plants to Army Air Forces bases, and other women filled Army administrative positions as members of the Women's Army Corps (WAC). Shown here are women at work on an aircraft assembly line. (NASM)

Above: *This photo shows some of the 12,677 Boeing B-17s built during World War II. Most of these aircraft were destined for service with the Eighth Air Force in Great Britain, but B-17s served in every war theater. (USAF)*

Above: *Giant floodlights light up the far corners of the airfield at Randolph Field during the first phase of Air Corps night training. The BT-9 was used as a basic trainer. (USAF)*

Right: *This 1942 photo shows the assembly of U.S. Mustang aircraft in Great Britain. The performance of these early Mustangs with Allison engines proved disappointing at altitude. When later teamed with the Rolls-Royce Merlin engine, the Mustang overcame these problems. (NASM)*

Concurrently with the beginning of Lend-Lease, Allied war planners feverishly devised, revised, and improvised. The first strategic discussions between Britain and America took place in March 1941. The necessity of an air campaign against Germany and other Axis-controlled zones was never in doubt.

The American plan for war against Germany, approved by the Army-Navy Board, was called Rainbow 5. This plan formed the foundation for 1941 materiel production requirements. In less than two weeks that summer, the Air War Plans Division created an Air Annex—known

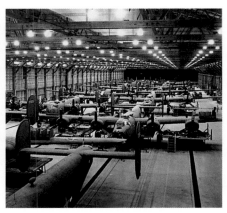

Left: *This Douglas Aircraft Company production line in Santa Monica, California, shows construction of some of the many Douglas aircraft built for the Army Air Forces during World War II. (NASM)*

Below: *The Consolidated Vultee Aircraft Corporation assembles B-24 Liberator bombers for the Army Air Forces at their Tucson, Arizona, plant. (USAF)*

as AWPD-1—to the Rainbow plan. America's air plan provided for strategic bombardment of the German homeland, tactical support to Allied ground forces, home defense, and defensive strategy against Japan. This was America's air war plan on 7 December 1941.

As the air arm expanded, reorganization and restructuring of the War Department became an obvious necessity. With the establishment of the Army Air Forces in June 1941, General Arnold was named overall

Below: *In 1941, President Franklin D. Roosevelt ordered Curtiss P-40s to Iceland to defend that Danish island from German occupation. This photo shows an early P-40 crated for transport. After crating, the planes were loaded aboard ship for deployment. (USAF)*

The Tuskegee Airmen

Colonel Alan L. Gropman, USAF (Ret)

In 1941, President Franklin D. Roosevelt directed the Army Air Corps to accept black Americans into aviation cadet training. The Air Corps, like all other components of the United States armed forces, decided to segregate black aviators into all-black squadrons. By the end of World War II, nearly a thousand black Americans had earned their wings as Army flyers. Fired by a determination to prove their patriotism, valor, and skill in combat, these black aviators, forever called the Tuskegee airmen, struck a significant blow against racism in America.

The first Tuskegee airmen to fight were members of the 99th Fighter Squadron, a unit commanded by black West Point graduate and future Air Force general officer, Colonel Benjamin O. Davis Jr. Over Anzio on 27 January 1944, pilots from the 99th, flying obsolete P-40s, downed nine superior Focke-Wulf 190s. As the 99th continued scoring kills, the 332nd Fighter Group, another unit manned by Tuskegee airmen, arrived in Italy with obsolete P-39 ground-attack fighters. In the spring of 1944, these segregated units transitioned to P-47 Thunderbolts, then a month later to P-51 Mustangs, and began flying bomber-escort missions.

The 332nd flew escort missions from 9 June 1944 until the German surrender in the spring of 1945. By a large margin, the Tuskegee airmen destroyed more aircraft than they lost. They shot down 111 enemy aircraft in air-to-air combat—losing sixty-six of their own aircraft to all causes, including seven shot down. On 200 escort missions, they never lost a single friendly bomber to an enemy fighter.

Tuskegee airmen fulfilled their mission uniquely well—no other fighter group that had stayed in the hunt half as long could claim no bomber losses to enemy fighters. While the 322nd Fighter Group fought in Europe, the segregated 477th Bomb Group, manned by Tuskegee airmen, was activated in 1944 at Selfridge Field, Michigan. Relocated several times during the next eighteen months and slowed in its preparations for war because training was sacrificed to maintain segregation, the 477th achieved operational readiness too late to be shipped overseas.

Nevertheless, by their performance, the Tuskegee airmen struck a significant blow to the poison of racism in America. They demolished bigotry by their actions in the skies over North Africa, the Mediterranean, Sicily, Italy, Austria, Yugoslavia, France, Romania, and Germany. With that record they dispelled myths, opened eyes, rewrote history, and prepared the United States Air Force to be the first armed service to integrate racially.

Bottom, left: Charles McGee of the Tuskegee Airmen flies his P-51B over an enemy airfield. McGee went on to fly fighter missions in the Korean War and the war in Southeast Asia before retiring from the Air Force in the rank of colonel. ("A Perfect Record," Stan Stokes)

Bottom, right: Tuskegee aviation cadets and their instructor.

commander, and Robert Lovett was appointed Assistant Secretary of War for Air. As chief of the Army Air Forces, Arnold also acted as General Marshall's Deputy Chief of Staff for Air. The War Department General Staff reorganization in March 1942 recognized Army Air Forces as co-equal with Army Ground Forces and Army Services of Supply.

By the spring of 1942, Arnold was a member of the Joint Chiefs of Staff. In that capacity, he was responsible to the Secretary of War and to the Army Chief of Staff for all Army air operations. Unity of command was finally achieved within Army aviation. Thereafter, Arnold, now the commanding general of the Army Air Forces, ensured continued preparations for war while also encouraging scientific and technological advances in his blossoming command.

Despite the pressures to standardize and accelerate production during the massive buildup of airplanes, Arnold still found time to push for exceptional technology that demonstrated military potential. For example, when he learned of the British "Whittle" jet engine, Arnold contacted Air Chief Marshal Portal requesting the engine and a copy of the plans. Arnold directed Colonel Benjamin J. Chidlaw, chief of the Materiel Command Engineering Branch, to get an American jet-powered aircraft in the air.

An engineering team assembled the engine at Lynn, Massachusetts, under the project title Super-charger Type #1. Workers were segregated from each other so that even team members were not sure what they were building. On 2 October 1942, the jet-powered Bell XP-59A flew three times. Bob Stanley, a Bell test pilot, made the first two flights. Colonel Laurence Craigie, the Army Air Forces project officer, flew the third. The plane had actually lifted into the air for the first time during taxi tests, but Larry Bell of Bell aircraft insisted that the first flight was not "official" until the generals were present as witnesses.

Craigie, the first American military man to fly the jet, recalled that the atomic bomb was the only project during the war that was more secret than Super-charger Type #1. He never revealed his mission—not even to his wife—who only found out about it in January 1944 when the *Washington Post* broke the story to the country.

Above: *Cadets and instructors head for another flight at Randolph Field. After training an average of fewer than 300 pilots per month during the 1930s, Army Air Forces Training Command graduated 11,411 pilots in November 1943. (USAF)*

The Bell XP-59, America's first jet plane, flew on 2 October 1942. The team that made that flight possible included (from left): Bob Stanley, chief test pilot; Colonel Benjamin N. Chidlaw; Don Keirn, project officer; Ralph Swofford, project officer; and Larry Bell, president of Bell Aircraft Company. (USAF)

Black Thursday

Cadet First Class Scott Snider, U.S. Air Force Academy

Major Charles Normand's B-17 reverberated from the incessant hammering of its .50-caliber guns. Tossed mercilessly by flak and rocket explosions, the aircraft shuddered and absorbed heavy gunfire from another wave of Luftwaffe fighters. The B-17 gunners returned fire, but the sheer number of enemy fighters assailing the bomber formation from every direction proved overwhelming. ME-109s and FW-190s dove through B-17 formations spraying bullets and 20mm cannon shells that tore gaping holes in the bombers, ripping aircraft and men apart. To the rear and out of range of the gunners, ME-110s, ME-210s, and JU-88s fired aerial rockets that exploded in giant fireballs among the B-17s. No Eighth Air Force bomber went unscathed.

Normand's aircraft intercom fell silent. The gunners stopped warning of attacking fighters because there were too many to count. Gunners only broke the silence with quick reports about the fall of another B-17 and the number of parachutes observed—or reports of B-17s catching direct hits from aerial rockets and in a split second becoming fiery smears across the sky. No survivors. The losses weighed more heavily on Normand because he was leading the 305th Bomb Group on the mission. He had departed England with 15 aircraft. Approaching the target, only three remained.

On 14 October 1943, a date subsequently known as "Black Thursday," Eighth Air Force planners decided to go after the Schweinfurt ball-bearing facility again, hoping this attempt would fare better than the previous mission on 17 August 1943 when the Eighth lost 60 bombers—16 percent. Tragically, both missions had similar results. On "Black Thursday," a smaller force went to Schweinfurt and lost another 60 bombers—20 percent—and 600 airmen. This mission would be the last unescorted high altitude daylight-bombing mission to penetrate deep into Germany without long-range fighter escort. The losses inflicted by the Luftwaffe proved unacceptable. The 305th Bomb Group suffered most. Of the 15 aircraft under Normand's command at the beginning of the mission, only two returned to England.

B-17Gs of the 100th Bomb Group en route to Schweinfurt, Germany, in 1943. ("Fortress Engaged," Keith Ferris)

Air War in the European Theater

By August 1942, AWPD-1 had been replaced by AWPD-42, an expanded and much more complex attempt to deal with the global nature of World War II in the air. Emphasis was placed upon gaining and maintaining "complete air ascendancy" over Axis forces. Allied planners recognized that freedom to operate in the air, in large measure, permitted freedom to operate on the ground and over the seas.

As the American Eighth Air Force gathered strength in the European Theater of Operations, British night area bombing doctrine and American daylight precision bombing doctrine appeared contradictory. Eighth Air Force bombing during 1942 had shown less than stellar results. The British called for the Americans to switch to night bombing. American commanders defended the concept of daylight precision bombing, claiming that the diversion of Eighth Air Force resources to support the North

Top: These American P-40 "tomahawk" aircraft, part of the British Desert Air Force in North Africa, show shark markings like those of the American Volunteer Group in China that flew similar Curtiss aircraft. (USAF)

Above, left: The P-51 Mustang, equipped with drop tanks for extended range, became a decisive weapon in the fight for air superiority over Germany. Bomber crews called the fighters "Little Friends." With drop tanks, the "Little Friends" could now go all the way to the target and back with the bombers. (USAF)

Above, right: B-26s of the 386th Bomb Group return to home station after an attack against enemy positions in northern France. Initially, the B-26 suffered from unsatisfactory low-speed handling characteristics and was nearly cancelled. After those problems were resolved, Martin built more than 5,000 of these aircraft. ("Marauder Mission," Robert Taylor)

African campaign had hindered the concentration of airpower over Germany and negatively impacted combat effectiveness.

In January 1943, the Allies met at Casablanca, Morocco, to solidify plans to defeat the Axis. This conference was the most important for American airpower during the entire war. Averell Harriman and Harry Hopkins, Roosevelt's assistants, informed Arnold that the British were planning to push hard for American night bombing. Arnold summoned Major General Ira C. Eaker, Eighth Air Force commander, to plead the American case directly to Prime Minister Winston Churchill. Arnold and his commanders advocated the "continuous application of massed air-power against critical objectives," arguing that both day and night attack would challenge the Luftwaffe and stretch German resources.

Although Churchill may have already been leaning toward a combi-nation of day and night operations, Eaker drove the American argument home. Churchill agreed to an Allied air campaign subsequently called the Combined Bomber Offensive. The "Casablanca Directive" established the air objective for the remainder of the war in Europe: the progressive destruction and dislocation of the German military, industrial, and eco-nomic system, and the undermining of the morale of the German people to a point where their capacity for armed resistance was fatally weak-ened. To accomplish this, the Combined Chiefs of Staff established five

Major General Nathan F. Twining (left), commander of 15th Air Force; Lieutenant General Ira C. Eaker, commander of Mediter-ranean Allied Air Forces; and Major General John K. Cannon, commander of 12th Air Force, plan air support for operations south of Rome. (USAF)

specific target sets: German submarine construction yards; German aircraft industry; transportation; oil refineries; and other enemy war industries including ball bearings and rubber. Additionally, they confirmed the defeat of Germany as the top war priority while the Pacific battle was relegated to a holding action. After plans were finalized in May, the combination of Royal Air Force night attacks and Army Air Forces daylight attacks resumed the systematic destruction of Germany's war machine.

Above: *The Whittle engine, designed by Sir Frank Whittle (shown) and developed by Power Jets, Ltd. (UK), for the Royal Air Force. In April 1941, the experimental W1X powered the British Gloster E. 28/39 aircraft during taxiing trials. The Gloster made short, straight hops causing the W1X to become the unofficial first British turbojet to become airborne. (USAF)*

Left: *Colonel Joseph A. Moller, commander of the 390th Bomb Group, in a B-17 cockpit. Discharged from the Air Service soon after completing pilot training in November 1918, Moller rejoined the Army Air Forces in the early days of World War II and flew more than fifty combat missions over Europe in B-17s. (Dorothy Moller)*

45

A mid-air collision with a German Focke-Wulf 190 nearly severed the tail of this B-17, but the crew managed to fly the damaged aircraft back to England. (USAF)

A P-47 is readied to support the D-Day landings in France. Colonel Francis "Gabby" Gabreski flew this 56th Fighter Group aircraft. ("Calm Before the Storm," Jim Laurier)

During the fall of 1943, American commanders suspended Combined Bomber Offensive operations temporarily following catastrophic losses on daylight raids against targets in Ploesti, Romania, and Schweinfurt, Germany. Over the European Continent, between August and October, the Army Air Forces lost nearly 10 percent of the attack force along with approximately two thousand airmen. The bomber, it appeared, would not always get through. American attacks against central Germany did not resume until the advent of the P-47 Thunderbolt and the Merlin-powered P-51 Mustang—effective fighters with external drop tanks for extended range. Until the spring of 1944, the Luftwaffe remained a powerful adversary.

When American operations against Germany resumed in 1944, the tale was different. Late in February, the Royal Air Force and the U.S. Army Air Forces began a devastating series of around-the-clock raids against the German aviation industry. Together, these air forces flew over 6,000 sorties and dropped 20,000 tons of bombs in one week. The Allied air forces lost over 400 aircraft—nearly 7 percent. The rate of German fighter losses to the American escorts was even higher. Big Week, as it came to be known, initiated the final collapse of the Luftwaffe. By April, the rate of German fighter pilot attrition soared to 25 percent. The German air force had been defeated.

During May and June, Allied air forces prepared the landing zones for the cross-channel effort. Operation Overlord took place on 6 June 1944 under an umbrella of complete air supremacy resulting from months of bombing efforts and sacrifice by Allied aviators. Once a beachhead was established in France, the Allied strategic air forces were relieved from many tactical support obligations and returned to a punishing campaign striking deep into the heart of Germany.

Above: Airmen working munitions for the
388th Bomb Group penned a personal
message on their ordnance before loading.
Sentiments are still expressed on ordnance
to be delivered on a specific location. (USAF)

From July 1944 through May 1945, Allied bombers dropped over
70 percent of the total tonnage of bombs employed against Germany
during the entire war. As a comparison, in 1943 the Allies had dropped
over 220,000 tons of bombs in the European Theater. In 1944, that
number more than quadrupled to 1.2 million tons.

This Douglas A-26 Invader readies for
another mission against German targets in
1945. ("Rat Poison," Nicolas Trudgian)

P-51s, C-47s, and gliders in invasion markings begin the air assault over Normandy on 6 June 1944. ("D-Day The Airborne Assault," Robert Taylor)

Lieutenant General James H. "Jimmy" Doolittle commanded Eighth Air Force from January 1944 to September 1945. He is shown here standing before a British aircraft on one of his many visits with the Royal Air Force. (USAF)

These accomplishments were truly remarkable. In 1939, United States industry produced just 2,141 military aircraft. In 1944, American factories built more than 96,000 airplanes, an increase of forty-fold. American aircraft production shocked everyone, including the Army General Staff. Arnold's leadership, the dedication of American factory workers—many of them women—and the can-do enthusiasm of industry leaders were major reasons for American airpower's evolution into a massive, largely independent, technological system by 1944.

By the last year of the war, the Army Air Forces had grown from a mere 26,500 men and 2,200 planes to over 2.4 million men and women, and nearly 200,000 combat and training aircraft. America's Eighth Air Force flew its last combat mission against Germany on 25 April 1945. Many of the aircrew soon shipped out for Pacific bases to fly more strategic bombing missions.

Air War in the Pacific Theater

The Boeing B-29 "Superfortress" was the chosen instrument for strategic bombing in the Pacific Theater. The B-29 was originally intended for use in Europe when Army Air Corps leaders feared a German victory over England and anticipated that operating bases for air attacks against Germany might be more distant from Europe. When the Royal Air Force successfully defended Great Britain against the German onslaught in 1940, the Superfortress was allocated to the Pacific Theater where strikes against Japan would require the B-29's tremendous range.

The first American air attack against Japan underscored the need for long-range aircraft and disclosed the intention, if not the destructive

The Hump Airlift

Colonel Drue L. DeBerry, USAF (Ret)

In early April 1942, Colonel Caleb V. Haynes arrived in northeast India. His task: to take command of 10 commandeered Pan American DC-3s and four Army C-47s and deliver aviation fuel to China for the Doolittle Raiders. Japanese forces had closed the Burma Road, the last overland access to China. The only remaining access was by air—a 500-mile and five-hour flight by C-47. As Colonel Haynes looked east toward Burma with China beyond, he could see the Naga Hills rising more than 10,000 feet. Beyond, towering more than 20,000 feet, lay the Himalayan Mountains. Americans called this aerial route to China "the Hump."

Haynes delivered the fuel to China, but neither he nor anyone else could have foreseen that this modest beginning would lead to a massive three-year airlift of munitions, medicine, fuel, and everything else needed to sustain all American forces in China as well as several Chinese armies. President Roosevelt was determined to keep China in the war and to hold open the basing of American bombers in China for the assault on Japan. From the trickle of supplies delivered by Haynes, the airlift grew to a torrent, but the task was never easy.

The C-47s and the other aircraft used could not fly above the mountains. Instead, pilots flew between peaks, day and night, crossing mountain passes that were higher than the summit of Pike's Peak in the United States. Japanese fighters occasionally patrolled the Hump, and they shot down transports, but the most dangerous enemy was the weather. Violent, unpredictable storms, with ice, snow, and winds in excess of 200 miles per hour occurred year-round. Pilots reported updrafts and downdrafts inverting their aircraft and tossing them several thousand feet higher or lower, sometimes with disastrous results. On the night of 6 January 1945, 14 aircraft and 42 people were lost in one storm. Little wonder that the Hump route was also known as "the aluminum trail" for the thousand crewmen and 600 aircraft scattered across the mountains.

The initial cadre of pilots who flew the hump were Air Corps reserve officers called to duty in 1942, many former airline pilots with considerable experience flying in weather at night. In addition to more aircraft, by 1943, newly trained Army pilots began arriving, many of them enlisted pilots. Of the 102 technical sergeants completing pilot training in class 42-I at Lubbock, Texas, in October 1942, more than 30 began flying the Hump in December of that same year. The challenging environment for the Hump mission, along with a range in pilot experience from many years flying commercial airliners to only a few hours in twin-engine aircraft, posed challenging leadership issues.

The Hump airlift delivered 500 thousand tons of cargo to China in 1943, well below requirements. Brigadier General William H. Tunner took command in August 1944. In the final eight months of the war, Tunner's airlifters delivered more than 500 thousand tons of cargo, 76 percent of the total delivered between December 1942 and V-J Day..

The Curtiss C-46 Commando, lesser known than the Douglas C-47, had greater lift capacity and better performance at altitude than the C-47. The C-46 was the workhorse of the Hump airlift between India and China. (USAF)

Top, left: *In late 1944, General Arnold became impatient with the progress of B-29 attacks against Japan. In this photo, Major General Curtis LeMay, the new commander of the XXI Bomber Command confers with Brigadier General Haywood "Possum" Hansell, the outgoing commander. (USAF)*

Top, right: *Sixteen North American B-25 Mitchell bombers launched from the U.S. aircraft carrier* Hornet *in April 1942 and staged a surprise attack against targets in Japan. The successful bombing of Japan bolstered an American public battered by a string of stinging defeats. Japanese leaders, morale shaken by air strikes against their homeland, diverted resources from conquest to home defense. In this painting, Doolittle's B-25 sets course for Tokyo. ("I Could Never Be So Lucky Again," William S. Phillips)*

Environmental conditions in the Southwest Pacific posed particularly difficult operational problems for the Army Air Forces. Here, airmen stand ankle-deep in mud while attempting to maintain high-frequency communications links. (USAF)

capability, of the Army Air Forces in the Pacific Theater. In 1942, a small, select group of airmen led by Lieutenant Colonel James H. "Jimmy" Doolittle flew sixteen North American B-25 Mitchell bombers on a one-way mission against the Japanese mainland. Planners designed the "Doolittle Raid," launched from the aircraft carrier *Hornet*, to demonstrate American resolve and to boost national morale in the early years of the war. Arnold personally selected Doolittle to lead the raid. Although not tactically powerful, the raid's strategic impact on Japan and the positive boost to American self-confidence rightfully earned Doolittle the Medal of Honor and a promotion from lieutenant colonel to brigadier general.

The air operations that evolved against Japan differed significantly from air operations against Germany. Arnold selected Major General Curtis E. LeMay to direct the final air assault against Japan, moving him from the European Theater to succeed Brigadier General Haywood S. "Possum" Hansell, Jr., as commander of XXI Bomber Command. Initial B-29 raids had been disappointing. Arnold directed LeMay to make better use of the new B-29 Superfortress, which represented a quantum leap in aircraft technology.

Poor weather over Japan frequently prevented visual acquisition of targets and forced less-than-accurate radar bombing. LeMay, understanding that General Arnold was a man of results and not excuses, was driven to action. The new Pacific commander realized that only by flying below the clouds could his bombers maintain visual contact and hit the desired targets. He ordered low-level attack—it was his only option. After shifting from high-altitude to low-altitude bombardment, LeMay wrote Arnold and explained that weather forced the change in tactics. Almost immediately, LeMay's decision dramatically improved bombing effectiveness against Japan.

Bombing in the Pacific Theater was anything but precise. The Army Air Forces flew three-quarters of the raids against Japan at night. The B-29s pummeled more than sixty Japanese cities and industrial centers with incendiary weapons. LeMay's planners selected incendiary weapons because Japanese cities were vulnerable to fire and because cottage industries, dispersed within the most congested parts of Japanese cities, constituted an important strategic component of Japan's industrial strength. Incendiary attacks started massive fires in urban areas, destroying industry

The Doolittle Raiders

Colonel Drue L. DeBerry, USAF (Ret)

On 18 April 1942, USS Hornet *turned into the wind. Army Air Force mechanics removed engine covers and topped off fuel tanks on 16 B-25s lashed to the carrier's heaving deck. Cold Pacific Ocean spray whipping across the flight deck pelted sailors standing by to move Lieutenant Colonel Jimmy Doolittle's aircraft into takeoff position.*

Four months into war, America reeled from staggering defeats. Wrecked ships littered Pearl Harbor. Wake Island and Guam had fallen to Japanese invaders. American and Philippine forces had surrendered at Bataan. General Wainwright's command, the last organized American defenders in the Philippines, faced imminent defeat on the besieged island of Corregidor.

Doolittle, now in position a mere 467 feet from the forward end of the carrier's deck, engines running, brakes set, signaled readiness for takeoff. The deck officer raised a checkered flag. Doolittle advanced engine throttles to full power and watched as Hornet *'s bow plunged into a 30-foot trough, then lifted. As the bow neared the crest of the next wave, the deck officer's flag flashed down. Doolittle released brakes.*

The heavily loaded B-25 lurched forward, skimmed over the edge of the deck, and settled toward the ocean. Gradually, the aircraft leveled, then climbed. Doolittle circled Hornet *once so navigator Lieutenant Henry Potter could align the aircraft compass with the carrier's deck, then set course for Tokyo. The remaining aircraft followed, with each successive pilot claiming the few additional feet of deck made available by the departure of the aircraft now circling overhead.*

Sighted by a Japanese trawler, Hornet *had been forced to launch the Doolittle Raiders several hours and 200 miles farther from Japan than intended. Planning to bomb Japanese targets then crash-land in China beyond Japanese lines, Doolittle and his men knew their early launch compromised an already thin margin of safety. Would fuel reserves take them beyond areas of China controlled by Japan? The sixteen B-25s proceeded independently to assigned targets and the uncertain conclusion to a dangerous mission.*

Of the eighty men who flew the mission, sixty-four, including Doolittle, bailed out over China, evaded capture, and returned to the United States. Five were interred in the Soviet Union, then neutral in the war between the United States and Japan. Three died from injuries sustained bailing out. Of eight crewmen captured by the Japanese, three were executed, one died in captivity, and four survived as prisoners of war.

All eyes follow Jimmy Doolittle's B-25 as it rolls down the deck of the aircraft carrier *Hornet*. Doolittle and his men prepared for this first-ever launch of Army land-based aircraft from a carrier by practicing takeoffs from runways marked to simulate the length of a carrier deck. (USAF)

Mission to Hiroshima

Lieutenant Colonel Michael J. McCarthy, USAF

Colonel Paul W. Tibbets held the overweight B-29 on the runway, building enough speed to lift the plane and its special payload into the air. Captain Robert A. Lewis, the copilot, reached for the controls as he saw the end of the runway and the dark waters of the Pacific rushing toward him. At the last moment, Tibbets pulled back on the wheel, lifting the Enola Gay into the sky. It was 2:45 in the morning, 6 August 1945, and the first mission of the atomic age.

Tibbets had been preparing for this flight for almost a year. He had been selected to form and train the 509th Composite Group, deploy it to Tinian, and lead it in atomic bombing missions against Japan. During that entire period, he never told his men the true nature of the weapons they would employ. Tibbets kept that secret almost to the end. Four hours after takeoff, when Little Boy was ready and armed, he finally informed his crew: "We are carrying the world's first atomic bomb."

Tibbets wasn't actually flying the Enola Gay when Little Boy was dropped on Hiroshima. With final heading adjustments from Major Thomas W. Ferebee, the bombardier, Tibbets lined up the aircraft on the Aioi Bridge in the center of the city. With less than two minutes to go on the final bomb run, he passed the controls to Ferebee. As the distinctive T-shaped bridge came into view in his bombsight, Ferebee initiated the procedure that would release Little Boy. In an eerie foreshadowing of the Cold War, the first atomic bomb was released not by human hands, but by an automated machine.

As Little Boy tumbled away, the Enola Gay lurched into the sky, freed of its awesome burden. Tibbets immediately regained the controls, throwing the aircraft into a sharp 150-degree turn and diving to pick up speed. He had less than a minute to get away. The seconds ticked by, measured off by the crew. At first they thought the bomb was a dud—it hadn't exploded at the forty-three second count. Then, suddenly, the sky lit up like a ball of fire, filling the Enola Gay with a bright light. A minute later, the shock wave from the explosion hit the aircraft, bouncing the crewmembers in their seats. It was so violent that Tibbets first thought they had been hit by anti-aircraft fire. After a second, smaller shock wave passed, Tibbets knew they were safe and headed home. Ten hours and thirteen minutes after takeoff, Tibbets returned to Tinian. His mission would change the world forever.

Bottom, left: The *Enola Gay* returns to Tinian Island from its 6 August 1945 atomic bombing mission against Hiroshima. (USAF)

Bottom, right: The *Enola Gay* crew. From the left, standing: LtCol John Porter, maintenance officer; Capt Theodore J. Van Kirk, navigator; Major Thomas W. Ferebee, bombardier; Col Paul W. Tibbets, pilot; Capt Robert Lewis, co-pilot; Lt Jacob Beser, radar countermeasures. Kneeling, Sgt Joseph S. Stiborik, radar operator; Sgt George Caron, tail gunner; Pfc Richard H Nelson, radio operator; Sgt Robert H. Shumard, assistant engineer; and Sgt Wyatt Duzenbury, flight engineer. (USAF)

Opposite: The second bomb, dropped on 9 August 1945, detonated near Nagasaki, Japan. (USAF)

The Bell XP-59, America's first jet-powered aircraft, rises above the test field on 2 October 1942. ("The Beginning," Mike Machat)

Carl A. "Tooey" Spaatz (center) became the first Chief of Staff of the independent United States Air Force on 18 September 1947. Here he meets with Arnold in Europe during the Allied advance after D-Day. (Robert Arnold Collection)

General Henry H. Arnold (left) with Robert Lovett at the first ever Army Air Forces "Dining In." Lovett, a quiet, persistent, Wall Street banker, served as the Secretary of War for Air from 1940 until the end of the war. (Robert Arnold Collection)

already slowed by shortages of raw materials, disrupting the economy, and undermining Japanese morale.

Meanwhile, during Allied conferences in Berlin after the defeat of Nazi Germany, the most contested decision of the war between U.S. military and political leadership—whether or not to drop the atomic bomb—surfaced only briefly. Best evidence indicates that President Harry S. Truman decided in mid-June to use the atomic bomb against Japanese targets despite opposition from his Joint Chiefs of Staff. Although Arnold's views against dropping such weapons were known, he himself was in the Pacific when Truman made the final decision. Neither Arnold nor the other military chiefs endorsed the most Clausewitzian decision of the war.

Early on the morning of 6 August 1945, a B-29 from the 509th Bomb Group lifted off a coral runway on Tinian Island. Colonel Paul Tibbets and the crew of the *Enola Gay* set course for Japan. A little more than six hours after takeoff, over the city of Hiroshima, they dropped *Little Boy*, the first atomic bomb, destroying a significant portion of the city's downtown area. Three days later, a second atomic bomb on Nagasaki finished the job, changing the world for all time.

Role of Airpower in Victory

After the war, the Japanese reported over one-half million casualties and the destruction of 2.5 million buildings resulting from the American aerial assault. The United States lost 400 B-29s and more than a thousand airmen. In terms of U.S. aircrew losses, the bombing effort against Japan cost one-tenth that of the strategic bombing campaign against Germany—and no land invasion was required to finish the job.

In the end, airpower in the Pacific played a vital role in the defeat of Japan. Naval aircraft and U.S. ships destroyed the Japanese navy allowing ground forces to capture vital staging bases closer to Japan.

Above: *A pair of Boeing B-29s based in India drop bombs on a large Japanese depot in Rangoon, Burma, in 1944. The B-29 resulted from Arnold's 1940 request that aircraft manufacturers submit proposals for a very long-range bomber. Boeing flew the prototype aircraft in 1942 and began delivering production aircraft in 1943. (USAF)*

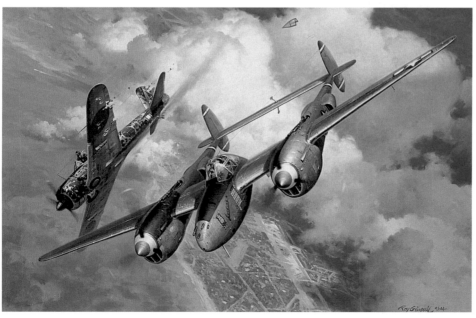

Left: *A Lockheed P-38 Lightning downs a Japanese Zero. A valued asset in all theaters, the P-38 was particularly deadly in the Pacific where it is credited with destroying more Japanese aircraft than any other fighter. ("High Noon Over Alicante," Roy Grinnell)*

This photo shows the second test firing of the MX-774 in September 1948. Development of this ballistic missile was cancelled due to lack of funding. (USAF)

Captain Charles E. "Chuck" Yeager made world history on 14 October 1947, when he became the first man to fly faster than the speed of sound. (USAF)

The Bell X-1, named Glamorous Glennis *by Yeager, streaks into the history books leaving a visible shock wave in the exhaust plume. (USAF)*

Ground forces valiantly stormed the beaches into hostile enemy gunfire enabling the establishment of forward airfields. The political decision to use atomic weapons prevented the loss of untold human lives that might have been sacrificed during an invasion of Japan.

Airpower advocates were both right and wrong concerning the effectiveness of the air weapon in World War II. On one hand, air forces denied the enemy free use of the third dimension of the battlefield—the air. On the other hand, airpower was not singularly decisive—but it was a vital contributor to Allied victories around the globe. The battle for "complete air ascendancy" called for in AWPD-42 proved costly. The Army Air Forces suffered more casualties during World War II than the combined totals in the Navy and the Marine Corps.

The air war constituted an important element in a complex military effort. In Europe, the British, standing alone, shouldered a tremendous burden opposing the Luftwaffe. The valiant effort of the Royal Air Force during the Battle of Britain remains one of the most heroic human endeavors in the history of warfare. The German high command furiously and erroneously changed targets in England, allowing the fight to continue. Later, the Combined Bomber Offensive tested Allied fortitude, challenged doctrinal principles, and cost those who fought in the skies over Europe dearly in both lives and equipment.

In the Pacific, the Japanese attack on Pearl Harbor was a tactical masterpiece. Surprise, mass, unity of command, and deception led to a stunning tactical victory. Strategically, the Pearl Harbor attack provoked the devastation of Japan's industrial infrastructure and the destruction of uncounted acres in over sixty cities. The final blow, the unleashing of the atom bomb against those who had "awakened the sleeping giant" only four years before, put the world on notice that the United States would use its awesome power if the cause was perceived as just. The bombs dropped on Hiroshima and Nagasaki ended the war and set an ominous tone for the future.

The Birth of the United States Air Force

While the Allies attacked Japan from air, land, and sea, General Arnold attacked the problem of long-term scientific and technological planning for the postwar Army Air Forces by establishing several working groups that would focus on technological developments. Influenced by Professor Theodore von Kármán's report, *Where We Stand*, Arnold's vision for the future was reinforced.

By January 1946, Arnold had allocated $10 million of his military budget to Douglas Aircraft Corporation, funding a one-year study of future warfare. Called Project RAND, this study was to provide a program of research on the broad subject of intercontinental warfare and offer long-term, unbiased research to Air Force planners. By 1950, over 800 men and women were employed supporting that task. Thirty-four million dollars had been allocated to twenty-eight different guided missile projects. In 1947, however, Congress slashed the military budget in typical postwar downsizing. The guided missile budget fell from $34 million to $13 million, forcing cancellation of ten programs already underway. Of the surviving programs, only one was a long-range, rocket-propelled ballistic missile—the MX-774B—under contract to Consolidated Vultee Aircraft Corporation. Budget constraints limited future Air Force missile programs until an external threat in the 1950s again altered the national political climate.

Realizing that he had effectively forged an American Air Force and that his health was rapidly deteriorating—he had endured a critical heart condition since 1943—General Arnold retired from active service in February 1946. Although he witnessed the birth of the independent Air Force, he was unhappy with the final compromise that produced that independence. The 1947 National Security Act and Executive Order 9877 left broad holes in the definition of roles and missions expected of each service.

Generals Marshall and Eisenhower had both advocated three co-equal military branches. Arnold, Spaatz, Eaker, Doolittle, and others envisioned all land-based air resources placed under one single air commander. Navy flag officers did not agree. Bickering between the Navy and the AAF eventually resulted in a political compromise resulting in the appearance of national defense unification. Lieutenant General Doolittle called the resultant legislation "an unfortunate compromise" that left two American air forces rather than one. The argument over strategic airpower eventually resulted in a deadlock between the Air Force, the Navy, and civilian leadership in the Pentagon.

Despite this, President Truman recognized General Arnold as America's top airman during World War II and officially made him the first, and to this date the only, General of the Air Force—the only man to hold five-star rank in two services. Arnold died of a massive heart attack on 15 January 1950, on a cool, crisp, still morning—perfect for flying.

When Major General Henry H. Arnold took command of the Army Air Corps in 1938, the prospect of war opened the door for his dynamic leadership. He immediately set about applying his World War I experience in production and training, overcoming two decades of institutional neglect in a mere five years. Additionally, Arnold acted as the Army air arm's liaison with science. Familiar with current technologies and always interested in future possibilities, he earned the respect of many gifted scientists. During the closing years of World War II, Arnold's quest for technological development led to America's acquisition of jet engines, guided missiles, the pursuit of ICBM theory, and advanced aeronautical designs.

His decisions also influenced American society. Arnold selected Jackie Cochran to lead the Woman's Air Service Pilots, the WASPS. These dedicated and skilled women filled vital roles for the Army Air Forces, from factory testing to ferrying aircraft to combat theaters. Arnold encouraged the employment of women in American factories during wartime, and the number of women working in defense plants soared.

During Arnold's command, career lessons he had internalized forged the foundation of America's air arm. Others, Arnold's trusted inner circle of officers, as commanders of the newly independent United States Air Force under the command of General Carl A. "Tooey" Spaatz, carried his vision and beliefs into the early years of the Cold War.

General Henry H. Arnold successfully led the massive expansion of the Army Air Forces during World War II. When Arnold took command, the Army Air Corps included 21,000 personnel and 1,600 aircraft of all types. At its height during World War II, the United States Army Air Forces numbered more than two million men and women and deployed more than 20,000 first-line combat aircraft overseas. (USAF Art Collection)

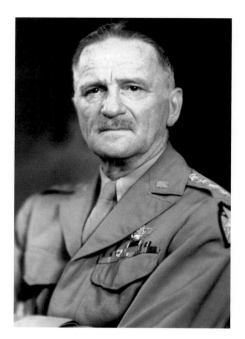

General Carl Spaatz was the last commander of the Army Air Forces and the first Chief of Staff of the United States Air Force. (USAF)

Cold War
Air Force

Cold War Air Force

Colonel Walter J. Boyne, USAF (Ret)

The Allied victory in 1945 over Germany and Japan raised hopes for an era of peace and recovery after years of war and destruction. The creation of a new organization, the United Nations, strengthened expectations for the peaceful resolution of future international disputes. However, victory also sowed the seeds of future conflict between the Western Allies and the Soviet Union as the good intentions voiced at Teheran and Yalta disappeared. The Soviet Union imposed its will through puppet governments in the Baltic States, Poland, and Rumania. Others would follow. Western suspicion and mistrust sprouted in the wake of the Soviet occupation of Eastern Europe behind an "Iron Curtain" of totalitarian secrecy. The Soviet Union followed Russian tradition by expanding its borders as rapidly as possible and rejecting Western Allied overtures to participate in the Marshall Plan. Instead, Soviet paranoia saw sinister purposes in Western policies to "contain" communism. These perceptions set the stage for the decades-long conflict between East and West that came to be known as the Cold War.

A brilliant group of officers had managed the growth of the United States Army Air Forces from very small beginnings to the largest air force in history. General of the Army Henry H. Arnold and Generals Carl Spaatz, Ira Eaker, George Kenney, Lawrence Kuter, Orvil Anderson, Hoyt Vandenberg, Lauris Norstad, and others had definite ideas about how airpower should be deployed after World War II had been won. Wishing to avoid a repetition of the dismal days of the 1930s when the United States lagged behind all major nations in both the number and the quality of its aircraft, they were determined to have an independent air force of adequate size and quality to maintain the peace.

Under their leadership, the United States Army Air Forces had reached a wartime peak of 218 groups with 2,253,000 military and 318,514 civilian personnel. Basing their planning on the hard experience gained in fighting Germany and Japan, these leaders determined that the United States would require an air force of at least seventy-five groups and about 550,000 personnel to keep the nation secure. Size was determined by the worldwide responsibilities of the United States

Top, left: President of the Air Force Association James H. Doolittle (seated left), Assistant Secretary of War for Air W. Stuart Symington (seated right), Major General Lauris Norstad, (standing right), and Lieutenant General Hoyt S. Vandenberg, look on as President Harry S. Truman signs a proclamation declaring 1 August Air Force Day in honor of Americans who contributed to the growth of airpower in the United States. (USAF)

Top, right: Chief Justice Fred M. Vinson swears in General Hoyt S. Vandenberg as the new Chief of Staff of the Air Force. Others present (from left) are Secretary of Defense James V. Forrestal, retiring Air Force Chief of Staff General Carl A. Spaatz, and Air Force Secretary W. Stuart Symington. (USAF)

Page 58–59: Strategic Air Command Boeing B-47s in formation over Canada leave contrails interspersed with those of their fighter escorts. (U.S. Air Force Art Collection)

Opposite: Over the nearly fifty-year Cold War standoff between the United States and the Soviet Union, the Strategic Air Command (SAC) was rightly seen as both the shield and the sword of the United States and the western democracies. This illustration captures the sense of that awesome responsibility and the power marshaled to meet it. ("Cold War Warriors," John Young)

When established in 1946, the Strategic Air Command possessed 148 Boeing B-29s like the one shown in this photograph. Lacking forward bases and in-flight refueling capability, B-29 crews faced the prospect of a one-way mission should hostilities erupt between the United States and the Soviet Union. (Boeing)

Between victory in Europe and victory in the Pacific, thousands of American fighters were hurried to Liverpool, England, for shipment to Pacific destinations for the invasion of Japan. This photo shows 145 P-47 fighters—none having flown more than 100 combat hours—awaiting disassembly for shipment. (USAF)

and by the knowledge that maintaining an adequate industrial base required annual procurement of a respectable number of aircraft and ancillary equipment. Requirements for research, development, and training were implicit within these overall goals.

This carefully crafted plan collapsed in the light of post war budgets and the incredibly wasteful haste of demobilization. A war-weary public demanded an immediate return to peacetime conditions and clamored for all service personnel to be brought home as soon as possible. Congress responded with alacrity. By December 1946, the once powerful United States Army Air Forces had only fifty-two groups, of which only two were combat ready. Where it once had some 60 percent of its 70,000 aircraft ready for operations, the Army Air Forces could now achieve only a 20 percent readiness of the diminished fleet of 25,000 planes.

The aviation industry, which had delivered 324,750 airplanes between 1939 and 1945, suffered a similar precipitous decline. After delivering 96,318 military aircraft in 1944, and another 47,714 in 1945, it delivered only 700 in 1946. Production cuts devastated the aircraft industry, forcing manufacturers and subcontractors out of business and causing skilled employees to seek jobs elsewhere.

Three rays of hope illuminated this otherwise discouraging situation. The first was the temporary but still important American monopoly on atomic weapons that seemed to promise at least a decade of freedom from war. The second was the immutable fact that jet engines had altered aircraft design so that the production of new jet fighters and bombers was imperative. The third bright ray—more important than the other two combined—was the continued research and development resulting from Hap Arnold's prescient insistence on the priority of research and development within the Air Force and the array of brilliant military and civilian minds that he called upon to foster that effort.

The Cold War Begins

In American public opinion, the Soviet Union had passed from being an imponderable anomaly in the 1920s to a social threat in the 1930s to a gallant ally in the early 1940s. Despite visible evidence of the extension of the Soviet sphere of influence, a general recognition of the Cold War did not materialize in the United States until Sir Winston Churchill's famous iron curtain speech at Fulton, Missouri, on 5 March 1946.

Coincidentally, just sixteen days later the United States Army Air Forces created the Strategic Air Command, the Tactical Air Command, and the Air Defense Command. These three combat commands—understrength, ill equipped, and without fully defined missions—would eventually shoulder major responsibilities for containing the Cold War.

Although exhausted by the savage fighting in what it called the Great Patriotic War, the Soviet Union did not demobilize as did the United States and soon presented a new and growing strength. The Soviet Union's military recuperation stemmed in large part from its exploitation of the satellite states it had established as a buffer in the West, and in part from a basic flaw in its system, one which would ultimately doom it. The Soviet Union maintained its buildup of forces at the expense of economic growth and the vital domestic needs of its society. Communist leaders did not recognize that in time an economy geared almost entirely to the production of military goods would bankrupt even a country so rich in resources as the Soviet Union. Indeed, that bankruptcy was too far in the future for anyone in the East or the West to recognize.

It was, however, easy to recognize the buildup in Soviet military strength, as evidenced first by its introduction of the Tupolev Tu-4 bomber, a reverse-engineered Boeing B-29, and then by its unexpected early attainment of a nuclear capability. These were just the preliminary steps in the incredible arms race of the Cold War that would include a proliferation of nuclear weapons on a scale that now seems absurd but at the time was accepted as necessary.

The Early Days of the Strategic Air Command

When the Strategic Air Command, known as SAC, was organized, it included the Eighth and Fifteenth Air Forces and 279 operational aircraft, 148 of which were Boeing B-29s. The B-29, while the finest bomber of World War II, did not have intercontinental range. Only a few of them were capable of carrying atomic weapons, and those weapons were in very short supply and under the control of the Atomic Energy Commission.

This Tupolev TU-4 Bull on static display is one of 420 to 1,200 (estimates vary) Russian aircraft built on plans derived from the disassembly of an American Boeing B-29 interned in Russia before the Soviet Union entered World War II against Japan. Like the American B-29, the Soviet TU-4 could deliver nuclear weapons. (Russian Power)

Aerial refueling was the key to intercontinental capability for bombers. The first SAC tankers, converted B-29s, used a hose system developed by the British. This photo shows the Lucky Lady II *practicing for the record-setting, non-stop around-the-world flight conducted between 26 February and 2 March 1949. The 23,452-mile flight took 94 hours and one minute and required four in-flight refuelings. The flight sent a message to the Soviet Union: SAC is intercontinental. (USAF)*

General George C. Kenney was the first commander of the Strategic Air Command. (USAF)

The Convair B-36 Peacemaker was the source of much controversy, but ultimately proved itself with thirteen years of first line service. Originally designed to allow the United States to bomb European targets from the North American continent, the ten-engine B-36D possessed a top speed of 439 mph and a range of 7,500 miles. (USAF)

From left to right, Brigadier General William F. McKee, Major General Curtis LeMay, and Major General Earl E. Partridge use a scale model of Bikini Atoll to review plans for atom bomb tests on that Pacific island. (USAF)

SAC's first commander, General George C. Kenney, distinguished himself during World War II as the commander of Fifth Air Force in the Southwest Pacific. Yet Kenney chose the creation of an independent United States Air Force as his primary goal after the war, and he did not devote the time or talent necessary to make SAC an effective command. In practical terms, the infant Strategic Air Command was more like an elite flying club that paid its members to fly than a serious combat organization. The relaxed standards of performance and safety resulted in a lack of mission capability and a tragically high accident rate.

In April 1948, the Soviet Union seized Czechoslovakia. President Harry S. Truman clearly defined the Cold War emergency by citing the Soviet Union as a potential enemy. The Communist blockade of Berlin beginning on 22 June 1948 removed all doubt about Truman's assessment. Using the C-47s assigned to his command, Lieutenant General Curtis E. LeMay began airlifting supplies into Berlin on 26 June. Meanwhile, the Air Force moved larger C-54 aircraft to Europe to supplement and eventually replace the C-47s. Air Force Chief of Staff General Vandenberg also ordered the deployment of a Military Air Transport Service task force to Europe commanded by Major General William H. Tunner, a master of airlift management. Tunner organized a multinational airlift operation that sustained the city and broke the back of the blockade.

While the blockade was under way, General LeMay was recalled to the United States for an even more challenging assignment, command of the Strategic Air Command. LeMay had a distinguished record in both the European and Pacific Theaters during World War II. In a post-war conversation, General Ira Eaker called LeMay his "best combat commander." Lieutenant General Jimmy Doolittle agreed, going on to say that he believed LeMay the best air combat commander the United States—or any other nation—ever produced. Most observers familiar with LeMay's leadership style and the results he achieved would agree with those assessments.

It was SAC's great good fortune that LeMay became its commander on 19 October 1948. LeMay found a force that had grown in size, if not proficiency, since its inception. SAC now possessed 837 aircraft, including fifty Convair B-36 and fifty Boeing B-50 intercontinental bombers.

LeMay went to work rebuilding SAC to his own exacting standards. As a test, he called for a simulated combat mission—a maximum effort as would have been required if the United States suddenly went to war. The only difference was that targets were simulated and located in the United States at the mid-point of the long mission rather than in the Soviet Union. He was dissatisfied but not surprised at the results: many aircraft aborted the mission, and not one aircraft reached its target.

Contrary to the legends, LeMay did not fire a single commander because of the fiasco. Instead, he began his rebuilding process by concentrating on the 509th Bombardment Group, famous for its attacks on Hiroshima and Nagasaki. He created a staff at SAC Headquarters that could evaluate performance and see to it that the unit came up to his high expectations. In a relatively short time, it did, and the procedure was then applied to another unit, and then another. Proficiency increased, as did pride. The accident rate decreased. Not everyone liked LeMay or his technique, but everyone liked his results.

As the training continued, SAC expanded, getting more and better equipment. By 1957, SAC was a force of 224,000 personnel, operating 2,700 aircraft, including 127 B-36s, 243 B-52s, 1,501 B-47s and RB-47s, 742 KC-97s and 24 KC-135s. This intercontinental force was fully equipped with an array of nuclear weapons that were now under USAF control.

With a 230-foot wingspan and a 162-foot fuselage, the B-36 was a very large aircraft. This photo shows a B-36 being refueled. Note the airmen performing maintenance on the leading edge of the wing. (National Archives)

The Boeing B-50D was equipped with the flying-boom refueling system. A derivative of the B-29, it featured the much more powerful Pratt & Whitney R-4360 engines along with numerous structural and equipment refinements.

General Curtis E. LeMay is shown here reunited with an old friend, a Boeing B-17. His peers regarded LeMay, the guiding light of the Strategic Air Command, as the finest combat air commander in history. This photograph was taken on 1 February 1965, the day General LeMay, then Air Force Chief of Staff, retired. (Air Force Association)

A Boeing KC-97 Stratotanker refuels a B-47 at sunset over the Rocky Mountains. The KC-97 was a derivative of the B-29, using the wing, tail, and engines designed for the bomber. This illustration also shows the flying boom method of in-flight refueling. ("Silver King at the Pump," Robert Watts)

LeMay had used his prodigious analytical powers to select the equipment, establish the standards of crew proficiency, and lay out the training requirements to achieve those standards. In the process, he refined the nature of SAC's mission, which, under his interpretation, was to be so obviously strong that no nation would dare risk an attack upon the United States. He wanted the leaders in the Kremlin to recognize that against the United States, an act of war, no matter how powerful or with what degree of surprise, would result in the utter destruction of the Soviet Union. In a phrase of the time, LeMay guaranteed there would be "no more Pearl Harbors."

SAC adopted LeMay's personal rigorous operational philosophy and became the most powerful armed force in history. While the United States faced a continuing series of minor wars, there was no global nuclear war. SAC's power established a Pax Americana that eventually saw the Cold War won. In the process, the Soviet Union achieved great strength before it crumbled and fell under the weight of its system. The Soviets were unable to compete with a dynamic American economy that allowed the United States to be both powerful and prosperous.

The peak of SAC's bomber force effectiveness may have occurred during the Cuban Missile Crisis of 1962 when 625 SAC bombers, out of 1,595 available, were placed on alert. Soviet Premier Nikita Khrushchev later remarked that all during the negotiations over Cuba he could not get the thought of orbiting B-52s out of his mind.

LeMay's obvious success with SAC had many advantages for the United States Air Force, one of which was receipt of the lion's share of

For former B-29 and B-50 pilots, one of the most stirring aspects of the B-47 was its 6,000 foot-per-minute rate of descent on penetrations from altitude. The aft main gear and the outriggers were extended to act as dive brakes. (Boeing)

the military budget during his tenure. Over time, other USAF commands began to adopt SAC methods, a process that accelerated after 1957 when LeMay became first Air Force Vice Chief of Staff, and then, on 30 June 1961, Chief of Staff. He saw to it that commanders who had done well in SAC were transferred to head other commands and there impose SAC methods and standards.

Ironically, LeMay was less effective as a Chief of Staff than as Commander of SAC. He became Chief at a time when President John F. Kennedy was accepting the guidance of Secretary of Defense Robert S. McNamara. McNamara advocated a policy of "flexible response" toward Communist provocation—a policy put forward by the Chairman of the Joint Chiefs of Staff, Army General Maxwell D. Taylor.

President Johnson ignored LeMay's advice against getting involved in a war in Southeast Asia. When the fighting there began in earnest, the President ignored LeMay's advice on the proper conduct of the air war.

LeMay retired in 1965. Despite his frustrations as Chief, he could look back on his career with pride, for the SAC that he created was still powerful and, even with the demands of the war in Southeast Asia, still able to deter the Soviet Union from a first strike. SAC's ability to do this

Top: *A photo from the days when the USAF bought bombers not by the score but by the thousands! More than 2,000 B-47s were procured from Boeing, Lockheed, and Douglas, and they provided SAC with an unparalleled nuclear capability. These B-47 bombers and RB-47 reconnaissance planes are being assembled at the gigantic Wichita, Kansas, plant. (Boeing)*

Above: *SAC ran its far-flung operations from an underground command post at Offutt Air Force Base, Nebraska. The hours were long, the work was serious, and the faces were often grim. (USAF)*

In the navigation compartment of a B-36, a lieutenant completes an entry on his flight plan while a captain, probably a flight examiner, checks his work. Two other crewmembers concentrate on their instruments. (National Archives)

An RB-36 crewman replaces a camera component in preparation for another reconnaissance run. SAC operated more than a hundred RB-36s, each equipped with a dozen cameras. The typical RB-36 crew numbered twenty-two. (USAF)

derived in large part from the equipment for which LeMay had created the requirements.

Initially SAC was equipped with the Boeing B-29 Superfortress and the first intercontinental bomber, the Convair B-36. The "Peacemaker" as the B-36 was called—and as it was in fact—was the biggest USAF bomber ever, with a 230-foot wingspan. Its design had begun in 1941 when it seemed that Great Britain might be conquered and it would become necessary to bomb European targets from bases within the continental United States. When Germany failed to overcome Great Britain, B-36 development was slowed in favor of producing more Consolidated B-24s. The first XB-36 did not fly until 8 August 1946.

In 1948 and 1949, the B-36 became the subject of a bitter controversy, the famous "Revolt of the Admirals." The Navy charged that the B-36 was a "billion dollar blunder" and alleged contractual improprieties. A congressional investigation showed that the procurement of the B-36 had been both proper and appropriate, but anger over the dispute lingered for years.

The addition of four jet engines improved performance of the B-36, and it eventually attained a top speed of 435 miles per hour and a service ceiling of 45,000 feet. The last B-36 was retired from SAC on 12 February 1959, ending thirteen years of service in which it never dropped a bomb in anger, but served the cause of peace with its intercontinental capability to deliver nuclear weapons.

SAC Aircraft Alert Force

General James P. McCarthy, USAF (Ret)

The klaxon alert horn shocked me awake. I glanced at the clock. Three forty-five a.m. I scrambled into flight suit and boots, and then ran down the alert facility corridor out into the night to our alert truck. Freezing rain brought me further awake. The navigator and I tumbled into the truck. The copilot drove the 100 yards to the dark B-47 sitting on the ramp. As I climbed the entry ladder, our crew chief started the ground power unit, applied power to the aircraft, and then manned the fire bottle. I put on my helmet and heard the wing command post transmitting the alert message in code. As I started engines, the navigator called, "Exercise Cocoa message. Working authentication." The copilot and navigator confirmed authentication, then I taxied toward the runway. Visibility was very poor but I saw 11 other alert bombers and tankers falling into line. We crossed the runway hold line 11 minutes after the klaxon sounded, then taxied back to our parking space, having demonstrated once again that the SAC alert force could get airborne in less than 15 minutes.

During the Cold War, Strategic Air Command constantly maintained more than 300 aircraft on alert as a deterrent force. SAC exercised the force, day and night, to ensure responsiveness in all conditions. Crews averaged more than one week out of three on alert. While on alert, we received daily briefings on operations, weather, and intelligence, studied assigned targets, or trained in simulators. We ate and slept in the alert facility. On Sundays, families brought picnic lunches to an area adjacent to the alert facility.

After a Friday changeover to the replacement crew, we were off duty until Tuesday afternoon. One month out of three, we deployed to England for alert duty. The routine was similar. We spent a week on alert, a week off, a week on, three days off, and then a week on before redeploying. On average, SAC crews spent 40 percent of their lives on alert or deployed until the end of the Cold War.

This scene of an alert crew racing to its aircraft was repeated thousands of times over the years. The crews never became jaded. Any one of the alerts could have been the real thing, signaling a nuclear first strike by the Soviets with all the terrible implications that had for the world—and for every individual crewman's family. It was a sobering time, when the airman going to war had a greater chance for survival than the family he left behind. (USAF)

Top: *The Boeing KC-135, with its flying boom system, was perfectly compatible with both the B-47 and the B-52, and made them into true intercontinental bombers. Soon, both fighters and transports would come to depend upon aerial tankers for mission capability. (USAF)*

Above: *In-flight refueling looks relatively simple—line one aircraft up behind the other. Reality is far different. Two huge aircraft (here, a B-52) fly at more than 300 knots in close proximity, often at night and in bad weather. It is an art as well as a skill. (USAF)*

The McDonnell-Douglas KC-10 Extender is a converted DC-10 equipped with additional fuel cells, a refueling boom and a boom operator's station, and a refueling receptacle. The Extender is also equipped to serve as an airlifter when needed in that role. The Air Force acquired sixty of these aircraft between 1981 and 1990. (USAF)

In-flight Refueling: The Essential Discipline

A clear forecast of the future of SAC came about in 1947 with the first flight of the Boeing B-50 bomber. The vastly improved B-50D appeared in 1949, equipped to receive fuel from new flying boom tankers. To all appearances an upgraded version of the B-29 with more powerful engines, the B-50D heralded a new age in bomber warfare, for it ushered in aerial refueling as a standard tactical procedure.

The early tankers were KB-29s, converted bombers that used the trailing hose technique adapted from British practice. Boeing revolutionized the world of aerial refueling with its introduction of the flying boom system on first the KB-29P and then the Boeing KC-97 and KB-50. Use of the flying boom sped up and simplified the hook-up procedure, permitting a much higher rate of fuel transfer.

Although not generally perceived at the time, the adoption of this new method of in-flight refueling would transform the entire Air Force. Where initially tankers were devoted primarily to SAC's intercontinental mission, it became possible to take advantage of the tactical flexibility and utility they would confer first on fighters, and much later, on transport aircraft. In time, the tanker fleet became central to Air Force doctrine, planning, deployment, and operations.

The production run for the long-lived KC-135 that made its first flight on 31 August 1956 totaled 732 aircraft. Like the B-52, these have been continually modified and upgraded over time, the most significant change being the incorporation of turbofan engines in the KC-135R. The McDonnell Douglas KC-10 tanker, a derivative of the DC-10 transport, made its first flight on 12 July 1980. The Air Force purchased sixty of these aircraft.

Tanker crews have received comparatively little public acclaim despite the fact that aerial refueling is a dangerous operation requiring a high level of skill on the part of both the tanker and receiver crews.

When, as is done so often, the refueling is carried out at night, in bad weather, under radio silence, and sometimes within range of enemy defenses, it is extremely hazardous. The skill of the crews and the frequency with which aerial refueling occurs have dulled public appreciation of the difficulty of the operation. In stark contrast, no one appreciates the tanker crews more than the receivers, for tankers have saved countless aircraft and crews over the years.

Strategic Air Command Bombers

On 17 December 1947, the Boeing XB-47, the most important multiengine jet aircraft in history, made its first flight. A joint product of Boeing's long experience in building bombers and a flood of new information from

Above: This photo shows the view of an aerial refueling from a B-47 cockpit. The tanker is a KC-97. (USAF)

This photo from the cockpit of an FB-111 shows one of the bombers waiting to refuel while another prepares to receive fuel from a KC-135 tanker. (USAF)

The Boeing B-47 blazed the way not only for military follow-on aircraft such as the KC-135 and B-52, but also for a host of civilian airliners, from the 707 down through the 777. Virtually invulnerable to interception in its early days in service, the B-47 was a demanding aircraft to fly. It is shown here making a rocket assisted takeoff. (USAF)

The EC-135 airborne command post aircraft were ready to assume control of SAC's intercontinental-range bombers and missiles should SAC ground commands become inoperative. The aircraft, carrying all necessary communications equipment, a general officer, and a skilled team of operations specialists, were airborne around the clock. Before one EC-135 would land, another was already in the air. (USAF)

There is no element of the USAF more beloved by the people it serves than the Air Rescue Service. The Sikorsky SH-19 helicopter shown here is practicing the rescue of a downed airman from a life raft in open sea. (USAF)

SAC's bombers went supersonic with Convair's B-58 Hustler. With a top speed of 1,358 mph and a service ceiling of 63,080 feet, the Hustler was a brilliant weapon hampered by a relatively short combat radius of 1,550 miles. Only the 43rd and the 305th Bomb Wings operated the B-58, which was retired in 1970, the victim of high operating costs and a high accident rate. (USAF)

German research available after World War II, the XB-47 featured six jet engines suspended in pods and thirty-five degrees of sweep on its wing and tail. The importance of the XB-47 stems from its prominence as SAC's primary jet bomber for many years as well as from the myriad aircraft that derived from its design. Its distinctive shape is retained to this day by its direct derivatives such as the Boeing 707 through 777 and many airliners built by other companies.

The B-47 was truly revolutionary, and, as might be expected, suffered many engineering problems during its development. SAC eventually purchased more than 2,000 of the aircraft and with them established an aerial dominance that ensured peace. With a combat speed of 557 miles per hour at 38,500 feet, the B-47 was, for much of its life, a difficult aircraft to intercept. The performance of the new tanker was compatible with the B-47, and over the next five decades, with a host of other aircraft. The B-47's capability was extended by the introduction of the KC-135 tanker.

As advanced as the B-47 was, General LeMay wanted an even larger and more capable follow-on aircraft. Although he did not use the term at the time, it is clear that LeMay saw the follow-on aircraft as a "platform" large enough to accommodate new equipment that would be developed in the future.

The YB-52 made its first flight on 15 April 1952. If the B-47 was the most important jet bomber in history, the B-52 Stratofortress would earn the title of longest-lived and most useful, for it would be continually updated and modified over the years. Boeing built 744 B-52s, the last one being a B-52H delivered on 26 October 1962. The mission of the B-52 changed radically over time. It started life as "SAC's long rifle," a high altitude nuclear bomber that could penetrate as a single aircraft or as part of a small group to the heart of the Soviet Union. With its 600-mile per hour top speed and 50,000-foot altitude capability, the B-52 presented Soviet interceptors with a difficult task. However, when Soviet missiles made high-altitude missions dangerous, the Stratofortress became a terrain-follower, flying below the Soviet radar screen.

In Southeast Asia, the B-52 became a formidable tactical bomber, dropping huge loads of conventional weapons on enemy positions and even performing close air support missions. As each decade has passed, B-52s have demonstrated the ability to assume new roles, including delivery of air-launched cruise missiles as well as precision-guided munitions. No one, not even LeMay or the Boeing design staff, would have predicted that the B-52 would be in service until well into the 21st century and that grandchildren would someday fly the same aircraft crewed by their grandfathers.

Three other bombers were important to SAC. The first supersonic bomber in the world, the Convair B-58 Hustler, was a beautiful, awe-inspiring aircraft with a formidable speed. First flown on 11 November 1956, the Hustler had a maximum speed of 1,385 miles per hour and a combat radius of 1,550 miles. Unfortunately, the accident rate was high for B-58s, and they were so expensive to operate and maintain that they were withdrawn from service in 1970.

The General Dynamics swing-wing FB-111, first flown on 30 July 1967, was an improvisation intended as a successor to the B-58 and as a replacement for some B-52s. Only seventy-six were purchased—enough to equip two wings. The FB-111A had a top speed of 1,453 miles per hour and an un-refueled ferry range of 4,786 miles. LeMay considered it too small to be useful.

The last bomber built for the Strategic Air Command during the Cold War was the Rockwell B-1A, an aircraft whose history illustrates not only the technology but also the politics of its era. Originally begun in 1961 as a supersonic replacement for the B-52, the B-1A did not fly until 23 December 1974. Four B-1A prototypes were successfully tested before President Jimmy Carter killed the program in 1977. His decision was reversed in October 1981 when President Ronald Reagan announced that 100 follow-on B-1B aircraft would be built. A secret decision had been made at the same time to proceed with what would become known as the Northrop B-2 stealth bomber.

The B-1B differed in many significant ways from the original B-1A, the most important change being the incorporation of stealth technology that reduced the B-1B's radar cross section. The top speed requirement for the aircraft was reduced to Mach 1.25, and the design was optimized for the carriage of cruise missiles. The aircraft went through a long series of development problems and had particular difficulty with its electronic warfare suites, but it matured into a capable bomber able to deliver nuclear weapons, cruise missiles, precision guided munitions, and conventional bombs.

Between 1952 and 1962, the Air Force purchased 744 Boeing B-52 bombers in models from A to H. This illustration of a B-52 B (foreground) and a B-52G shows some of the external changes between early and late models of this remarkable bomber. The last B-52H was built in 1962, yet these rugged and versatile aircraft are scheduled to remain in service well into the 2030s. ("B-52s: They Keep On Ticking." Stan Stokes)

This FB-111 with wings extended is preparing to land. The General Dynamics FB-111 could fly at top speeds of 1,450 mph (Mach 2.2) and carry SRAM missiles or up to 37,000 pounds of conventional bombs. (USAF)

Over the years, SAC bombers and tankers worked together to carry out the nuclear deterrence mission and a tactical mission with conventional bombs. In the 1950s, SAC also possessed other aircraft, including Douglas C-124s for use in strategic support squadrons, Republic F-84 escort fighters, and North American F-86 fighters for air base defense.

Strategic Air Command also operated several different reconnaissance aircraft including the Republic RF-84F, the Boeing RB-50, RB-47, and EB-47, the Martin RB-57, the Lockheed U-2, and the magnificent Lockheed SR-71. In addition, SAC operated the vitally important EC-135 Looking Glass aircraft as well as the Boeing E-4B National Emergency Airborne Command Post.

From SAC's electronic experience, an entirely new array of intelligence gathering and airborne battlefield command and control systems emerged using both KC-135 and C-130 aircraft platforms. These highly classified operations, implicit force-multipliers, assume ever-greater importance with each passing year. They loom large in the design and operation of future fighter, bomber, and reconnaissance aircraft, both manned and unmanned.

A decisive change in SAC's nuclear deterrence posture took place from 1959 on as aircraft were supplemented—but not supplanted— by an increasingly powerful force of missiles. The U.S. fleet of ballistic missiles was the product of a technical and industrial revolution managed by one of the greatest leaders of the era, General Bernard A. "Bennie" Schriever.

The advent of the intercontinental ballistic missile (ICBM) brought profound changes in SAC. However, SAC organization and training procedures were applicable to the new weapon systems, and a massive effort was made to insure that ICBM crews felt as appreciated as crews of bombers and tankers. Here Major General David Wade, commander of the 1st Missile Division and Colonel Rex Dowtin, the Deputy for Operations at Vandenberg AFB, California, brief SAC commander, General Thomas S. Power. (USAF)

Schriever and the ICBM Revolution

In the continuing battle for a larger share of the relatively small budgets of the time, the services pressed for a decision on the roles and missions for missiles. In 1956, Secretary of Defense Charles E. Wilson decided that the USAF would have responsibility for the intercontinental ballistic missile (ICBM) and share, with the Army, responsibility for the intermediate range ballistic missile.

Missileers on Alert

Lieutenant General Arlen D. Jameson, USAF (Ret)

The crackling, piercing, alerting tone wailed from the whirring bank of electronic equipment, followed immediately by "Sky Bird, this is Looking Glass with a White Dot message for the Primary Alert Force." More than a hundred miles east of Rapid City and deep beneath the rolling plains of South Dakota, SAC Combat Crew S-056 threw open Top Secret checklists and prepared to copy a message from the SAC Airborne Command Post.

The Primary Alert System speaker box blared, "Charlie, Sierra, Whiskey, Lima, Foxtrot, Bravo. The time is zero three zero one five five. Authentication is Romeo November. Acknowledge now. This is Looking Glass out." Major Earl Andy Anderson, crew commander, shouted out checklist actions and Second Lieutenant Dirk Jameson simulated the response. It was another test communication to let everyone, including the Soviets, know that SAC was ready no matter what was going on topside.

Springtime in the Dakotas could be brutal as the March 1964 storm was proving to S-056 and their fellow missileers. The harrowing three-hour drive over snow-covered backcountry roads to Minuteman launch control facility Echo 01 was negotiated successfully even as the glowering sky signaled a bruising, wind-whipped blizzard. With crew changeover finally complete and the eight-ton blast door locked securely in place, we turned full attention to managing young troops scattered over the hundred square miles that were home to Echo Flight and ten Minuteman ICBMs. From arrival in the capsule what seemed like eons ago, this alert had been a bear. Alerts were supposed to be 24 hours long but in this case Mother Nature, in her fury, prevented relief crews from leaving the base for three consecutive days.

The nasty weather was causing numerous launch facility security alarms requiring the security forces to respond. Commercial electricity was fluctuating at several remote sites and two Emergency War Order messages interrupted our alert turnover procedures. The storm was bearing down on the missile field when an electronic maintenance team arrived at Echo 10 to change out a guidance and control missile part. Penetrating a nuclear missile site requires strict security, encoded combinations, and aggressive safety measures all made more challenging by subzero conditions. The team finished the maintenance effort in six hours despite the weather. Wind chill temperatures dropped to minus 40 and lower, causing survival conditions on mostly impassable roads.

We were lucky! All maintenance teams managed to scramble back to the warmth of the launch control facility. Out in the howling blizzard, three security camper teams hunkered down in pickup campers guarding missile sites that had lost all power.

As she always does, Mother Nature let up and digging out went full bore. The missiles came through at the ready and Missileers went about their work as they continue to do to this day.

Left: Fifty feet under the Montana prairie, encased in tons of steel and concrete, a two-man Minuteman Missile Combat Crew prepares to go on strategic alert. (USAF)

Opposite: Strategic Air Command's manned aircraft strike forces were augmented by the advanced missile systems such as the Minuteman. This ICBM is shown during a test launch from Edwards AFB, California. (USAF)

Above: *Major General Bernard Schriever, shown here in 1958 when he commanded the Ballistic Missiles Division of Air Research and Development Command, led the effort to develop ballistic missiles for the Air Force. (USAF)*

Right: *Missile technology advanced with amazing speed, setting the stage for the exploration of space. The solid-fuel Minuteman series of missiles could carry a wide variety of warheads and were a tremendous advance over their liquid-fueled predecessors. Boeing was the airframe contractor for the Minuteman. (USAF)*

Below: *Any missile launch was impressive, and none more so than that of the massive Titan II. Martin Marietta was the airframe contractor for the Titan II, which carried a six-megaton warhead. (USAF)*

Enormous difficulties accompanied creating an ICBM, ranging from building a rocket able to carry the huge warheads then required to problems of guidance and control, engine staging, reentry, and so on. To lift a thermonuclear warhead, engineers estimated that the Atlas rocket under design by Convair would weigh 440,000 pounds.

A breakthrough occurred in 1953 when Dr. Edward Teller and Dr. John von Neumann independently concluded that a thermonuclear warhead weighing only 1,500 pounds was feasible. A high-level board of scientists, known informally as the "Teapot Committee," recommended that the Atlas rocket be developed to carry the new lightweight high yield warhead. Brigadier General Schriever was picked to organize and lead the Ballistic Missiles Division of Air Research and Development Command, the organization charged with Atlas development.

Schriever was the right man at the right time. He possessed rapport with the scientific, military, and industrial communities and melded them

into an efficient team. The ICBM program received top priority within the Air Force. Using the Western Development Division as a military integrating facility to combine efforts of science and industry, Schriever introduced an entirely new management style.

The organization Schriever headed eclipsed the Manhattan Project in terms of scientific difficulty, budget, and urgency. The Soviet Union launched Sputnik into orbit on 4 October 1957 and trumpeted their lead to the world. Had Schriever and his team failed, the United States would have been at the mercy of an adversary equipped with nuclear-capable ICBMs.

Fortunately, Schriever elicited miraculous achievements from the military-scientific-industrial organization, fielding no fewer than three operational ICBMs and one intermediate range ballistic missile in less than eight years. These included the Atlas, Titan, and Minuteman ICBMs and the Thor intermediate range ballistic missile. Later developments saw the Peacekeeper ICBM join the force.

By 1989, SAC's tremendous power was divided between its aircraft and missile systems. It possessed more than 1,000 strategic aircraft, including ninety-six B-1Bs, 254 B-52s, sixty-one FB-111s, 506 KC-135s, fifty-eight KC-10s, four E-4s, and a number of strategic reconnaissance aircraft. SAC's missile strength included 950 Minuteman IIs and IIIs and fifty Peacekeepers. Warheads had become more sophisticated over time, as illustrated by the introduction of multiple independently targetable reentry vehicles, which expanded the number of targets that the missile force could cover.

As effective as the B-47 was, General LeMay wanted a bigger, more capable aircraft, and got it in the Boeing B-52, shown here equipped with Hound Dog missiles. Although no faster than the B-47, the B-52 possessed a higher ceiling, longer range, and was large enough to serve as a platform to accommodate succeeding generations of new equipment. (USAF)

The Minuteman gave the SAC ICBM fleet an unprecedented reliability and a much shorter reaction time. Here, a Minuteman II is poised in its silo at an ICBM launch facility. (USAF)

The Air Defense Command was initially equipped with World War II vintage aircraft, including the North American F-82 Twin Mustang. While an excellent aircraft (one would score the first aerial victory in Korea in 1950), the F-82 was far from ideal as an interceptor for protecting the United States. (USAF)

Above: *When specialized all-weather aircraft proved troublesome in development, the USAF turned to Lockheed to develop the basic P-80/T-33 design yet a little further. The result was the F-94 Starfighter, shown here in the F-94C version. The Starfighter carried twenty-four 2.75-inch folding-fin rockets in its nose, and twelve each in two wing pods. Top speed was 585 mph and service ceiling was 51,400 feet. (USAF)*

Right: *The Northrop F-89 Scorpion's first contract was let on 3 May 1946, but the aircraft did not enter service until 1950. After initially troublesome development, the aircraft proved to be very reliable. The F-89H carried forty-two 2.75-inch air-to-air rockets and six Hughes Falcon guided missiles. (Northrop)*

Air Defense Command

The leaders of the USAF had to contend with what they thought the Soviet Union *could* do, not what they thought it *would* do. From the early post-World War II years, the Soviet Union could have launched a one-way atomic attack upon the continental United States. To defend against this threat, the USAF had to develop an adequate air defense system despite the tremendous expense involved.

Air Defense Command (ADC) was formed on 21 March 1946 under the command of Lieutenant General George E. Stratemeyer. Composed of the First, Second, Fourth, Tenth, Eleventh, and Fourteenth Air Forces, ADC originally was equipped with North American P-51, P-82, and Lockheed P-80C aircraft, which would have had difficulty intercepting Soviet Tu-4s.

The emergence of the Soviet threat prompted a rapid growth in ADC and the production of a succession of all-weather fighters by the aviation industry. The task was not easy. The early aircraft, including the Lockheed F-94, Northrop F-89, and North American F-86D, all had problems that took years of service to resolve. They were followed in amazingly short order by the so-called century series of fighters—aircraft

like the F-101 identified by three digits. These newer aircraft had much better performance despite each having its own development problems.

The first USAF aircraft armed only with guided missiles and unguided rockets—the Convair YF-102 Delta Dagger, always called "the Deuce"—made its first flight on 24 October 1953. It had to undergo extensive development before it entered service in mid-1956, but ultimately it served with thirty-six squadrons. Perceived deficiencies in the F-102 were fixed in the Convair F-106 Delta Dart, which was fitted with the sophisticated Hughes MA-1 electronic guidance and fire control system. First flown on 26 December 1956, the well-liked Delta Dart eventually equipped fourteen squadrons and remained in service until 1988.

The sensational Lockheed XF-104 made its first flight on 7 February 1954. The F-104A, with its tremendous rate of climb and Mach 2 speed, seemed ideally suited to the ADC interceptor role. It lacked the necessary equipment to be an all-weather fighter, however, and was soon sidelined by more capable aircraft. The McDonnell F-101B first flew on 27 March 1957. It was armed with two Douglas MB-1 Genie nuclear unguided rockets in addition to three AIM-4 Falcon missiles. Slower than the F-104A, it had the advantage of a second crew member to operate the radar system.

The Bomarc, a medium-range ground-based interceptor missile, complemented ADC's airborne defenses. ADC deployed thirty-six squadrons of Bomarcs. The Mach 3 missile, first flown in 1952, was the first with an active homing system. Bomarc served for twenty years.

An extensively modified version of the F-102, the Convair F-106 was fitted with the Hughes MA-1 electronic guidance and fire control system and operated with the Semi-Automatic Ground Environment (SAGE) defense system. With a top speed of 1,327 mph and a combat radius of 730 miles, the F-106 was an ideal interceptor, remaining in front line service from 1959 through 1988. (USAF)

The BOMARC (IM-99) pilotless surface-to-air interceptor missile shown at McGuire AFB, New Jersey, in 1962. The BOMARC interceptor was tied into the SAGE air defense network. BOMARC was designed to intercept either manned bombers or air-breathing missiles. (USAF)

81

Above: In the 1950s the Air National Guard assumed an ever more important role in air defense of the North American continent. Here, Montana Air National Guard Convair F-102s patrol the northern border of the United States. The wing planform of the F-102 gave rise to its official name, the Delta Dagger. After a very long development process, the aircraft proved itself as an interceptor, equipping thirty-two ADC squadrons. It also served in Vietnam, flying combat missions from 1962 through 1969. (USAF)

Right: Air defense radar sites stretching across Canada and Greenland provided warning of aerial assault across polar routes, the most likely flight path of Russian bombers. (USAF)

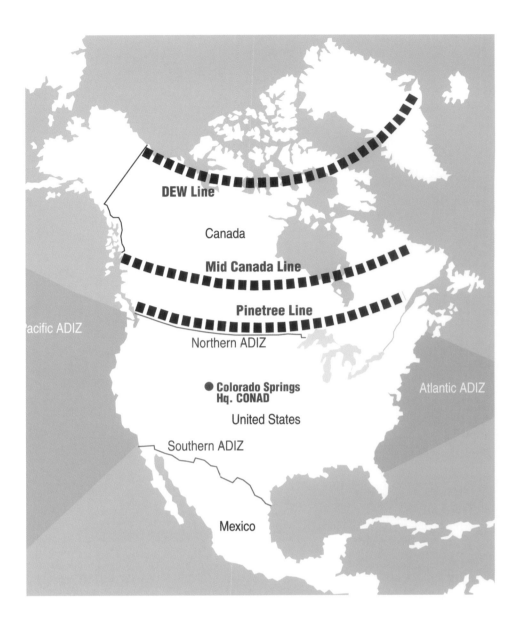

In addition to land-based radars, the Air Force built a number of radar sites at a considerable distance off shore from the United States on platforms developed for drilling oil wells on the ocean floor. Duty on these "Texas Towers" demanded much from those who manned and maintained our air defense system. (USAF)

Air Defense aircraft and missiles relied upon an extensive ground-based radar system. Radar equipment was in short supply, and in the early years of the Cold War, the Ground Observer Corps was revived. Thousands of volunteers watched the skies while the first continental radar system, appropriately called "Lashup," was improvised. The Soviet threat was serious enough to require building a series of radar installations known as the Distant Early Warning (DEW) line. Stretching more than 3,000 miles along the 69th parallel in northern Canada, this monumental engineering achievement was completed in 1955.

Two more radar lines were also built—the Pinetree line about 1,000 miles south of the DEW line, and the Mid-Canada line built across the 55th parallel from Labrador to Hudson Bay. In addition, ADC employed airborne early warning aircraft and Texas Tower sites—manned radar stations built on modified deep-water oil-drilling platforms in the North Atlantic Ocean. In 1959, work began on three Ballistic Missile Early Warning Sites, one at Point Clear Alaska, one at Thule Air Base Greenland, and one at Fylingdales in Great Britain.

Both the ADC flying mission and the early warning mission required USAF personnel to be stationed at remote arctic bases where the weather was usually bad. Air Defense Command maintained interceptor aircraft and

crews on alert at Thule AB, Greenland; Goose Bay AB, Labrador; and several other bases in Canada and Alaska. In the United States, ADC fighters were on alert at Air Force bases at Glasgow, Montana; Grand Forks and Minot in North Dakota; Marquette, Michigan; and other locations near the nation's northern border. In fair weather or foul, ADC crews launched within five minutes to intercept unidentified aircraft that might pose a threat to the United States or Canada. That ADC could fulfill this mission successfully while maintaining morale is a tribute to the command and to the men and women who served in it. The rigorous flying conditions severely tested ADC pilots. Those that survived were among the best in the Air Force.

The magnificent engineering and the highly talented personnel implicit in the employment of sophisticated century-series interceptors, supersonic missiles, and multilayered radar nets reached peak proficiency in the Semiautomatic Ground Environment (SAGE) system. SAGE, designed to process information from radar sites, the Ground Observer Corps, interceptors, and elsewhere, became operational in 1957. The system possessed the capability to identify targets, assign fighters to intercept them, and then control the battle as it evolved.

Ironically, ADC reached its highest capability just as the threat of a Soviet bomber attack began to decline. With that decline, ADC missions and assets began transferring to Air National Guard and Air Force Reserve Units. By 1980, ADC was deactivated, and its remaining assets were divided between SAC and Tactical Air Command (TAC).

The Lockheed P-80 Shooting Star began to enter the inventory in early 1945, and plans were drawn before the end of World War II to purchase 5,000. Those plans changed after V-J Day. Lockheed eventually built 1,732 P-80s for Air Force pursuit squadrons. Two of those aircraft are seen here from the Rim Highway in southern California. Only the exhaust gases of the third aircraft are visible in this illustration, but one future pilot has that lead aircraft in the sights of his cap pistol. ("Shootin' Stars of the 94th," Stan Vosburg)

The North American F-86 Sabre was immortalized in MiG Alley over the Yalu, but it served TAC long and well in many theaters. Here are four from the 44th Fighter Bomber Squadron over the Philippine Islands on 22 June 1954. (USAF)

The Tactical Air Command

Early post war planning had called for tactical aviation to be a part of the Continental Air Command, but General of the Army Dwight D. Eisenhower wanted a separate command for close air support work, and Tactical Air Command was created for that purpose. Like SAC and ADC, TAC was initially equipped with World War II-era aircraft. Its mission was to train forces for tactical operations anywhere. This slight disconnect—the training of forces for other commanders to use—resulted in a loss of TAC's bargaining power when it came to pressing for resources. The command conducted operations from three numbered air forces, the First at Langley AFB, the Ninth at Shaw AFB, and the Twelfth at Bergstrom AFB.

Unlike the other two major commands, TAC ran into an immediate organizational problem as its commander, Major General Elwood R. Quesada, feuded with General Hoyt S. Vandenberg, who became Chief of Staff on 30 April 1948.

The stringent budgets of the day caused cuts in the force structure, and TAC was reduced in status and incorporated within Continental Air Command in January 1949. The outbreak of the Korean War caused TAC to be reestablished in August 1950 with additional responsibilities for electronic countermeasures, tactical airlift, and air-to-ground operations.

Throughout its history, TAC furnished units and pilots of the utmost skill and bravery to overseas commands. The nature of U.S. policy meant that our wars were fought at long distances from the homeland, over enemy territory, and usually under disadvantageous conditions. None of this mattered to TAC crews who executed their missions brilliantly despite all obstacles.

After the Korean War, TAC changed rapidly, acquiring a host of capable new aircraft and gaining a nuclear weapons delivery mission. It was a golden time for the aviation industry, and TAC received a succession of excellent fighters and bombers. Fighters included the North American F-100, Lockheed F-104, McDonnell F/RF-101, McDonnell F/RF-4, Republic F-105, McDonnell Douglas F-15, and General Dynamics F-16. The bombers and attack planes included the Douglas B/RB-66, Martin B-57, and Fairchild A-10. TAC also operated Lockheed C-130 and EC-130 aircraft.

TAC still encountered difficulties acquiring enough resources to accomplish its assigned tasks. This resulted in many improvisations. In some cases, TAC converted older aircraft such as the Douglas A-26 Invader and, long after the aircraft was obsolete, used it effectively in a counter-insurgency role. TAC also modified trainer aircraft like the North American T-28 and Cessna T-37 into combat aircraft. TAC even adopted the Douglas Skyraider from the Navy and Marines to serve as a very effective Air Force attack plane in low-intensity conflict. Although these "recycled" aircraft were bravely flown, TAC still needed more purpose-built aircraft for its assigned missions.

The esprit of TAC aircrew and ground personnel enabled the command to respond forcefully and well to crises around the world like those in Lebanon and Formosa in 1958, Berlin in 1961, Cuba in 1962, and in Southeast Asia from 1964 through 1973. The in-flight refueling techniques that gave Strategic Air Command unlimited range and great flexibility did the same for TAC, which quickly adapted to the concept and employed it routinely. Initially, TAC only used in-flight refueling for long-distance deployments, but during the Vietnam War, aerial refueling became an essential component of tactical combat missions.

On 1 August 1961, General Walter Campbell Sweeney Jr., a SAC veteran, took command of TAC. Sweeney applied SAC's philosophy to the

The USAF's first operational jet bomber, the four-jet North American B-45 served with distinction from its first flight on 17 March 1947 until it left active service in 1958. The RB-45C reconnaissance version saw service in Korea and in Europe, some flying clandestine overflight missions. (USAF)

Above: *In the phrase of the day, TAC was "SACimzied" with the arrival of General Walter C. Sweeney Jr. who brought with him the concept of centralized control of operations that was key to SAC's success. Sweeney had distinguished himself as a commander during World War II, and led the first B-47 non-stop flight across the Pacific in 1954. He is shown here with Technical Sergeant Kellis E. Deaver, just after Deaver parachuted in as a part of a Tactical Air Command Combat Control Team. (USAF)*

Left: *The first of the "century-series" fighters, the North American F-100 was also the first U.S. fighter capable of supersonic speed in level flight. Entering service in 1953, the F-100 went on to give superb service in Vietnam. The Air National Guard flew the Super Sabre until November 1979. Many F-100s were later converted to drone aircraft. In this illustration, an airman pulls ordnance safety pins before the F-100D heads for the bombing range. ("Soon, Distant Thunder," John Young)*

The Douglas Invader not only served in three wars (World War II, Korea, and Vietnam) it had three designations. It was first the A-26, then the B-26, and then, in Vietnam, once again the A-26. First flown on 10 July 1942, the "little racer" as some pilots called it, was extremely versatile and well liked by crews. Here, in July 1953, Captain John J. Croston (left) and A/2C Charles T. Thompson, flight engineer, check the instrument panel prior to taking off on another night combat mission over Korea. (USAF)

command and this approach initially worked well. His efforts to central-ize complemented the management technique of Secretary of Defense Robert S. McNamara, who also believed in running a tight ship. These methods served well for TAC during the difficult years when 50 percent of the fighter force was deployed overseas.

The war in Southeast Asia saw TAC and SAC exchange roles. Tactical aircraft were formed into massive strike forces that included fighters, fighter-bombers, and electronic warfare aircraft. Great armadas of F-105, F-4, and EB-66 aircraft plunged deep into North Vietnam, executing strategic missions. Meanwhile, SAC B-52s per-formed tactical missions bombing suspected Viet Cong concentrations in South Vietnam.

As the Southeast Asia war ended, General Robert J. Dixon began the slow process of rebuilding TAC. Under funded, plagued with aging aircraft and difficult organizational issues, Dixon faced an uphill battle. He began by introducing a more realistic training exercise, Red Flag, which slowly restored the sharp edge to TAC combat capability.

General Wilber L. Creech, named to succeed General Dixon in 1978, expanded Red Flag and introduced decentralized, team-based management ideas, moving slowly at first and then accelerating the pace as people became accustomed to his methods. His credo was "command must be reasoned." He seemed to be everywhere at once in TAC, turning up on flight lines, in barracks, in mess halls, in motor pools. The ubiquitous Creech sought out the best ideas from his best people and applied them with an ethical rigor that proved startling to some.

He gained results almost immediately. The TAC accident rate dropped from one every 13,000 flying hours to one every 50,000 flying hours and kept on dropping. During that same interval, the aircraft sortie rate doubled because of improvements in maintenance that reduced the out-of-commission rate by 75 percent.

Top, left: *A workhorse of the Vietnam War, the Republic F-105 Thunderchief was known far better by the nickname "Thud." Designed originally as a nuclear bomber, the F-105 bore the brunt of long-range attacks on North Vietnamese targets for many years. (USAF)*

Top, right: *A Texas Air National Guard Boeing KC-97L tanker provides aerial refueling for a McDonnell F-4D from USAFE. The difference in normal cruising air speed is reflected in the angle of attack of the two aircraft, with the KC-97 flying nose-down, and the F-4D flying nose-up. (USAF)*

Above: *General Wilber L. Creech brought a new management philosophy to TAC when he assumed command. Here he listens to Chief Master Sergeant Watkins explain a maintenance procedure. (USAF)*

Left: *In 1958, TAC anticipated the future by creating a Composite Air Strike Force (CASF) designed for rapid deployment to any area of the world in response to "limited" wars. In this shot, a Boeing KB-50 tanker refuels three aircraft using the probe and drogue system. They are the North American F-100 at the right wing, the Douglas B-66 bomber at the center position, and the McDonnell F-101 on the left wing. Flanking the formation to the rear are two Lockheed C-130 turboprop transports carrying flyaway kits, personnel, and supplies necessary to keep the CASF in the field. (USAF)*

Top: *Few aircraft were better to fly than the Douglas C-54. it proved itself invaluable during the Berlin Airlift; doing a job for which it had not been designed and doing it well. (USAF)*

Above: *Hundreds of Douglas C-47s remained in service during the 1950s, and some were fitted with JATO units for special tasks, such as the rescue of downed crews inside enemy territory. (USAF)*

Airlift in Transition: From Gooney Bird to Galaxy

The U.S. concept of air transport grew from the primitive days before World War II when transports were procured in small numbers to the vast fleets of Douglas C-47s, which General Dwight D. Eisenhower identified as one of the five most important weapons of the war.

Modern USAF air cargo delivery can trace its ancestry directly back to the Air Transport Command (ATC), established on 30 April 1942. ATC conducted worldwide operations delivering personnel and materiel critical to the U.S. Army war effort. At its peak, ATC had 3,700 aircraft and more than 300,000 personnel.

The Naval Air Transport Service (NATS) had been formed on 12 December 1941, and though smaller than ATC, performed similar functions for the U.S. Navy. On 1 June 1948, ATC and NATS were inactivated, and a new joint command, the Military Air Transport Service (MATS), was formed under the command of Major General Lawrence S. Kuter, with Rear Admiral John P. Whitney, United States Navy, as vice commander.

General Kuter reported directly to the Chief of Staff of the United States Air Force. With 824 aircraft and 54,164 personnel assigned, MATS operated three divisions: Atlantic, Continental, and Pacific. The command also was responsible for managing the Airways and Air Communications Service, the Air Photographic and Charting Service, the Air Weather Service, the Air Rescue Service, and Flight Service.

MATS scored an important diplomatic victory for airpower when it successfully broke the Soviet blockade of Berlin. This was the first in a long series of compassionate missions in which MATS would be used to save lives. One of the most notable of these was the operation in the Congo, from July 1960 to January 1964, when MATS flew 2,128 relief

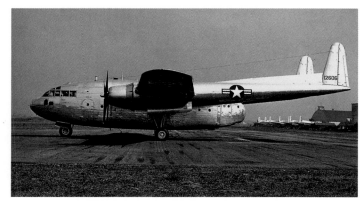

missions, transported almost 64,000 personnel, and delivered more than 18,000 tons of vital cargo. On 1 January 1966, MATS became the Military Airlift Command (MAC) and, in addition to its strategic airlift mission, gained the combat role of dropping paratroops and cargo.

The war in Southeast Asia made heavy demands upon MAC. The command provided the strategic airlift that moved troops and equipment from the United States to forward bases in the Southeast Asia Theater and also augmented theater tactical airlift keeping many ground units alive by aerial resupply. Airlift crews were heroically active during the siege of Khe Sanh, delivering vital equipment and evacuating the wounded.

During World War II, ATC had used the Douglas C-47 and Curtiss C-46 with distinction. The Douglas C-54 proved key in the Berlin Airlift. Korea saw the C-46s and C-47s return to the fray, with the addition of Fairchild C-119 aircraft. Although these aircraft functioned as well as could be expected, design deficiencies prompted the call for a more modern transport for theater operations. That aircraft proved to be the versatile, long-lived Lockheed C-130 Hercules, which first entered service in December 1956.

One thing learned from early airlift operations was that fewer large aircraft were more efficient than more numerous small aircraft. This realization led to the Douglas C-124, introduced to the fleet in 1950. The C-124 was followed in time by the much more modern Douglas C-133

Above: *Air Force humanitarian airlift operations range from the Arctic to Equatorial Africa. Here grain is unloaded from a Lockheed C-130 Hercules in Africa. (USAF)*

Right: *During the Korean War, TAC recognized the need for a much more capable and efficient cargo plane. The result was the magnificent Lockheed C-130 Hercules, designed by famed Willis Hawkins. It became tremendously successful in many roles, including gunship, tanker, electronic warfare, and electronic reconnaissance, but it has made its major mark in the world as an agent of compassion, delivering food and medicine to remote locations following flood, drought, or earthquake. ("On the Deck Over Scotland," Gil Cohen)*

Below: *The Douglas C-133 Cargomaster had four Pratt & Whitney T34 turboprops and was designed to transport very large military stores, including intercontinental ballistic missiles. The aircraft, troubled by a series of accidents, was withdrawn from service in the early 1970s. (USAF)*

turboprop—an aircraft designed specifically to transport ICBMs. Unfortunately, metal fatigue problems limited the useful service life of the C-133.

MAC entered the jet age in 1961 with the arrival of four squadrons of Boeing C-135 transports. Lockheed C-141 Starlifters began arriving in 1965 to be followed five years later by the controversial, but ultimately well-regarded, Lockheed C-5. These large, fast aircraft quite literally revolutionized air cargo operations, for they were designed as a part of a system that also included advanced materiel-handling equipment. The crews loved them, for they reduced the time required for long over-water flights.

Operation Nickel Grass, the aerial resupply of Israel with weapons, munitions, and materiel during the October War of 1973, demonstrated the immense value of these long-range large-capacity aircraft. Nickel Grass also revealed the vital necessity of using aerial refueling in MAC airlift operations to avoid dependence on foreign airfields. During this operation, the Lockheed C-5A proved its worth beyond all doubt to both the USAF and to the critics who had attacked it for years.

MAC's greatest challenge came during the Persian Gulf War, when all of the preparation, all of the training, and all of the effort paid off. As part of Operation Desert Shield and in preparation for Operation Desert Storm, the command airlifted the 82d Airborne Division, the 101st Airborne Division, and the 7th Marine Expeditionary Brigade from the United States to Saudi Arabia. From July 1990 to January 1991, MAC flew 15,402 missions airlifting 544,000 tons of equipment from the United States to the Arabian Peninsula. To assist in this massive airlift, MAC activated the Civil Reserve Air Fleet calling 154 civilian passenger and

Above: *The C-130 was tough enough to get in and out of short landing strips under enemy fire, but sometimes the LAPES (Low Altitude Parachute Extraction System) was the preferred way to get heavy equipment— like this Sheridan tank—on the ground in short order. (USAF)*

Below: *A derivative of the DC-9 commercial transport, the McDonnell Douglas C-9 Nightingale entered service in August 1968. Twenty-one were procured as aeromedical evacuation aircraft for service with the Military Airlift Command's 375th Aeromedical Airlift Wing. (USAF)*

Left: *The first Lockheed C-141A flew on 17 December 1963 and proved to be an immediate success. After years of service with the Military Air Transport Command, the aircraft was "stretched" by adding a twenty-three foot section to the fuselage. Designated the C-141B, the modified aircraft gave the Air Force a great increase in airlift capacity—the equivalent of increasing the C-141 fleet by some eighty-seven aircraft—at relatively modest cost. A C-141B is shown here at McMurdo Sound, Antarctica. ("Inspection Party," Keith Ferris)*

Few airplanes endured as much controversy as the Lockheed C-5A Galaxy, and few airplanes have proven to be as valuable to the USAF. The Galaxy particularly distinguished itself airlifting supplies to Israel during the October War of 1973 and airlifting supplies for coalition forces during the Gulf war. (USAF)

cargo aircraft along with crews to Federal service. This first ever activation of the Civil Reserve Air Fleet worked smoothly and provided a very substantial increase in MAC capabilities.

The Total Force

During the Cold War, the United States depended upon the superb support provided by both the Air National Guard and the Air Force Reserve. Guard and Reserve squadrons played a major role in Air Defense Command, providing interceptor crews at numerous bases in the United States. During the Korean War, the 1961 crisis in Europe over access to Berlin, the Vietnam War, and other emergencies, Guard and Reserve units and individuals served extended periods of active duty, augmenting regular Air Force organizations in the United States and overseas. The success of Guard and Reserve units in fulfilling air defense, airlift, and tactical missions led to even greater responsibilities.

In 1966, Air Force leaders proposed incorporating the USAF, the USAF Reserve, and the Air National Guard into what was called the "total force concept." In 1973, Secretary of Defense James R. Schlesinger called for the total force concept to be applied to all aspects of Air Force management, including planning, programming, and employment. Where once Air National Guard and Air Force Reserve personnel had been regarded as "weekend warriors" used primarily as a replacement pool,

Two Vought A-7D Corsairs loaded with practice bombs, take off from RAF Wittering, UK, on 17 June 1978. They were participating in Operation Coronet Teal, the first peace-time deployment of the Air National Guard to Europe. The A-7, an aircraft developed by the Navy and subsequently purchased by the Air Force, served well in Vietnam both in close support and in search and rescue operations. (USAF)

they were now expected to fulfill all of the proficiency requirements of the Air Force. Instead of second line aircraft, they received the most modern equipment available and were held to the highest USAF operational standards. The Air National Guard and the Air Force Reserve have proven the soundness of this concept time after time.

Summary

The Cold War Air Force confronted enormous responsibilities over a forty-year period. It was tasked to be strong enough to prevent a nuclear war, and simultaneously, to contain the expansion of communism. It fought long and bloody wars in Asia under adverse conditions while constrained by crippling rules of engagement. At the same time, the USAF was tasked to carry out compassionate missions throughout the world. The Air Force accomplished all of this with limited budgets and during times of great social change within the United States. Among these social changes was the challenge to fully integrate women and minorities, a challenge that the USAF met with greater success than most other agencies.

The success of the United States Air Force in achieving its many Cold War objectives may be attributed to a number of factors. The USAF was always a volunteer organization, one that embraced its duties freely and with passion. The combat commands—SAC, TAC, and ADC—were backed up by a marvelous system of logistics. Research and development was adequately funded for many years, and there was good liaison with both industry and the academic community, although support from the latter eroded during the Vietnam era.

The USAF, well led by dedicated officers who put the service first, was particularly fortunate in the selection of many of its top commanders. Yet in the last analysis, success depended upon the hundreds of thousands of non-commissioned officers and enlisted personnel who fulfilled their duties with imagination and rigor despite relatively low wages and challenges to family life resulting from frequent moves and remote assignments.

Economically, there never was a time when it made sense to stay in the service rather than seek employment in the civilian economy. Despite this, the patriotism and the valor of young men and women who embraced the values of the USAF kept its standards high.

The Air Force tried hard to improve conditions for enlisted personnel despite budget and operational considerations. The quality of the USAF enlisted force was brought home in the declining years of the Cold War by comments from Soviet officials visiting USAF bases. The Soviet officers accepted the material advantages evident in the United States, but they could not believe the quality they found in USAF enlisted personnel, nor in the responsibility that was placed on them. They said that there was simply no counterpart to this able and talented force in the armed forces of the Soviet Union. This is perhaps the highest accolade that could be paid to USAF enlisted personnel, compensating in part for all the sacrifices they made while contributing so much to winning the Cold War.

This photo shows the rugged C-130 landing on an unimproved strip carved out of a Peruvian mountainside to bring relief supplies after a 1970 earthquake. (USAF)

The McDonnell Douglas F-15 has a maximum speed well over Mach 2 and a thrust-to-weight ratio that provides a rocket-like rate of climb. (USAF)

United States
Air Forces
in Europe

United States Air Forces in Europe

Warren A. Trest

The rise of U.S. Air Force and North Atlantic Treaty Organization (NATO) airpower during the Cold War years occurred on a scale unimagined when the Western alliance was formed in 1949. An outgrowth of the Cold War, the North Atlantic Treaty Organization banded allies together for collective security after the "iron curtain" descended across Eastern Europe, and the USSR engaged in a war of intimidation against the West. Four decades later, the Cold War ended to the sounds of the Berlin Wall coming down and the Soviet Union crumbling. NATO's formidable tactical air forces backed up by U.S. strategic and tactical airpower had a leading role in the drama.

Throughout the Cold War, the U.S. Air Forces in Europe (USAFE) was the air component of the U.S. European Command (USEUCOM) and an essential element of NATO airpower. At the Cold War's denouement in 1989, USAFE commanded three numbered air forces from headquarters at Ramstein Air Base (AB), Germany. These lean tactical headquarters were Third Air Force at Mildenhall Royal Air Force Station (RAF Mildenhall) in the United Kingdom, Sixteenth Air Force at Torrejon AB, Spain, and Seventeenth Air Force at Sembach AB, Germany. Sixteenth Air Force headquarters was preparing for a move to Aviano AB, Italy, to meet the terms of a new bilateral agreement signed by the United States and Spanish governments requiring that all U.S. forces be withdrawn from Spain by 1992.

USAFE's force structure—including ten tactical fighter wings equipped with F-15C/D Eagles, F-16C/D Fighting Falcons, F-111F Aardvarks, F-4G Phantoms, and A-10 Thunderbolt IIs, and the 32d Tactical Fighter Squadron with F-15C/Ds at Soesterberg AB in the Netherlands—was

Above: An RF-4C Phantom flying a routine training mission strikes an elegant pose against the backdrop of a majestic German castle. This Phantom is from the 26th Tactical Reconnaissance Wing at Zweibrucken Air Base, Germany. (USAF)

Page 94–95: An F-15 Eagle (left), two F-16s, and an A-10—all from the 52d Tactical Fighter Wing at Spangdahlem AB, Germany— represent some of the American tactical aircraft committed to the defense of Western Europe during the Cold War. (USAF)

Opposite: The 48th Tactical Fighter Wing at RAF Lakenheath in the United Kingdom received the first F-15E Strike Eagles to be based in Europe. The advanced F-15E models are designed to carry out all-weather deep interdiction strikes in addition to their traditional air superiority mission. Earlier models of the F-15 had been in the USAFE inventory since the first Eagle squadron arrived in 1977. (USAF)

Right: The Fairchild A-10 Thunderbolt II is the only aircraft developed by the Air Force exclusively to support troops on the battlefield. The deadly ordnance load carried by the A-10 includes a 30-mm cannon that fires a projectile designed to penetrate the armor of tanks. In August 1978, the 81st Tactical Fighter Wing at RAF Bentwaters/Woodbridge became the first USAFE unit to add A-10s to its inventory. (USAF)

These three Air Force aircraft, a General Dynamics F-16 Fighting Falcon, a Republic A-10 Thunderbolt II, and a McDonnell Douglas F-15 Eagle, played important roles in NATO defense plans during the Cold War. (USAF)

Below: An F-16 Fighting Falcon from the 52d Tactical Fighter Wing at Spangdahlem AB, Germany, taxis into position for take-off. The first F-16s to be based in Europe were assigned to the 50th Tactical Fighter Wing at Hahn AB, Germany, in September 1981. (USAF)

primed and ready for any contingency, conventional or nuclear. Two tactical missile wings with ground-launched cruise missiles (GLCMs), a tactical reconnaissance wing of RF-4s, an electronic combat wing with EF-111As, and an array of supporting units backed up the fighters. The GLCM wings were on their way out because of the Intermediate-range Nuclear Forces Treaty signed by U.S. and Soviet leaders in 1987

General Michael J. Dugan, the U.S. Air Forces in Europe commander in chief (CINCUSAFE) at the end of the 1980s, was dual-hatted as commander of NATO's Allied Air Forces Central Europe (COMAAFCE). As COMAAFCE, he controlled some 2,000 tactical aircraft through the Second

and Fourth Allied Tactical Air Forces (ATAFs). These air resources came from Belgium, Canada, West Germany, the Netherlands, the United Kingdom, and the United States. On NATO's southern flank, Allied Air Forces Southern Europe at Naples, Italy, commanded two additional tactical air forces in Italy and Turkey. This combined force was backed up in wartime by U.S. strategic airpower and tactical forces deploying from the United States to seventy collocated operating bases (COBs) throughout NATO.

The imposing array of tactical airpower dotting the landscape of Western Europe had done its part to deter Warsaw Pact aggression and to end the Cold War. A daunting force of modern tactical fighters that could deliver crippling conventional or nuclear strikes with deadly accuracy, the combined NATO air posture comprised the best the West had to offer in

Above: *An F-111F of the 48th Tactical Fighter Wing based at RAF Lakenheath landing at RAF Alconbury, October 1977. The wing converted from F-4Ds to F-111Fs starting in March 1977. The first versions of the swept-wing fighter to be based in Europe were F-111Es, which entered the USAFE inventory in 1970 and were assigned to the 20th Tactical Fighter Wing's 79th Tactical Fighter Squadron at RAF Upper Heyford. (USAF)*

Below: *An artist's vision of a NATO airborne warning and control aircraft refueling over Germany. The artist had flown to Geilenkirchen, Germany, with the Ohio Air National Guard's 121st Air Refueling Wing to observe the refueling of AWACS aircraft. (John Clark, United States Air Force Art Collection)*

tactical aviation technology and fighter pilot ingenuity. A later USAFE commander in chief, General Michael E. Ryan, noted that during the Cold War tactical airpower developed "one year, one crisis, and one struggle at a time." Forty years in the making, the USAFE force structure evolved from a shoestring occupation arm left over in Europe from World War II.

Postwar Europe, 1945 to 1950

Postwar demobilization not only dismantled the mighty Army Air Forces that commanded the skies over Europe, but also resulted in a draw down of U.S. occupation forces overseas and a low state of military readiness at home. These actions sent the wrong message to the USSR about the willingness of the United States to defend Western Europe—and miscalculation on the part of the Soviets leading to a Communist takeover of Czechoslovakia and a rail blockade of Berlin in 1948. The Berlin Airlift carried out jointly by U.S. and British transports lifted the blockade of

the beleaguered city, but this was not the only allied response. These first hostile acts of the Cold War led to the establishment of NATO and set the stage for the return of U.S. airpower to the skies over Europe.

Before the Berlin crisis, USAFE's combat capability had been reduced to a single composite group of F-47 Thunderbolts and A-26 Invaders located at Neubiberg AB, Germany, and a few reconnaissance planes at nearby Furstenfeldbruck AB. In March 1947, the U.S. theater commander, General Joseph McNarney, informed the War Department that the few combat air forces left in Europe had become an administrative burden to his headquarters and were no longer needed. His planners recommended that combat air forces be permanently based in the United States and rotated to Europe for training and showing the U.S. flag.

At the start of the Berlin Blockade, to show U.S. resolve, President Harry S. Truman ordered a wing of jet fighters to Germany and two groups of B-29s to England. The 36th Fighter-Bomber Wing arrived in August by ship with seventy-five F-80 Shooting Star jet fighters and joined the 86th Wing at Neubiberg. Both wings were placed under the newly activated 2d Air Division at Wiesbaden AB. The two groups of B-29s were rotational units from Strategic Air Command (SAC) and remained under SAC control while in Europe.

Air Force leaders had the vision to plan for the return of combat air forces to overseas bases before the rail blockade of Berlin. Air Staff planning focused primarily on the development and deployment of strategic

Lockheed F-80 Shooting Stars arrive in Bremen, Germany, in 1946. After unloading, these aircraft were towed to a nearby airport, assembled, and delivered to the 55th Fighter Group based near Giebelstadt, Germany. (USAF)

Air Force transports forged a worldwide reputation for dependability during the Berlin Airlift. Each year airlift crews conduct a range of airlift missions from routine channel missions to unit moves to humanitarian relief—and they continue to deliver the goods. (USAF)

The Berlin Air Lift

Colonel Drue L. DeBerry, USAF (Ret)

"This is a hell of a way to run a railroad," Major General William H. Tunner thundered in the cockpit of his C-54 on Friday, 13 August 1948. Heavy rain and thick clouds obscured the runway at Tempelhof Airport in Berlin. Three aircraft tried to land; one overshot the runway and crashed; the second landed long and blew two tires on the runway; the third missed the primary runway completely, landing instead on an auxiliary runway and ground-looping. Arriving at three-minute intervals, the stream of aircraft waiting to land began to stack up over Berlin.

Tunner keyed his microphone. "This is Tunner. Send every airplane in the stack back to home base." A nervous ground controller asked him to confirm the order, then began redirecting air traffic.

In June, the Russians had closed all surface access to Berlin from the West. Britain, France, and the United States had the choice of withdrawing from Berlin or trying to supply—by air—the 4,500 tons of food and fuel needed daily to sustain their garrisons and the two million Germans living in their zones of the city. The Allies chose to airlift supplies into Berlin. Major General Curtis E. LeMay, commander of U.S. Air Forces in Europe, launched the airlift on 26 June 1948 with the 102 C-47s and two C-54s in his command.

Recognizing the inadequacy of the C-47 for the task, the Air Force rushed 200 of the larger C-54s to Germany and dispatched Major General William H. Tunner, experienced and successful commander of the China-Burma-India Hump airlift, to manage the operation. In his first fifteen days in command, Tunner had called for reopening several decommissioned bases in Germany to support the airlift, and he had directed that the airlift operate around the clock with the goal of one-minute separation between aircraft inbound to land at Berlin. He also directed that all aircraft fly to Berlin through two of the three corridors available for flights over the Russian zone, and that all returning aircraft fly the third corridor back to their home base. His staff established precise airspeeds for C-54 climb, cruise, and descent to maintain aircraft separation. After the August 13 fiasco, Tunner brought newly developed ground-controlled approach radars to Berlin and directed that all pilots make instrument landing approaches, regardless of weather, and that any pilot

Left: From the rubble of a destroyed city, children watch an American C-54 land in Berlin. Eighty percent of these flights delivered bagged coal. Workers unloaded 20,000 pounds of bagged coal in less than ten minutes. Thirty minutes after landing, aircraft departed. (USAF)

Above: Landing at Tempelhof. (USAF)

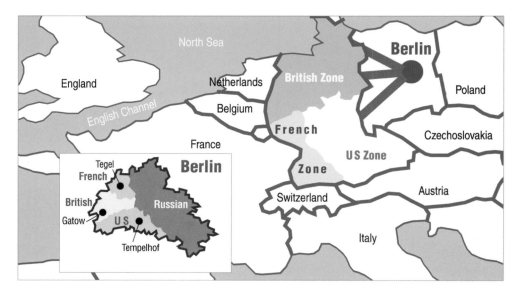

who failed to land on the first approach should return to home base with his cargo.

Daily airlift totals climbed steadily as airlifters fine-tuned the system. On 17 April 1949, airlift aircraft delivered 13,000 tons of cargo—including the equivalent of 600 railroad cars of coal—to Berlin. The Russians, tacitly acknowledging defeat, lifted the blockade the following month. The airlift continued through September. Between June 1948 and October 1949, Berlin Airlift crews from the United States and Great Britain completed 189,000 flights and delivered 2.3 million tons of cargo. Seventy-seven people—39 British, 31 Americans, and seven Germans—lost their lives to various causes during the airlift. The city of Berlin, surrounded by the Red army, remained a beacon of hope to all who opposed communism.

Top: During the airlift, an aircraft arrived at Tempelhof or departed the airport every ninety seconds, twenty-four hours a day. While German workers unloaded the aircraft, operations officers and weather officers briefed the crews at the airplane, and German Red Cross women served coffee and donuts. (USAF)

Above, left: Airlift aircraft were restricted to a twenty-mile-wide corridor over Soviet-controlled territory.

Above, right: Workers load fresh milk aboard a C-47 at Rhein Main AB for babies in Berlin. (USAF)

Left: When twenty-seven-year-old Lieutenant Gail Halvorsen discovered that the children of Berlin were doing without sweets, he began dropping handkerchief parachutes with candy and gum just before his aircraft landed. The practice became widespread. Here, Halvorsen is surrounded by some of the children expressing their appreciation. (USAF)

On their way to a British base, Strategic Air Command B-29s overfly Dover's cliffs. The Superfortresses became a common sight in the skies over England from the late 1940s through the mid-1950s when they rotated to the European theater on a regular basis. (USAF)

The first Republic F-84 Thunderjet fighter-bombers arrived in Europe in late 1950 and were assigned to the 36th Fighter Bomber Wing at Furstenfeldbruck as replacements for F-80s. By mid-1952, some F-84s were modified to carry tactical nuclear weapons. (USAF)

bombers as a nuclear deterrent, rather than on tactical air forces. In January 1946, General Carl A. Spaatz and Air Marshal Sir Arthur Tedder of the Royal Air Force negotiated access to bases in East Anglia for B-29 operations. A few months later six B-29s deployed to Germany as a show of force when two unarmed USAFE C-47s were shot down after straying across the Yugoslav border. The following summer, SAC began deploying rotational squadrons of B-29s to Europe and the Pacific on a regular basis. Rotational squadrons were so called because although based in the United States, they deployed to forward bases in Europe or Asia for several months each year.

The choice of Lieutenant General Curtis E. LeMay to command USAFE in October 1947 was an indication of the priority the Air Force placed on operating B-29s in the European environment. The giant bombers came off the assembly line too late to see action in Europe during World War II, but had been put to good use by LeMay in taking the war to the Japanese homeland. General LeMay immediately announced plans to improve the readiness of his new command. A year later, he turned the USAFE reins over to Lieutenant General John K. Cannon and returned to the United States to forge SAC into a viable nuclear deterrent.

The nuclear deterrent was more bluff than brawn during those perilous postwar years. The B-29s were not intercontinental bombers, and those deploying to NATO bases at the time were not armed with atomic bombs. General Dwight D. Eisenhower, who became NATO's first Supreme Allied Commander in December 1950, said that all the Soviets needed to march across Europe were enough pairs of shoes. Nonetheless, British

Above: *This air traffic controller communicates with aircraft arriving or departing Berlin through narrow corridors across Soviet-controlled territory. During the Berlin airlift, crews were required to maintain precise timing over check points to assure an even flow of air traffic into and out of the city. (USAF)*

Prime Minister Sir Winston Churchill credited U.S. airpower and the atomic bomb with having saved Europe from Soviet domination.

In the spring of 1951, General Eisenhower activated his new headquarters, Allied Command Europe and Supreme Headquarters Allied Powers, Europe (SHAPE) at Rocquencourt, near Paris. NATO's Allied Air Forces Central Europe (AAFCE) was formed at Fontainebleau, France, with CINCUSAFE serving in a dual role as the AAFCE commander. A year later, AAFCE organized NATO's air forces into the Second and Fourth Allied Tactical Air Forces. A USAFE numbered air force commander served dually as the head of the Fourth ATAF at Landsberg, Germany. The lines of authority for NATO's air forces changed in 1953 when command of AAFCE was given to a British officer.

Above: *The crew of the last flight of Operation Vittles, the airlift undertaken to defeat the Soviet blockade of Berlin, posed for a picture on September 30, 1949, before taking off from Rhein-Main. Brigadier General Edward H. Alexander, commander, 61st Troop Carrier Wing, shakes hands with pilot Captain Harry D. Immel. The rest of the crew, left to right, are First Lieutenant Charles N. Reece, First Lieutenant James C. Powell, Staff Sergeant Jerry G. Cooksy, and Technical Sergeant Matthew M. Terenzi. (USAF)*

While planning was underway to strengthen NATO's military posture, a chain of ominous events dramatically raised the stakes of the Cold War. Mao Tse-tung's rise to power in China and the Soviet Union's explosion of its first atomic bomb in 1949, followed in June 1950 by the outbreak of war in Korea, threatened world peace, and hastened rearmament in the West. The Truman Administration did not limit its military buildup to the fighting in Korea, but accelerated efforts to acquire more bases in Europe and to strengthen NATO's force posture. If the Communists were willing to risk a wider war in Korea, Western leaders worried that Germany might be next.

Rebuilding Airpower in Europe in the 1950s

The decade of the 1950s was a period of expansion for USAFE and NATO. At the start of the decade, USAFE was a skeletal force of approximately 30,000 military personnel and fewer than 400 aircraft, mostly support planes, spread around a dozen or so bases in England and Germany. The

Above: *These North American F-86 Sabre jets arrived with the Air National Guard's 116th Fighter Interceptor Squadron at RAF Shepards Grove, Suffolk, England, on 27 August 1951. The deployment was part of the theater build-up during the Korean War. (USAF)*

Above: *In July 1952 at Goose Bay Air Base, Labrador, dozens of F-84G Thunderjets en route to duty at Wethersfield, England, form a line as long as the eye can see. On arrival in England, they joined the 49th Air Division. (USAF)*

few USAFE combat aircraft were crammed onto three German bases shared with SAC's rotational B-29s. By the end of the 1950s, the command had grown to 67,000 military personnel and 1,600 aircraft. The USAFE base structure had expanded to 29 installations in nine countries—France, Germany, Italy, Libya, Morocco, the Netherlands, Spain, Turkey, and the United Kingdom. SAC operated nine additional bases in the theater.

The Korean War had first claim on combat resources at the start of the fifties. By the time the armistice was signed in July 1953, however, TAC had augmented USAFE with an air division, three fighter-bomber wings, two light bombardment wings, two troop carrier wings, one tactical reconnaissance wing, and some fifteen specialized units. In September 1950, the 36th Fighter-Bomber Wing at Furstenfeldbruck AB received the command's first F-84E Thunderjets as replacements for aging F-80 Shooting Stars. A year later, the 81st Fighter Interceptor Wing at RAF Bentwaters received new F-86 Sabres. The 86th Fighter-Bomber Wing at Landstuhl AB, Germany, received Sabres in 1953. Starting in the fall of 1954, TAC augmented USAFE by deploying units earmarked for NATO to Europe for six-month training periods.

Strategic Air Command received the lion's share of the defense budget during the 1950s and dominated the development and employment of Air Force weapon systems. The command owned all of the Air

Force aerial refueling assets, and it operated a sizeable force of tactical fighters and reconnaissance aircraft. In 1955, SAC had thirty-nine aerial refueling squadrons and a tactical force of 568 F-84s and RF-84s dispersed among six strategic fighter wings and one reconnaissance wing. By 1957, SAC had acquired the B-52 Stratofortress and no longer needed fighter escorts. The fighters were transferred to TAC, but the doctrine governing their employment through the end of the 1950s remained more strategic in orientation than tactical.

The Air Force implemented plans in the early 1950s to equip tactical air forces for a forward nuclear deterrent role. In the summer of 1952, the Air Staff sent the nuclear-capable 49th Air Division from TAC to RAF Sculthorpe in the United Kingdom. Two wings equipped with B-45s and F-84s were assigned to the division. Their mission was to conduct tactical nuclear operations, thereby freeing SAC's bombers for the strategic offensive. Under NATO planning, U.S. nuclear capabilities were combined with NATO forces to form the sword and shield of deterrence against the Soviet threat.

The threat against Western Europe grew more ominous when the Soviets tested a hydrogen bomb in August 1953, one month after shooting stopped in Korea. The end of the Korean War gave the Eisenhower Administration greater latitude in rearming Western Europe and in building up the U.S. strategic arsenal. The Administration's "New Look" at national defense proposed to arm and prepare allied nations to defend against local aggression under the umbrella of U.S. nuclear deterrence. In October 1953, the National Security Council issued NSC 162/2 formally adopting a strategy of massive retaliation. The paper gave notice that the Administration would retaliate with strategic nuclear weapons if the Soviets attacked the United States or its allies.

As it applied to NATO, the new "trip wire" strategy relied on tactical and strategic nuclear weapons to counter the Soviet advantage in conventional military forces. By 1956, all USAF tactical fighter squadrons assigned to NATO were trained and equipped to deliver nuclear weapons. Nuclear-capable B-57 Canberras were added to the USAFE force structure in 1955 and B-66 Destroyers the following year. In 1956 USAFE's first

Opposite, top: *Painting of an F-84 ready for take-off at Furstenfeldbruck AB, Germany. The painting was done in 1951 when Furstenfeldbruck was the hub of USAFE tactical air activity. The base was transferred to the German air force in December 1957. ("F-84s Ready for Takeoff," Francis H. Beaugureau, United States Air Force Art Collection)*

Above: *In March 1955, personnel from the 30th Tactical Reconnaissance Squadron at Sembach AB, Germany, check out the first Martin RB-57 Canberra assigned to the squadron. (USAF)*

Bottom, left: *In Labrador's 10-below-zero weather, parka-clad mechanics, Tech Sergeants George Haefer and Dan Cordell, members of the 21st Fighter Wing from George AFB, California, use a portable heater to pre-heat the engine of a North American F-86 Sabre jet. The 21st Fighter Wing was committed to NATO in 1954 and assigned to a new base under construction at Chambley, in northeastern France. The F-86s made the 6,000-mile flight from California to Europe by way of Labrador, Greenland, Iceland, and Scotland. Maintenance teams accompanied the Sabres to keep them in flying trim. (USAF)*

Bottom, right: *North American F-86 Sabres of the 21st Fighter Wing taxi out on a wintry morning at Goose Bay, Labrador, for the flight to Narsarsuaq, Greenland, en route to France. The wing's move from George AFB, California, was part of the continuing build-up of forces to bolster the defenses of Western Europe. (USAF)*

Above: *The Matador tactical missile, capable of delivering a nuclear warhead, was first deployed to Europe in 1954. By 1956, some twenty wings of aircraft and missiles provided a tactical nuclear deterrent for the defense of the NATO Alliance. (USAF)*

Right: *An RB-66 photo-reconnaissance aircraft assigned to the 30th Tactical Reconnaissance Squadron at Sembach AB, Germany, streaks toward its target during a routine training mission. The RB-66s, which arrived in the theater in 1956, performed both day and night reconnaissance missions. (USAF)*

A low noonday sun throws cold light on a squadron of F-86 Sabres on an air strip in southern Greenland. The photo was taken in September 1955. These F-86s of the 21st Fighter Wing are en route to Europe to bolster NATO's defenses. (USAF)

Opposite, bottom left: *This endless line of F-100s at a stateside base in 1962 awaits takeoff to conduct a firepower demonstration for President John F. Kennedy. Prior to 1961 and the deployment of F-105 aircraft, the North American F-100 had served as USAFE's primary nuclear alert aircraft. (USAF)*

Opposite, bottom right: *This 1963 painting depicts a three-plane formation of Convair F-102 Delta Daggers overflying a typical windmill landscape in the Netherlands. The F-102s belonged to the 32d Fighter Interceptor Squadron stationed at Soesterberg, the Netherlands. ("Air Guardian of the Netherlands," Don Dubois, United States Air Force Art Collection)*

Right: *Painting of F-100s on the flight line at Aviano AB, Italy, on 10 November 1970. (George Guzzi, United States Air Force Art Collection)*

F-100C Super Sabres began arriving in Europe to stand nuclear alert. The F-100 was the world's first supersonic aircraft. The models sent to USAFE were configured to carry extra fuel tanks and heavier bomb loads for the fighter-bomber role. The term "fighter-bomber" rankled many fighter pilots and did not last long after the 1950s. USAFE also activated the first Air Force tactical missile wing in 1956 to direct the operations of three Matador missile squadrons stationed at Hahn, Bitburg, and Sembach Air Bases in Germany.

By the end of the decade, many of USAFE's older interceptors had been replaced by more modern F-101 Voodoos and F-102 Delta Daggers. Mace missiles began arriving in 1959 to replace the Matadors. These newer missiles enhanced the command's ability to destroy fixed targets as part of the retardation mission intended to slow the advance of Soviet armies. The United States also began stockpiling nuclear warheads in Europe under an agreement whereby U.S. forces would control U.S. warheads, while the armed forces of NATO nations would operate their own respective delivery systems.

Tactical Air Command, meanwhile, had developed a composite air strike force (CASF) concept that was designed to respond to lesser contingencies or to augment tactical forces overseas when required. The CASFs were under TAC's Nineteenth Air Force, which became known as the "suitcase air force" because of its mobility. In 1958, simultaneous crises in

Above: Republic F-84s of the Air National Guard's squadrons called to active duty during the Berlin crisis of 1961-62 quickly settled into bases in France. The Thunderjets deployed to Europe as part of Operation Stair Step in October and November 1961. (USAF)

Above: *Two Air Force pilots review a checklist a an F-102 Delta Dagger alert hangar in Germany. (USAF)*

Above: *This C-124 Globemaster II of the Air Logistics Command sits on the ramp at Aviano AB, Italy. The C-124 was slow, but for many years these reliable aircraft delivered troops and equipment worldwide. (USAF)*

Above: *Double checking their parachutes and equipment, these 5th Aerial Port Squadron Combat Control Team members of the 322nd Air Division (Combat Cargo) at Evreux-Fauville AB, France, are the first to jump into a drop zone when Army and Air Force personnel conduct joint missions in Europe. (USAF)*

Right: *These F-100 Super Sabres and F-105 Thunderchiefs, seen here at an en route support base, are bound for Europe. Air Force units in Europe flew both aircraft during the 1960s. (USAF)*

Lebanon and Taiwan strained the capabilities of the U.S. armed forces to respond to non-nuclear contingencies. During the Lebanon crisis, USAFE sent nine F-86Ds to Incirlik AB, Turkey, and TAC deployed a composite strike force to NATO's southern flank to support the landing of U.S. ground troops. The CASF deployment from the United States—using tankers for refueling—went without a hitch. One of the hard lessons learned from the operation, however, was that TAC's aircrews were trained almost exclusively for the nuclear mission and unprepared for conventional operations.

Before the Lebanon crisis, the Eisenhower Administration had already begun modifying its position on massive retaliation—acknowledging that the West could not rely solely on nuclear weapons to deter Soviet aggression. For NATO, massive retaliation assumed central Europe would become a nuclear battleground. The alternative, defense with conventional forces, required that NATO allies build and maintain larger standing armies, navies, and air forces. The need for larger conventional forces to defend Europe raised questions about German rearmament. Holding the alliance together was not always easy. Differences over controversial issues such as stockpiling nuclear weapons in Europe or rearming Germany revealed cracks in NATO solidarity.

USAFE began equipping and training a new German Air Force in 1955, reaching this stage only after an uphill battle within the alliance. When the U.S. Government first proposed German rearmament in 1950, other NATO members stiffly opposed. France and some of its neighbors—fearing revived German militarism as much as they feared the Soviet threat—stalled the U.S. initiative until the mid-1950s. In 1956, USAFE transferred 15 F-84s and RF-84s to the new German Air Force at Furstenfeldbruck AB and graduated the first German jet pilots from flight training.

Control of U.S. nuclear weapons stored on French soil also threatened NATO unity. When President Charles De Gaulle's Fifth Republic demanded joint control of these weapons at the end of the 1950s, USAFE relocated its three French-based atomic fighter wings to bases in Germany and the United Kingdom. Continued disagreement over alliance military policies led France to withdraw its armed forces from NATO command in the mid-1960s and to evict all NATO headquarters and allied military units from

France. While France retained membership in the alliance, the removal of French armed forces from alliance contingency plans left a breach in NATO's defenses that lasted many years.

Meanwhile, the Soviet threat had not diminished. The bellicose actions of Soviet Premier Nikita Khrushchev, who rose to power in 1958, belied his espousal of peaceful coexistence with the West. The shoot down of a U-2 reconnaissance aircraft over the USSR and the capture of CIA-contracted pilot, Gary Powers, in May 1960 gave Khrushchev the provocation he needed to rail against U.S. aggression. For the remaining months of Eisenhower's presidency and after President John F. Kennedy's inauguration in 1961, the boorish Soviet dictator sought to undermine U.S. prestige on several fronts.

The North American F-100 Super Sabre was the workhorse of Europe-based fighter wings before being replaced by Republic F-105 Thunderchiefs beginning in the early 1960s. The F-100s were armed with four 20-mm cannon and carried the deadly Sidewinder missile. Super Sabres could also deliver napalm, as well as nuclear and non-nuclear bombs. (USAF)

USAFE and Flexible Response

Soon after taking office, President Kennedy announced his strategy of "flexible response" designed to respond to Communist aggression at any level of conflict—from counterinsurgency warfare to conventional or general war. Concern grew in the West about USSR support for armed insurgencies within emerging nations. That concern, however, did not divert attention away from central Europe where USAFE and NATO faced the brunt of the Soviet threat. USAFE continued to build and modernize its tactical nuclear capabilities. In May 1961, the 36th Tactical Fighter Wing at Bitburg AB, Germany, began converting from F-100s to Republic F-105D Thunderchiefs. Like the F-100, the F-105 was intended for nuclear missions.

F-105 Thunderchiefs being refueled for a combat mission. The first Europe-based F-105s were "D" models assigned to the 36th Tactical Fighter Wing at Bitburg AB, Germany. The F-105D was USAFE's first Mach-2 aircraft. (USAF)

Above: *A communist border guard peers over the Berlin Wall. The Wall, constructed in 1961, became an ugly symbol of the East-West standoff. (USAF)*

The shift in national policy from massive retaliation to flexible response caused mounting concern for USAFE planners due to the command's lack of conventional military capability. The USAFE posture mirrored the pervasive neglect of conventional arms throughout the military services under the strategy of massive retaliation. Under flexible response, however, U.S. forces would not respond with nuclear weapons unless the Soviets launched a nuclear attack against the United States or its allies. This initially placed USAFE and NATO at a disadvantage against the more powerful conventional forces of the Warsaw Pact. Perhaps Khrushchev sought to test this weakness in 1961 when he resumed nuclear testing and revived tensions over Berlin. When East Germany's puppet regime started constructing the Berlin Wall in August, President Kennedy ordered an accelerated buildup of tactical air and ground forces in Europe.

In early September, Tactical Air Command deployed a composite air strike force to USAFE as an interim measure until President Kennedy could mobilize Air National Guard units and reservists. The President ordered 148,000 reservists to active duty, including 27,000 Air Force personnel. Mobilized Guard units included twenty-one tactical fighter squadrons, four tactical reconnaissance squadrons, six air transport squadrons, and one tactical control squadron. Selected units began deploying to Europe as part of Operation Stair Step in late October and early November.

USAFE bedded down the Stair Step units at five bases in France—Chambley, Chaumont, Dreux, Etain, and Toul-Rosieres. In addition to the Air National Guard units, Tactical Air Command transferred the 102d Tactical Fighter Wing to USAFE, which the command also stationed in France at Phalsbourg AB. The Guard units remained in Europe less than a year, redeploying to the United States in the late summer of 1962. They returned home just in time to see the Cuban missile crisis bring the world to the brink of nuclear war. Their deployment to Europe had been a convincing show of force, but their integration into USAFE operations reminded Air Force planners that the United States was not prepared to fight a conventional war in Europe. Nevertheless, President Kennedy stood up to Khrushchev during both the Berlin crisis of 1961 and the Cuban missile crisis of 1962, and the Soviet leader backed down.

While responding to the Berlin crisis, USAFE concurrently supported United Nations (UN) peacekeeping operations in the strife-torn former Belgian Congo. Humanitarian airlift operations had become a routine part of the USAFE mission, but the Congo operation during the early 1960s was the largest since the Berlin Airlift. In 1960 and 1961, USAFE C-130s joined with C-124s of the Military Air Transport Service to airlift UN peacekeeping forces and supplies to the Congo. USAFE completed its support operations in October 1961, but MATS continued to support a reduced UN effort for two more years.

In November 1964, USAFE transports returned to the Congo on an urgent mission to airdrop a battalion of Belgian paratroopers at Stanleyville and Paulis to rescue 2,000 Americans and Europeans taken hostage by Congolese rebels. After the rescue, additional C-124s and C-130s under USAFE control began a sustained airlift of military and humanitarian supplies from bases in Europe to support the Congolese government. The transports delivered approximately 168 tons of cargo before the airlift ended in April 1965.

NATO's military leaders had concerns about the President's flexible response strategy at first. They believed it gave the Soviets the initiative of attacking Western Europe with weapons of their choosing. Flexible

Opposite, top: Combat assault troops of the 10th Infantry Division rush from a C-123B troop carrier during joint exercises at Kitzingen Army Airfield, Germany, in July 1956. The troops were flown to airheads simulated to be deep in enemy territory as a test for the C-123Bs that were assigned to USAFE. (USAF)

Republic F-84s of the Air National Guard's 166th Tactical Fighter Squadron in flight over France during the Berlin crisis of 1961–1962. The Thunderjets deployed to Europe as part of Operation Stair Step in October and November 1961. They redeployed to the United States in the late summer of 1962. (National Guard Bureau History Office)

Above: C-133s of the Military Airlift Command are seen here at Rhein-Main AB, Germany. The MAC transports joined with USAFE's assigned cargo planes to provide sustained airlift to the strife-torn Congo in the early 1960s. (USAF)

Left: Squadrons of Lockheed F-104C Starfighters also deployed to Europe during the Berlin crisis of 1961–1962. The multi-mission F-104s, assigned to TAC's composite air strike forces, joined with the Europe-based F-102 Delta Daggers for NATO air defense. (USAF)

An F-111F assigned to the 494th Tactical Fighter Squadron at RAF Lakenheath. Lakenheath's 48th Tactical Fighter Wing transitioned to F-111Fs from F-4Ds starting in early 1977. The 20th Tactical Fighter Wing at RAF Upper Heyford had been the first Europe-based unit to convert to the new swing-wing fighter. (USAF)

response was a boon to U.S. and NATO tactical air forces, however, because the strategy was the catalyst for developing modern conventional weapon systems and for ending strategic airpower's dominant role. The budding Vietnam War would further these goals, but the heavy cost of that protracted war also delayed many of NATO's plans to increase conventional strength.

Although NATO did not formally adopt the new strategy until 1967, the U.S. Air Force moved unilaterally to put its combat forces on both a conventional and nuclear footing. Modernization of USAFE's aircraft was a first step in this direction. In the spring of 1965, F-4 Phantoms began

Above: An F-4D from the 36th Tactical Fighter Wing at Bitburg lands at Erding Air Base on 25 February 1967 for a senior commanders orientation. The wing received its first F-4Ds in March 1965. (USAF)

Right: This painting shows an attentive ground crewman preparing an F-4 Phantom for launch at Hahn AB, Germany, in 1984. (Rodger P. Bechtold, United States Air Force Art Collection)

arriving in Europe to replace USAFE's Century-series fighters. Concurrently, the F-4Cs made their combat debut in the war against North Vietnam. The versatile fighters proved their merit in Southeast Asia and in Europe. The F-111—the first Air Force swing-wing aircraft—entered the USAFE inventory in 1970, but the F-4 Phantom in various configurations remained the command's primary tactical fighter through the 1980s. The Luftwaffe, having become a vital element of NATO's frontline defenses, began flying F-4Fs in the early 1970s.

Also affecting the transition to flexible response in Europe was a lack of adequate bases. The withdrawal from French bases—involving the loss of seven main operating bases, one depot, and sixty-eight other installations—created serious bed-down problems for USAFE's tactical forces. More tactical fighters, not less, would be needed to stop a conventional thrust into central Europe. USAFE inherited three bases in Spain when SAC's reflex operations ended there in the early 1960s, but these could not offset the loss of bases in France. Moreover, USAFE lost its primary weapons training center at Wheelus AB in Libya after Muamar Gaddafi overthrew the government in September 1969. The loss of Wheelus affected readiness because USAFE's fighter pilots and missile crews had rotated there for range training since the early 1950s from bases throughout Europe.

To make up for the loss in French bases, Secretary of Defense Robert McNamara directed the Air Force to implement a dual basing concept for the forces being withdrawn from France. The concept called for assigning the NATO-committed USAF units to bases in the United States and preparing main operating bases in Europe to receive them for exercises or emergencies.

Other factors had joined with dual basing to reduce USAFE air assets during the turbulent sixties. The rising costs of fighting the Vietnam War exacerbated concerns about balance-of-payment deficits and the depletion of U.S. gold reserves. Consequently, the USAFE inventory shrank from a peak of 1,595 aircraft during the buildup for the 1961 Berlin Crisis to 730 aircraft at the end of the decade. All of the command's surface-to-surface missiles were withdrawn when the last Mace missile unit, the 71st Tactical Missile Wing at Bitburg AB, was inactivated in 1969. Tactical units overall

Colonel Daniel "Chappie" James, Jr., assumed command at Wheelus Air Base, Libya, in October 1969. He stood up to the pressures applied on the Americans by Colonel Muammar Qadhafi to rush the closure of Wheelus in 1970. (USAF)

Use of technical data and the two-person concept can prevent mistakes in aircraft maintenance. Here, two airmen of the 86th Field Maintenance Squadron demonstrate the use of a tech order for work on an RF-4C at Zweibrucken AB, Germany. (USAF)

The U.S. flag comes down for the last time at Chateauroux Air Station, France. The American and French flags were lowered together during closure ceremonies held on 23 March 1967. (USAF)

U.S. airmen from Chateauroux Air Station, France, march behind a French Army unit to Place Lafayette in Chateauroux where wreaths were laid at the town's monument for war dead. First Lieutenant Willam F. Sautter, of the air police squadron at Chateauroux, led the 21-man flight. The event took place shortly before U.S. forces began withdrawing from French bases in 1966. (USAF)

F-4 Wild Weasel aircraft being refueled for a combat mission. By the 1960s, aerial refueling of jet fighters had become a routine part of overseas deployments and in-theater operations. The 81st Tactical Fighter Squadron, 52d Tactical Fighter Wing, at Spangdahlem AB, Germany, was the only Wild Weasel squadron in USAFE. The squadron converted from F-4Cs to F-4G advanced Wild Weasel aircraft in 1979. (USAF)

A formation of F-4 Phantoms over Europe during an annual Crested Cap exercise of dual-based forces. During the first Crested Cap exercise in 1969, TAC deployed a wing and a squadron of F-4Ds to Spangdahlem AB, Germany. (USAF)

were reduced from a total of sixteen in 1961 to eleven in 1969, with a corresponding reduction in military personnel from 77,000 to 46,000.

This draw down of forces came at a time when the Warsaw Pact had made a gradual buildup in conventional forces opposite NATO's central corridors and had made steady progress in modernizing its tactical air forces. Warsaw Pact armies were now supported by SU-19 and MiG-27 fighter-bombers carrying heavier payloads, laser-guided weapons, and nuclear bombs. Furthermore, the appearance of the MiG-25 fighter-interceptor in quantity ended an era of unchallenged Western technological superiority. Reinforcing the threat to central Europe, Warsaw Pact forces had reoriented training and tactics to emphasize offensive strikes and deep penetration of NATO territory. A thaw in Cold War relations after Khrushchev lost power in 1964 gave way to shock in the West in August 1968 when a Soviet invasion forced Moscow's will on Czechoslovakia. Moscow proved again that it would use military force to hold the Warsaw Pact together and to achieve its political objectives.

In 1969, the Air Force demonstrated its ability to rapidly deploy dual based forces to Europe. In January, TAC deployed the 9th Tactical Fighter Wing and 417th Tactical Fighter Squadron with their F-4Ds to Spangdahlem in the first annual Crested Cap exercise of dual based forces. Aerial refueling, which had become routine in the air campaign against North Vietnam, was a vital element in the rapid deployment of tactical fighters to Europe. While at Spangdahlem, the Crested Cap units participated in the first annual Reforger field training exercise of stateside ground forces earmarked for NATO. The Military Airlift Command airlifted the Army units to Europe.

Reorganizing USAFE

For two decades Western Europe had prospered under the collective security afforded by NATO. Member nations were contributing more to their own defense. U.S. defense budgets, on the other hand, were feeling the strain of balance of payments deficits, the war in Southeast Asia, and the mounting costs of worldwide military commitments. In 1970, the U.S. Congress directed a comprehensive review of the USAFE and USEUCOM commitments, missions, and capabilities. The review convinced congressional leaders that alliance partners should make an even larger financial contribution to NATO's costs, because their ability to do so had equaled, or surpassed that of the United States.

The Nixon Administration also engaged in NATO-Warsaw Pact Mutual and Balanced Force Reduction (MBFR) negotiations at the start of the seventies. Those negotiations and the continuation of strategic arms limitations talks (SALT) strengthened opportunities to further détente and to put brakes on the costly international arms race. A summit meeting in Moscow in May 1972 culminated in the SALT I agreement between the two opposing superpowers.

Concurrently, the winding down of the war in Vietnam let the administration refocus on NATO Europe, where the greater threat to

Pilots' flight gear is inspected by an airman at a personal equipment shop, Lindsey Air Station, Germany. The gear belongs to the USAFE 86th Air Division, flying F-102 Delta Dagger interceptors in a NATO air defense role. (USAF)

An overhead view captures the classic beauty of the F-4 Phantom Wild Weasel aircraft. The Phantom was the tip of the spear in NATO air defenses for nearly two decades, remaining in the USAFE inventory from the mid-1960s into the 1980s and beyond. (USAF)

Top, left: *The FB-111 (shown here) was SAC's version of the swept-wing aircraft developed by General Dynamics. Fighter versions of the F-111 added a vital all-weather system to NATO's strike capabilities. General Richard Ellis was particularly proud to have secured a second wing of F-111s for USAFE. (USAF)*

Top, right: *An artist captures the early morning return of a flight of F-111s to RAF Upper Heyford, England. (Louis F. Taylor, United States Air Force Art Collection)*

This F-4D fighter flies over the German countryside on 26 October 1979. It is loaded with auxilliary fuel tanks and an AN/ALQ-119 pod on its centerline. USAF)

An artist's drawing of an F-4G at Spangdahlem AB, Germany, in 1990. The nose view of the distinctive fighter readily distinguishes it from other aircraft. (James Consory, United States Air Force Art Collection)

world peace lay just beyond the Berlin Wall. U.S. military leaders were justifiably concerned that force reductions in Europe during the Vietnam era had put NATO at a disadvantage vis-à-vis the Soviet threat. Accordingly, in late 1970, President Nixon halted withdrawal of any additional U.S. forces from Europe except those negotiated under MBFR agreements.

Other NATO members shared U.S. concerns about European security at the start of the seventies. In September 1971, General David C. Jones assumed command of USAFE and began the task of harmonizing tactical air force capabilities with the aroused security concerns of NATO members and their renewed sense of commitment to strengthen the alliance. General Jones was one more in the succession of distinguished airmen who commanded USAFE.

General Jones began by moving all of USAFE's headquarters out of the cities and onto active air bases. The USAFE headquarters had been located at Lindsey Air Station, a former German army garrison in Wiesbaden, Germany, since 1954. Similarly, Third Air Force headquarters had been at South Ruislip in West London since its activation in 1951. Jones also believed the command's combat readiness would be improved by reducing the numbered air force headquarters and concentrating operational control of the wings at USAFE headquarters. In a related objective, he sought greater integration of USAFE's operations into the NATO environment and more centralized control of airpower in NATO's central region.

The withdrawal from France had resulted in NATO airpower becoming fragmented. In 1967, NATO established a new headquarters in Brussels, Belgium, and moved the Supreme Headquarters, Allied Powers Europe from Rocquencourt, France, to Casteau, near Mons, Belgium. A German army general commanded Allied Forces Central Europe (AFCENT) headquartered at Brunssum, the Netherlands. When Allied Air Force Central Europe (AAFCE) headquarters at Fontainebleau, France closed, airpower in the central region was divided into the Second Allied Tactical Air Force in the northern sector and the Fourth Allied Tactical Air Force in the south. The Royal Air Force dominated the north, while USAFE dominated the south. The two tactical air forces differed in approach, doctrine, and tactics, and operated without true centralized control.

Actions taken to reintegrate NATO's tactical airpower and to realign the USAFE and numbered air force headquarters were interrelated. While working through Secretary of Defense Melvin Laird to convince NATO of the need to examine the integration of air in the central region, General Jones got Air Force approval for the USAFE reorganization. USAFE reduced the manning in its three numbered air force headquarters by 70 percent, moved HQ Third Air Force from South Ruislip to RAF Mildenhall in mid-1972, and relocated HQ Seventeenth Air Force from Ramstein AB to Sembach AB, Germany, later in the year. Relocating the Seventeenth's headquarters to Sembach made room for HQ USAFE at Ramstein. Sixteenth Air Force's headquarters remained at Torrejon AB, Spain.

The move to Ramstein in March 1973 collocated the commander with his wartime headquarters. Since most of USAFE's strike and reconnaissance forces passed to NATO's Fourth Allied Tactical Air Force at Ramstein, it seemed logical that USAFE would be better prepared to respond to a crisis or war if the two headquarters were collocated. In a related move, Jones arranged to have the Sixteenth Air Force commander dual-hatted as commander of Allied Air Forces Southern Europe at Naples, Italy. This was done in the hopes of improving US-NATO planning and cooperation and easing the transition from peacetime to wartime operations in the southern region.

Reestablishing Allied Air Forces Central Europe to regain centralized control over the two tactical air forces in the central region was more complicated. The Supreme Allied Commander, General Andrew J. Goodpaster, asked General Jones to head a special group studying needed improvements in the employment of tactical air power in the central region. The study was carried out in Brunssum at AFCENT headquarters. Under Jones's leadership, the study group concluded that the most efficient way to control tactical airpower in the central region was to reestablish AAFCE at Ramstein under the USAFE commander. It took months of negotiating, however, to convince the allies, particularly the British, that change was needed.

Although General Jones took the lead in restoring AAFCE, he did not get to don the second hat. By the time SHAPE activated the AAFCE headquarters at Ramstein in mid-1974, Jones was back in Washington assuming his new duties as Air Force chief of staff. A new USAFE commander, General John W. Vogt, assumed responsibility for NATO air operations throughout the central region.

After assuming command of Allied Air Forces Central Europe, General Vogt turned over command of Fourth Allied Tactical Air Force to German air force Lieutenant General Carl-Heinz Greve. Six years later, in August 1980, the ATAF headquarters moved from Ramstein to Heidelberg. AAFCE headquarters remained at Ramstein still dually commanded by the USAFE commander-in-chief. The arrangement improved wartime planning and cooperation and demonstrated that it would ease the transition from peacetime to wartime operations.

The E-3A airborne early warning and control aircraft, which made a demonstration flight to Europe in 1973, held great potential for enhancing command and control of NATO air forces. General Jones, who admitted to being "a zealot for the AWACS," briefed the NATO military committee on the system's ability to look deep into eastern Europe and back into France. Jones believed the AWACS could be used for more than just an air defense

Dual-based F-4 Phantoms from Holloman AFB, New Mexico, taxiing out in Germany during a Crested Cap exercise in 1976. The parent unit, the 49th Tactical Fighter Wing, was stationed at Spangdahlem AB, Germany, before being relocated to Holloman as a dual-based unit in July 1968. (USAF)

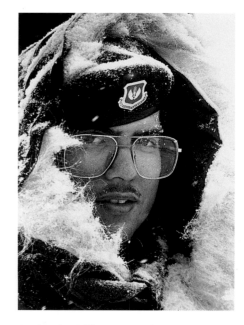

During the Cold War, United States Air Forces in Europe (USAFE) exercised year-round to remain prepared for any hostilities. Airman First Class Warren Moore of the 86th Security Police Squadron at Ramstein, Germany, stands guard at a Ramstein flight line entry point on a cold winter day. (USAF)

The E-3 Sentry is an airborne warning and control system (AWACS) aircraft that provides all-weather surveillance, command, control and communications needed by commanders. Mission specialists on the aircraft detect, identify, and track enemy and friendly aircraft within 250 miles of the Sentry. (USAF)

Boeing E-3A Airborne Warning and Control System aircraft over Europe. The first overseas deployment of the AWACS aircraft was hosted by USAFE in April 1973. Demonstrations of the E-3A's capabilities in the European environment led to NATO's procurement of AWACS aircraft. (USAF)

An aircraft maintenance specialist with the 26th Tactical Reconnaissance Wing at Zweibrucken AB, Germany, prepares to download camera equipment from an RF-4C aircraft assigned to the wing. (USAF)

warning system. He envisioned that it would keep the commander informed on the total battle area and facilitate his command of the battle.

General Richard H. Ellis recalled that the AWACS was "on the front burner" during his tour as CINCUSAFE, and that NATO's commanders "recognized the potential of the AWACS system." The E-3A became a familiar sight in the skies over central Europe as these aircraft participated in a variety of USAFE and NATO exercises. In 1980, four E-3A aircraft deployed to Riyadh, Saudi Arabia, to help protect Saudi airspace during the Iran-Iraq war. Around the same time, NATO established its airborne early warning force at Geilenkirchen AB, Germany. The first NATO E-3A aircraft arrived at Geilenkirchen in February 1981. General Ellis described the NATO AWACS force as "a giant step in upgrading the combat capability of the NATO air forces."

General Ellis spent much of his two years as USAFE commander improving exercises and refining command and control techniques. He also worked to improve coordination with the French air force, which had been separated from NATO for nearly a decade. In October 1975, the French air force established a liaison office at Ramstein, and began participating in NATO training and exercises.

Even as NATO sought to improve relations with the French armed forces, new rifts shook the alliance. Greece and Turkey, alliance members, nearly went to war with each other when Turkish troops invaded Cyprus in the summer of 1974. The United Nations arranged a cease-fire, but tensions remained high in the region. When the United States suspended the sale of arms to Turkey over the incident, the Turkish government retaliated by taking over all bases occupied by U.S. forces, with the exception of Incirlik. Relations between Turkey and the United States did not return to normal until military assistance was reinstated in 1978. A new government in Greece, however, withdrew its military forces from NATO as France had done in the 1960s.

Other ongoing initiatives included improving the survivability of USAFE bases and developing a better bed-down posture for augmentation forces. While the numbers of active and standby bases fluctuated over the years, there were enough to accommodate wartime reinforcements in the early phases of a European war. In the early 1960s, the loss of bases in France coupled with dual basing and the increase in follow-on forces required to fight a conventional war caused planners to take another look at wartime base requirements. A 1967 European air base study explored the use of allied air bases to accommodate augmentation forces from outside USAFE. The command's NATO partners had built some 220 airfields in the theater, and many of these could support USAF squadrons in addition to their own national forces.

Secretary of Defense McNamara authorized discussions with the allies, but the high costs of making required improvements for U.S. forces at collocated operating bases became a sticking point in negotiations. The Department of Defense, in a time of fiscal constraint, was reluctant to invest American dollars to improve non-U.S. installations. Host nations were no more enthusiastic about building facilities for U.S. squadrons based on the other side of the Atlantic. Cost-sharing arrangements for financing the collocated operating base (COB) program were eventually worked out within NATO, but it was a painfully slow process.

In May 1970, General Joseph R. Holzapple signed an agreement with the Canadian Forces Europe commander making Lahr AB, Germany, USAFE's first collocated operating base. That was only a start, however, because planners had identified a wartime requirement for forty-five COBs

F-4E Phantom IIs taxi toward their launch area during the 1974 Coronet Viking exercise in Norway. The fighters were deployed to Europe from the 4th Tactical Fighter Wing at Seymour Johnson AFB, North Carolina. (USAF)

This painting shows a KC-135 of the Illinois Air National Guard on a refueling mission in support of the NATO AWACS somewhere over Germany. (Thomas A. Morgan, United States Air Force Art Collection)

Above: *F-4E Phantom IIs arriving in Norway during Coronet Minuteman deployment in 1976. The F-4Es were assigned to the 334th Fighter Squadron at Seymour Johnson AFB, North Carolina. (USAF)*

Right: *A crew chief guides a 49th Tactical Fighter Wing F-4 Phantom out of a TAB-V shelter in Germany during an annual Crested Cap exercise of dual-based forces in 1976. The wing's home base was Holloman AFB, New Mexico. (USAF)*

Brigadier General Charles E. Yeager (left), vice commander of Seventeenth Air Force, and Colonel Austin O. Davis, commander of the 32nd Tactical Fighter Wing, welcome F-4E pilot Captain Bill Malerba to the air base at Camp New Amsterdam, Netherlands. (USAF)

An F-4 Phantom of the 36th Tactical Fighter Wing sits outside its hardened shelter at Bitburg AB, Germany, before the wing converted to F-15 Eagles in 1977. (USAF)

in the northern, southern, and central regions of Western Europe. That requirement eventually expanded to seventy bases. In April 1974, General Jones established a special group within his headquarters to manage the COB program making it one of USAFE's highest priority projects.

In July 1975, the Air Force began deploying tactical squadrons to their collocated operating bases in Europe on a regular basis. The first deployments were made to USAFE bases, with some elements visiting the COBs while they were in Europe. Eighteen F-4Es of the 335th Tactical Fighter Squadron from Seymour-Johnson AFB, North Carolina, made the initial deployment, arriving at Spangdahlem AB, Germany, on 11 July. Squadrons soon began deploying from their home bases directly to the COBs, starting with Lechfeld AB, Germany, in August 1976.

The survivability of NATO bases had been a concern from the earliest days of the Cold War. During the 1950s, an elaborate plan of dispersal bases, revetments, camouflage, and air defense evolved to protect USAFE's tactical nuclear alert forces. The project encountered funding problems and diplomatic complications, however, and was never fully developed. When the French government refused to allow the storage of nuclear weapons on its territory, for instance, USAFE's strike units in France had to establish forward detachments at bases in Germany to meet their alert commitments.

The vulnerability of USAFE aircraft to conventional strikes became a critical planning factor with the adoption of flexible response under the Kennedy Administration. The Air Force funded a 1962 proposal by USAFE to construct aircraft shelters at forward bases, but several years passed before funds were made available because Secretary McNamara wanted more study of the problem. In 1964 he directed the Air Force to conduct a theater air base vulnerability study, which became known as TAB-V.

USAFE experienced further delays in the shelter program due to the competing requirements of the war in Vietnam and to the uncertainty created by the loss of bases in France. That changed after the Israeli air force, during its Six-Day War with Egypt in 1967, demonstrated the ease with which an enemy's unsheltered aircraft could be destroyed. USAFE

accelerated its shelter program, and NATO took steps to improve survivability for both in-place and dual based aircraft at bases throughout Europe. On the other side of the Berlin Wall, the Soviet Union also accelerated hardening and dispersal on the Warsaw Pact's forward air bases.

The TAB-V program resulted in the construction of 342 aircraft shelters on seven bases in Germany, thirty-six shelters at Incirlik AB, Turkey, and eighteen at Aviano AB, Italy. An expanded shelter program, approved in the mid-1970s, included bases in the United Kingdom judged vulnerable to conventional attack by a new generation of longer-range Soviet aircraft. By the 1980s, under this expanded program USAFE constructed an additional 229 shelters at eleven bases. Another 203 shelters were either under construction or under design.

The "Yom Kippur War" in October 1973 conclusively demonstrated the value of shelters and active air defense. Israeli air strikes proved less successful in 1973 than in 1967 because Syrian and Egyptian bases were less vulnerable to air attack. During the 1973 war, USAFE provided extensive support for Operation Nickel Grass, the U.S. airlift of weapons and ammunition to Israel. After Israel and Egypt agreed to a cease-fire, USAFE provided airlift support for the United Nations peacekeeping force to Egypt.

Winning the Cold War in Europe: The 1980s

Terrorist attacks against USAFE and NATO personnel, on and off base, increased during the 1970s and 1980s. Some Middle East and North African countries supported local terrorists in NATO countries. In August 1981 a German leftist group set off an explosion at Ramstein AB causing extensive damage to the USAFE headquarters building and injuring fourteen people. USAFE responded with extraordinary measures to protect personnel and to keep the terrorist threat from affecting the mission.

Muammar Qadhafi's militant regime in Libya was suspected of sponsoring terrorism against the United States and its allies. On 5 April 1986 the Libyan government was linked to a terrorist explosion in a Berlin discotheque that killed one American serviceman and his girlfriend and

Top, left: A Military Airlift Command C-5 taxis toward the cargo ramp at Ramstein AB, Germany, in support of the annual Reforger exercise in September 1975. The Military Airlift Command provided the aerial lifeline between the United States and its armed forces overseas. (USAF)

Top, right: A Lockheed C-141 just before touching down at Berlin's Tempelhof airport in July 1966. The scene is in sharp contrast to pictures of C-54s hauling tons of food, fuel, and clothing during the Berlin Airlift of 1948–1949. (USAF)

A weapons load crew at Bitburg Air Base, Germany, load an AIM-9 Sidewinder missile on an F-15 This activity is taking place inside a TAB-V shelter. (USAF)

Right: *These three aircraft types constituted the bulk of the USAF El Dorado Canyon strike force. KC-135 tankers refueled KC-10s, which in turn refueled the attacking F-111Fs. (USAF)*

Above: *On 14 April 1986, F-111Fs of the 48th Tactical Fighter Wing prepare for takeoff from RAF Lakenheath to deliver punishing strikes against Libya for its active support of terrorism against U.S. interests overseas. (USAF)*

This pencil drawing depicts an Air Force Reserve KC-10 refueling an F-111 during the early stages of the bombing mission against Libya. Aerial refueling became particularly critical in Operation El Dorado Canyon when Spain and France denied overflight rights for the attack against Libya. Having to skirt these two countries greatly lengthened the time, distance, and fuel requirements for the missions. (Robert D. Coffman, Jr., United States Air Force Art Collection)

At Gilze Rijen Air Base, Netherlands, a truck is loaded aboard a C-130 Hercules from the 136th Tactical Airlift Wing during a Reforger exercise in 1983. The Lockheed C-130, which entered Air Force service in December 1956, remains a principal aircraft used for tactical airlift decades later. (USAF)

injured 200 others, including seventy-five Americans. Ten days later USAFE and Navy aircraft struck back at Libya in operation El Dorado Canyon. Eighteen F-111Fs from the 48th Tactical Fighter Wing at RAF Lakenheath joined fifteen Navy A-6 and A-7 attack planes from carriers in the Mediterranean to bomb terrorist-related targets at Tripoli and Benghazi, Libya.

Political opposition within NATO, while predictable, hindered the operation. France and Spain, opposed to the Libyan raid, denied requests for overflight by the F-111 strike force. Taking a circuitous over-water route added an additional 6,000 miles to the lengthy round-trip flight from RAF Lakenheath to Libya. SAC's European Tanker Task Force provided required in-flight refueling from KC-135s and KC-10s.

Aerial refueling had long been an integral element of USAFE operations. The command got its own aerial refueling unit, the 420th Aerial Refueling Squadron, equipped with KB-50s at RAF Sculthorpe in 1955. In 1964 SAC KC-135s replaced the 420th and began supporting tactical deployments to Europe and meeting USAFE's theater requirements. From 1967 to 1976, due to the Vietnam War's drain on SAC's tanker resources, Air National Guard KC-97L rotational units, known as Creek Party, supported USAFE and NATO. By 1976, the growth of refueling operations in Europe required activation of the 306th Strategic Wing. In 1978, 7th Air Division, activated at Ramstein AB Germany, assumed management responsibilities for all USAFE inflight refueling needs.

Operational readiness of USAFE and NATO forces was always the paramount concern to commanders. After General Ellis assumed command in 1975, he created a USAFE Readiness Center that identified and monitored areas where the command could improve its fighting ability. General John W. Pauly, commander of USAFE during 1978–80, characterized the command as "the strongest fighting entity within NATO." A USAFE historian noted that readiness was essential "to contribute unprecedented surges of combat sorties to help the alliance cope with the intensity of warfare that would result from a Warsaw Pact general offensive."

F-111 Raid on Libya

Colonel Robert Venkus, USAF

Late in the afternoon of 14 April 1986, 24 F-111F Aardvark aircraft of the 48th Tactical Fighter Wing taxied into takeoff position at Royal Air Force (RAF) Lakenheath in England. President Ronald Reagan had decided to send a message to Libya and to all nations supporting terrorism. Denied overflight of French or Spanish territory to reach Libya, the F-111 attack force would fly a 5,000-mile 14-hour circuitous round-trip over the Atlantic Ocean, through the Straits of Gibraltar, and across the Mediterranean—the longest fighter combat mission in history.

After several night refueling hookups with KC-10 tanker Debar 88, the three F-111s in Karma element approached the target. The entire task force had been forced to accelerate over the Mediterranean to meet planned time over target. Despite the refuelings, the Aardvarks were already concerned about fuel. Afterburners needed to sustain high attack speed were consuming fuel at rates higher than planned.

Dozens of Navy and Air Force aircraft converged on Libya. The F-111Fs struck three targets at Tripoli. Navy jets from the carriers America and Coral Sea attacked targets near Benghazi. Navy EA-6B electronic jamming aircraft joined with Air Force EF-111s to suppress Libyan air defenses.

Delivering a message to the Libyan dictator, Muammar Qadhafi, was not on the minds of Karma 51's crew as they began their bombing run. As the crew of the seventh of nine aircraft attacking Qadhafi's Azziziyah Barracks headquarters, the pilot, a combat veteran, and his weapon systems officer (WSO) knew the risks ahead. When they crossed the target, Libyan defenses would be fully alerted. A glance forward confirmed that conclusion. The night sky over Tripoli blazed with arcing tracers, surface-to-air missiles (SAMs), and exploding ordnance.

Despite heavy defensive fire, the three Karma aircraft pressed the attack. Fate and their perilous position in the stream of attacking aircraft that night would deny them the success achieved by their fellow F-111Fs. Karma 51's laser-guided bombs fell unguided, missing the target and causing collateral damage. Close behind Karma 51, Karma 52 exploded in a brilliant flash, probably falling to a SAM. Karma 53 thundered across the target but aborted weapons release due to a navigation system malfunction.

As the two-man crew on Karma 51 turned homeward in formation with their tanker, both knew that one and perhaps two Aardvarks had been lost on the mission. Back at RAF Lakenheath, a commander and an Air Force chaplain would soon arrive at a friend's home with the news that a husband and father would not be returning. One can only imagine the feelings of the pilot and WSO in the cockpit of Karma 51 as they listened to Armed Forces Radio play "The Air Force Song" saluting their lost wingmen. The Air Force war on terrorism had begun.

An F-111F on a training mission over its base at RAF Lakenheath. Visible are four GBU-24 "Paveway 2" laser guided bombs. Most of the El Dorado Canyon attackers flew in this configuration. (General Dynamics Corp.)

Two F-15s break left over the Dutch countryside, revealing the air-to-air missiles that,
linked with sophisticated onboard avionics,
made this McDonnell Douglas Eagle the
premier air superiority fighter of the 1980s.
(USAF)

USAFE activated an F-5E "aggressor" squadron in 1976 to hone the
combat-edge of fighter and reconnaissance crews. The aggressor squadron,
using Warsaw Pact tactics, engaged NATO squadrons in simulated air-to-air
combat and demonstrated the enemy tactics that could be expected in an
actual conflict. In 1988 USAFE began using F-16s in the aggressor role.

The glue that held the alliance together was the need for collective
defense—the preservation of nuclear and conventional forces that were
powerful enough to deter aggression, but ready and capable of fighting and
winning a war if deterrence failed. The end to the Vietnam War along with

Opposite: *A formation of F-15Es from the 4th
Tactical Fighter Wing at Seymour Johnson
AFB, North Carolina, en route to a collocated
operating base in Europe. (USAF)*

Right: *F-4 Phantoms of the 334th Fighter
Squadron, the "Fighting Eagles," arrive at
Flesland Air Station, Norway, on Coronet
Minuteman deployment in 1976. During
the Cold War, dual-based units such as the
Fighting Eagles were a vital element of
NATO's wartime planning. (USAF)*

Above: *An air-to-air right side view of an F-15E Eagle aircraft in flight in 1987. The F-15E was armed with four AIM-7 Sparrow missiles. (USAF)*

Armed F-16s awaiting take-off on a bombing mission. After its arrival in 1981, the versatile F-16 replaced the F-4 as the tactical workhorse in USAFE. (USAF)

economic stability in Western Europe finally gave NATO air forces the resources needed to modernize and to improve the readiness of their tactical units. Learning from its Vietnam experience, the U.S. Air Force directed more effort toward modernizing tactical air forces than at any previous time in its history.

Three new tactical aircraft, the A-10 Thunderbolt II, the F-15 Eagle, and the F-16 Fighting Falcon, entered the Air Force inventory during the post-Vietnam era. Working with the Army, the Air Force developed the A-10 as a tank-killer for direct support of ground operations. The 81st Tactical Fighter Wing at RAF Bentwaters received the first squadron of A-10s in 1978. By the end of the 1980s, USAFE activated additional A-10 squadrons at RAF Bentwaters and RAF Alconbury, and had established limited forward operating locations in Germany for the A-10s to train with ground forces and to meet wartime requirements.

The Air Force designed the F-15 Eagle primarily as an air superiority fighter, but it could be used in a variety of roles. In 1977, the 36th Tactical Fighter Wing at Bitburg, Germany, became the first overseas USAF unit equipped with F-15s. Four years later, the wing converted to newer C and D models. The 32d Tactical Fighter Squadron at Soesterberg AB, Netherlands, also flew the F-15C/Ds.

More versatile was the F-16 Fighting Falcon, a compact, multirole aircraft that was hailed as "the world's most advanced lightweight fighter." The 50th Tactical Fighter Wing at Hahn AB, Germany, received the command's first operational F-16s in 1981. The first C and D model F-16s were assigned to the 86th Tactical Fighter Wing at Ramstein in 1985. By decade's end, USAFE had five tactical fighter wings equipped with F-16C/Ds—the 50th, 86th, and 52d at Spangdahlem AB, Germany, the 81st at RAF Bentwaters, and the 401st at Torrejon AB, Spain. The 401st was scheduled to relocate to Aviano along with Sixteenth Air Force headquarters in 1992. To suppress enemy defenses, the 52d Tactical Fighter Wing also operated F-4G Wild Weasel aircraft and the 20th Tactical Fighter Wing at RAF Upper Heyford was equipped with EF-111s.

Modernization of other NATO tactical air forces had progressed as well. The British and French joined in a cooperative effort to produce new Jaguar light attack aircraft. The RAF purchased 160 Jaguars for tactical roles, permitting the transfer of its F-4 Phantoms to air defense. By the end of the 1980s, the aircraft industries of Great Britain, West Germany, and Italy were engaged in a cooperative effort to produce a multirole combat aircraft for their air forces. Within the Luftwaffe and the Italian air force, the new multirole fighters would replace the aging F-104s. The Netherlands, Belgium, Norway, and Denmark decided to replace their F-104s with F-16s.

Winning the Cold War in Europe

East-West relations worsened after the Soviet invasion of Afghanistan in December 1979. President Jimmy Carter deferred ratification of the SALT II treaty because of the invasion. When Ronald Reagan entered the White House in 1981, NATO had already agreed to deploy 108 improved Pershing II missiles and 464 ground launched cruise missiles (GLCMs) to counter the threat of Soviet SS-20s from Eastern Europe. As the Soviet war with Afghanistan wore on, U.S. military leaders could not help but draw a parallel with America's protracted war in Vietnam. It was soon evident to Kremlin watchers that the protracted arms race with the West and the unpopular war in Afghanistan had taken their toll on a failing Soviet economy.

The standoff between East and West, the threatened deployment of U.S. GLCMs and Soviet SS-20s, and the potential cost to both sides led to a treaty, signed by Ronald Reagan and Mikhail Gorbachev in December 1987, to eliminate intermediate-range nuclear forces worldwide. In the wake of improved East-West relations resulting from the treaty, a dramatic sequence of events unfolded. Free elections were allowed in eastern Europe, the Berlin Wall came down, Germany was reunified, the Warsaw Pact broke up, and the Soviet Union fell apart. The Cold War was over.

In the West, the striking power of NATO's tactical air forces had never been stronger. The dramatic rise of tactical airpower in Western Europe during the Cold War is a central theme in Cold War history. That history reveals the unrelenting Air Force commitment to prepare USAFE and NATO to fulfill wartime missions. The Air Force men and women assigned to USAFE were consistently among the best our country had to offer. The bonds that these service members established with their NATO counterparts and with the people of Western Europe represent a legacy with bold promises for the future. With the Cold War over, the past again became prologue as new missions for USAFE and NATO tactical airpower loomed over the horizon.

An overhead view of the durable F-4 Phantom. The F-4 provided air superiority around the globe for nearly three decades. (USAF)

The first deployment of ground launch cruise missiles (GLCMs) was at Greenham Common in the United Kingdom. Arms control negotiations stopped further deployments in Europe and closed down GLCM operations at Greenham Common. (USAF)

THE
Air Force in
the Korean War

THE
Air Force in the Korean War

Kenneth P. Werrell, Ph.D.

Above: *This North American F-82 Twin Mustang night fighter lifts into the Korean twilight for another mission. By removing the left wing and the right wing from two F-51s and joining two modified fuselages with a parallel wing section and a tail plane with elevator, North American created the F-82. The F model in this illustration carries radar in the large centerline pod. (USAF)*

Page 130–131: *A formation of F-86E Sabres of the 4th Fighter Interceptor Group fly over Korea. The advent of the MiG-15 in November 1950 left the U.N. force of F-51s and F-80s outmatched. The USAF responded with the deployment of the F-86 equipped 4th Group. By 17 December, the first MiG-15 was downed by a Sabre. ("Glory in the Sun," Harley Copic, U.S. Air Force Art Collection)*

The North Korean invasion of the South on 25 June 1950 caught the world and the United States military by surprise. America was ill prepared physically and psychologically to respond to this attack in an area that civilian and military leaders agreed was not vital to United States interests. Nevertheless, the threat of further Communist actions, echoes of German and Japanese aggression only a decade before, and the presence of U.S. forces and bases close to Korea were major factors in the American decision to intervene. Speed was critical as the tough, experienced, and well-equipped Korean army steadily pushed the lightly armed South Koreans aside. Could the United States field an adequate counter force before the North Koreans overran the peninsula?

At first, American decision makers hoped that the threat of a United States response, or at least the application of airpower and sea power, would suffice. Equipped with leftover World War II prop-powered F-51 and F-82 fighters and its first combat jet, the F-80, the USAF quickly neutralized the small Korean air force that flew about 130 World War II prop-powered fighters and attack bombers. While the combatant's prop equipment was near equivalent, American pilots had far superior training and experience, and were more aggressive. The first American aerial victory was credited to First Lieutenant William G. Hudson, who destroyed a Yak-11 on 27 June 1950. By the end of July, the Americans claimed air superiority after destroying almost all North Korean aircraft—twenty in air-to-air combat and the rest on the ground. This gave the United Nations (U.N.) forces aerial freedom, allowing them to use airpower as they pleased.

F-51s of the 18th Fighter Bomber Wing are joined on the ramp of a Korean air base in November 1951 by similar aircraft from No. 2 Squadron of the South African Air Force. Returning fighters are rearmed with bombs and rockets seen here in the foreground, refueled, and ready to fly again in an average of seven minutes. (USAF)

Runway conditions were appalling, especially after a spring rain. This North American F-51 Mustang taxis through several inches of standing water on the way to the takeoff runway for another mission. (USAF)

Japanese women concentrate on the care of their rice paddy as a Lockheed F-80 Shooting Star takes off for a mission against the invading North Korean army in August 1950. Bases in Japan not only supported tactical operations during the war, but also served as the logistics hub for supplies and equipment flowing in to support United Nations forces deployed in Korea. (USAF)

Mechanics check out the left engine of a North American F-82 at an airfield in Korea. F-82 squadrons based in Japan were the first American fighter-bomber units to arrive in Korea. F-82s claimed three of the victories on the first day of the air-to-air fighting, 27 June 1950. F-80s claimed the other four. (USAF)

Nevertheless, the Red tide continued to roll south over the disintegrating South Korean army and hastily dispatched, poorly trained, and inadequately equipped U.S. Army forces.

The USAF attempted to stem the North Korean advance with fighters, B-26 attack bombers, and even America's premier World War II heavy bomber, the B-29. The battle was close, but the North Koreans were stopped at the Pusan perimeter. Airpower played a major role in this action, battering the men and supplies of the Korean army. In fact, this may well have been the most important contribution of airpower to the U.N. cause in the course of the war. Lieutenant General Walton H. Walker, the Army ground commander, declared, "I will gladly lay my cards right on the table and state that if it had not been for the air support that we received from the Fifth Air Force we would not have been able to stay in Korea." Despite the considerable punishment meted out by airpower, the outnumbered North Koreans maintained the offensive until several days after U.N. forces launched an amphibious assault at Inchon, hundreds of miles behind Communist lines. In short order, the course of the war reversed as U.N. forces mounted an offensive thrust northward across the 38th parallel, the former boundary separating the two Koreas.

With the Korean army now in retreat, Americans believed that the war was over, or would be by Thanksgiving, and that the troops would be home for Christmas. However, this was not to be. As victorious U.N. forces approached the Chinese and Russian frontiers, the war took another turn. The Chinese intervened, surprised, and overwhelmed U.N.

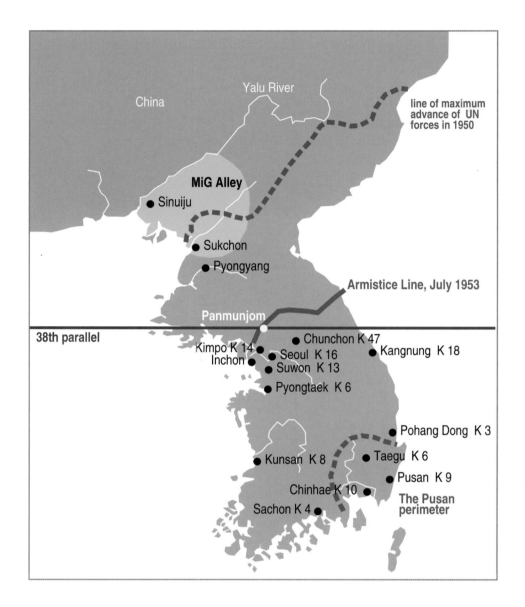

line of maximum advance of UN forces in 1950

China

Yalu River

MiG Alley

● Sinuiju

● Sukchon

● Pyongyang

Armistice Line, July 1953

Panmunjom

38th parallel

Kimpo K 14 ●
Inchon ●
● Seoul K 16
● Suwon K 13
● Chunchon K 47
● Kangnung K 18
● Pyongtaek K 6

● Pohang Dong K 3

● Kunsan K 8
● Taegu K 6
● Pusan K 9
Chinhae K 10 ●
Sachon K 4 ●
The Pusan perimeter

Above: *In Korea, many Air Force aircraft operated off primitive airfields that used pierced steel planking (PSP) rather than concrete for runways. Maintaining the integrity of the PSP surface was a daily task. Here, a member of the 930th Engineer Group of the U.S. Army welds PSP together. (USAF)*

Left: *This map shows the June 1950 border between North Korea and South Korea, the border between North Korea and communist China, principal cities and airfields, and the lines of maximum advance for the North Korean army and for United Nations forces. (Air Force Magazine)*

Maintenance facilities in Korea were frequently inadequate for the task at hand, but Air Force maintenance crews seemed to always find a way to deliver a safe and functional aircraft to combat crews. These maintenance men of the 18th Fighter Bomber Wing—more fortunate than most—have a hanger for the repair of this Mustang. (USAF)

forces with a large, rugged, and experienced army. United Nations ground forces fell back in disorder. Concurrently the Communists escalated the air war by introducing large numbers of their best fighter, the MiG-15. It became an entirely new war.

Sabres to the Rescue

Perhaps the best known, most successful, and most romantic Air Force operation in the Korean War was the duel between Americans and Communists over "MiG Alley." Although the outmoded American prop and jet fighters downed some MiGs, the Russian fighter, with vastly better performance compared to American aircraft in the theater, threatened U.N. air superiority. To make matters more difficult, unlike World War II where Americans won command of the air by pounding enemy aircraft factories, savaging airfields, and engaging in air-to-air combat, U.S. airmen in Korea were limited by political restrictions to only the latter. To rub salt into the wounds, American fliers could clearly see the enemy's airfields and observe his takeoffs just beyond the Yalu River that separated North Korea from China. Nevertheless, the Americans were not allowed to engage these lucrative targets. Thus MiG factories and airfields in China were never bombed.

Here a communist pilot ejects from a MiG-15 after being hit by a F-86. Second Lieutenant Edwin E. "Buzz" Aldrin got credit for this victory; he later was to be the second man to walk on the moon.

Right: *A North Korean defector received a $100,000 reward for delivering this Mikoyan-Gurevich MiG-15 to an American air base in South Korea on 21 September 1953. After being flight-tested in Okinawa, the aircraft was delivered to Wright-Patterson AFB, Ohio, for further testing before being placed on display at the Air Force Museum. (USAF)*

Opposite, top: On 17 December 1950, Lieutenant Colonel Bruce Hinton of the 4th Fighter Interceptor Group encountered a Chinese MiG-15 near the Yalu River. The ensuing dogfight was the first between jet swept-wing fighters. In this illustration, Hinton has damaged the MiG, now trailing smoke and fire from its engine, and has extended his speed brakes to get a closer look. Hinton was credited with a kill, the first of many by the Sabres. ("First Swept Wing Encounter," by Keith Ferris)

Above: *Major General Albert Boyd, commander of Wright Air Development Center, was one of five American pilots to fly a MiG-15 delivered to a USAF base in South Korea by a defecting North Korean pilot. Boyd described the MiG as "a light airplane with a big engine." Two of the other American pilots who flew the MiG were Captain Charles "Chuck" Yeager, who earlier was the first man to break the sound barrier in level flight, and Captain Tom Collins, later an astronaut. (USAF)*

Right: *On 8 November 1950, First Lieutenant Russell J. Brown in an F-80C downed a MiG-15 over Sinanju, Korea, in the first aerial combat between two jet fighters. The MiG-15s outclassed the F-80s in air-to-air combat, nevertheless, Shooting Star pilots claimed six MiGs destroyed of their total of 37 aircraft downed in air battles. The USAF lost 277 F-80s on operations, 143 to enemy action. ("Russell Brown Downs a MiG," Keith Ferris)*

The introduction of the MiG-15 prompted the USAF to send its best fighter to the theater, albeit in small numbers. The USAF did this with great trepidation as it had only about 420 of the sleek North American F-86 Sabres in service and feared involvement in this peripheral war when a direct conflict with the Soviet Union in Western Europe seemed highly likely. In any case, the Air Force responded quickly to the 1 November 1950 appearance of the MiG-15. Within a week, the 4th Fighter-Interceptor Wing received deployment orders, arrived in Japan within a month, and went into combat in mid-December. Much to the shock of the American military and public, the MiG proved superior to the F-86 in a number of performance areas. In addition, the MiGs, flying from sanctuaries in China, had the advantages of the initiative and a vast superiority in numbers.

Despite these Communist advantages, the U.S. airmen racked up impressive scores. They won air superiority the hard way—aircraft–

against-aircraft, pilot-versus-pilot, air-to-air, one kill at a time. Better training, more experience, and aggressiveness were probably the most important factors to explain the lopsided results. Other factors fueling Sabre successes included better tactics, a superior though capricious gunsight, and some performance advantages with a faster rate of roll, greater dive speed, and superior handling. Another U.N. advantage in waging the air war was control of Cho-do, an island just off the North Korean coast over a hundred miles behind enemy lines. It served as radar and radio interception site, as well as a base for both special operations and air sea rescue.

While precise American victory claims remain controversial, F-86 pilots won a clear victory, downing about eight MiGs for every Sabre lost in combat. Some Sabre victories were probably earned on the "wrong side" of the Yalu River against the stated rules of engagement. We now know that Soviet pilots initially manned the MiGs, joined later by Chinese pilots, and by the end of the war, by North Korean pilots.

Although the first MiG fell to an F-80 flown by First Lieutenant Russell J. Brown and the second to RB-29 gunner Sergeant Harry J. LaVene, F-86s waged the bulk of the air-to-air battle. On the Sabre's first combat mission on 17 December 1950, Lieutenant Colonel Bruce Hinton claimed a MiG. Other kills followed, and on 20 May 1951, despite a hung-up drop tank, Captain James Jabara became the first jet ace when he destroyed two Communist fighters. In all, thirty-nine Sabre pilots achieved ace status and claimed 305 of the 818 MiGs destroyed during

A smiling Airman Harry J. LaVene emerges from an RB-29 tail gunner's compartment after shooting down a MiG. Although MiGs proved to be a serious threat to unescorted B-29s, B-29 gunners shot down nearly two dozen MiGs in the course of the conflict. (USAF)

Captain James Jabara became the first American jet ace when he downed two MiGs on 20 May 1951. Pulled out of combat with six victories, he returned (as a Major) to fly a second tour and ended the war as the second leading American ace with 15 credits. Here he describes an encounter in a post-mission debriefing to an intelligence officer as interested Sabre pilots look on. (USAF)

Bottom, left: On 8 November 1950, while flying an F-80, First Lieutenant Russell J. Brown (right) downed a MiG-15 over Sinanju, Korea, in the first aerial combat between two jet fighters. Over Sinanju, in what came to be known as "MiG Alley," fighting was fierce through much of the Korean War. (Dick Escola)

Bottom, center: Captain Joseph C. McConnell, shown here climbing into the cockpit of his F-86, was the highest scoring USAF ace of the Korean War with sixteen confirmed kills. (USAF)

Bottom, right: Major George A. Davis, Jr., was credited with destroying twelve enemy planes before attacking a formation of enemy fighters on 10 February 1952 to protect allied fighter-bombers conducting a low-level bombing operation. After destroying two of the MiGs, Davis deployed his speed brakes, deliberately sacrificing his superior speed to attack a third plane. His F-86 was hit and he crashed into a mountain. He was awarded the Medal of Honor posthumously. (USAF)

the war. Jabara scored a total of fifteen victories, one less than the top American ace in Korea, Captain Joseph C. McConnell.

The other highest scoring pilots included Captain Manuel Fernandez with fourteen and a half kills, Major George Davis with fourteen, and Colonel Royal Baker with thirteen. Davis died in action on 10 February 1952 after downing two MiGs. He was posthumously awarded the Medal of Honor. A World War II ace, Davis was the top scoring American jet pilot at the time of his death. A number of the other F-86 pilots had also flown in World War II. Six of the Korean War aces were already World War II aces, and a further seven had scored victories in the big war, which helps account for the relatively older age of the successful pilots.

More than just the glamour and the glory, the Sabre pilots achieved a true victory. Despite numerous obstacles, they outfought their opponents and protected most air operations. Most importantly, with the

USAF Aces
Of The Korean War

McConnell, Capt. Joseph C., Jr.	16
Jabara, Maj. James	15*
Fernandez, Capt. Manuel J.	14.5
Davis, Maj. George A., Jr.	14*
Baker, Col. Royal N.	13*
Blesse, Maj. Frederick C.	10
Fischer, Capt. Harold E.	10
Garrison, LtCol. Vermont	10*
Johnson, Col. James K.	10*
Moore, Capt. Lonnie R.	10
Parr, Capt. Ralph S., Jr.	10
Foster, Capt. Cecil G.	9
Low, 1stLt. James F.	9
Hagerstrom, Maj. James P.	8.5*
Risner, Capt. Robinson	8
Ruddell, LtCol. George I.	8*
Buttelmann, 1stLt. Henry	7
Jolley, Capt. Clifford D.	7
Lilley, Capt. Leonard W.	7
Adams, Maj. Donald E.	6.5
Gabreski, Col. Francis S.	6.5*
Jones, LtCol. George L.	6.5
Marshall, Maj. Winton W.	6.5
Kasler, 1stLt. James H.	6
Love, Capt. Robert J.	6
Whisner, Maj. William T., Jr.	5.5*
Baldwin, Col. Robert P.	5
Becker, Capt. Richard S.	5
Bettinger, Maj. Stephen C.	5
Creighton, Maj. Richard D.	5*
Curtin, Capt. Clyde A.	5
Gibson, Capt. Ralph D.	5
Kincheloe, Capt. Iven C., Jr.	5
Latshaw, Capt. Robert T, Jr.	5
Moore, Capt. Robert H.	5
Overton, Capt. Dolphin D., III	5
Thyng, Col. Harrison R.	5*
Wescott, Maj. William H.	5

* In addition to World War II Victories

exception of nuisance operations—the infamous and pesky "Bed Check Charlie"—no sustained or major enemy air attacks occurred against friendly ground forces. Command of the air was an important U.N. advantage in the Korean War.

Prop Bombers in a Jet-Powered War

The Boeing B-29 Superfortress was clearly the best bomber of World War II as it proved in the exceptionally effective campaign against the Japanese homeland. In 1950, the USAF had two B-29 bomb groups, now designated medium bombers, assigned to the Pacific Theater. The B-29s quickly went into action. A WB-29 weather reconnaissance version of the bomber flew missions one day after the North Korean invasion. On 27 June, B-29 crews flew their first bombing missions against North Korean forces. The desperate situation on the ground forced airmen to use the strategic bomber in unanticipated roles—interdiction and close air support. Most notably, on 16 August the B-29 force, now increased to five-groups, dispatched almost 100 aircraft to carpet bomb North Korean forces threatening the Pusan perimeter. While this bombing had little physical impact on the Communists, it did boost the morale of beleaguered United Nations forces.

Although clearly secondary to ground support, the B-29s did fly against strategic targets. The first mission hit Wonsan on 13 July. However, few strategic targets existed inside North Korea and the concerns of European allies constrained attacking some of these. Washington excluded two key targets—the city of Rashin, one of North Korea's five major industrial areas, only seventeen miles from the Soviet border—and the Suiho dams, the world's fourth largest hydroelectric facility located adjacent to the Chinese border. The Joint Chiefs of Staff identified eighteen strategic targets, which U.S. airmen eliminated by mid-September 1950.

Following the conclusion of World War II, hundreds of B-29s were covered with "cocoon" material and stored at Davis-Monthan Air Force Base, Tucson, Arizona. In this photo, workmen are removing the protective "cocoon" and preparing these aircraft for return to active service. (Boeing Aircraft Company)

During this period, the bombers flew 4,000 sorties and dropped 30,000 tons of bombs for the cost of only four bombers. With the destruction of approved strategic targets and the successful Inchon invasion, the USAF sent two B-29 groups back to the United States in October. It appeared that the war was over. The main difficulty was the weather. That soon changed.

The intervention of Chinese forces in November 1950 altered everything, in the air as well as on the ground. The strategic air war

Top, left: *The "Mission Inn," a B-29 assigned to the Far East Bomber Command, displays the kind of nose art that became popular with crews during World War II and remained popular during the Korean War. (USAF)*

Above: *B-29s assigned to Bomber Command of Far East Air Forces rained tons of bombs on Chinese communist forces pushing down the Korean peninsula in January 1951. The USAF lost fifty-seven Superfortresses on operations, twenty-four to enemy action; in exchange the B-29 crews claimed eighteen communist aircraft destroyed in aerial combat, all but two of which were MiGs. The Boeing bomber dropped 44 percent of the bomb tonnage dropped by the USAF in the war. (USAF)*

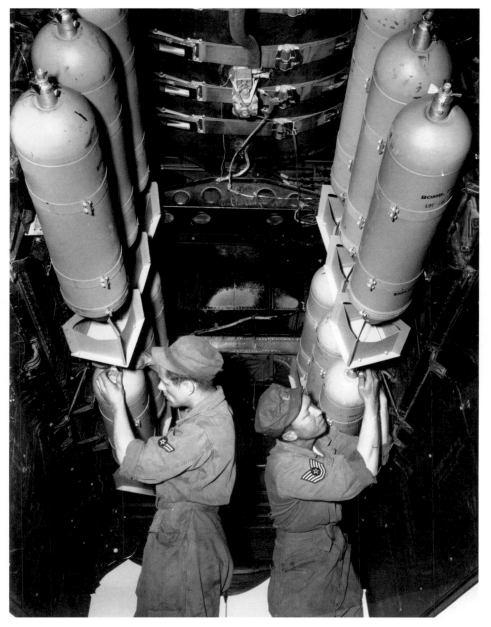

Above: *Mobile scaffolding is rolled into place to perform a service inspection and replace an engine on this B-29 of the 28th Bomber Squadron, on Okinawa in 1950. (USAF)*

Left: *Nightly, RB-26s patrolled the skies over North Korea looking for troop concentrations or vehicles as well as results of earlier bombing strikes. In this photograph, armament technicians insert nose fuses into photoflash bombs used to illuminate targets for RB-26 cameras. (USAF)*

Above: *Initially, F-86 fighters, wrapped in layers of protective material designed to prevent corrosion by saltwater, arrived in the Far East by ship. Soon after the Korean War ended, with rapid advances in air refueling techniques, most aircraft were flown to overseas deployments rather than shipped. (USAF)*

Above: *The Douglas A-26 Invader entered combat over Europe in 1944 and remained in active service after the war. Redesignated B-26, it prowled the night skies over Korea in interdiction missions against the communist transportation system. (USAF)*

Above: *Ground Control Approach radar was still a new technology in the early 1950s, but it proved particularly useful during the Korean War. Weather in Korea and Japan sometimes posed a more serious threat than enemy fighters. Here, an Air Force Staff Sergeant guides a pilot to a safe landing. (USAF)*

escalated. In an effort to stem the Chinese advance, the U.S. government authorized the bombers to hit Yalu bridges, but only the south side. This was a difficult, if not impossible technical task as well as a dangerous tactical one because it forced the bombers to attack the bridges from a right angle while Communist gunners fired away, many from positions in China, protected from air attack. In November 1950, the Joint Chiefs of Staff removed the prohibition on using incendiary bombs, and in January, raids destroyed 35 percent of Pyongyang, the North Korean capital. In August 1951, the B-29s, escorted by Navy fighters, attacked Rashin.

The MiG-15 proved more dangerous than Chinese antiaircraft fire. The speedy Communist fighter, designed specifically to combat B-29s, could elude defending fighters and severely punish the bombers—and it did both. Between November 1950 and November 1951, the USAF lost sixteen B-29s, even though the airmen employed fighter escort. In early 1951, losses forced the USAF to curtail deep Superfortress strikes. The Air Force also employed fighter-bombers in the strategic offensive. In a June 1952 "air pressure" campaign designed to inflict heavy losses on the enemy's high value targets and thus force him to settle the war, Air Force, Navy, and Marine fighter-bombers attacked the massive Suiho hydroelectric facility. Four days of attacks cut off 90 percent of North

Korean electricity, as well as electricity to other Communist countries. Even more effective were fighter-bomber attacks in May 1953 that extensively damaged irrigation dams and threatened North Korea's agriculture.

Airfields made up another critical target set in North Korea. In January 1951, the Communists attempted to extend a chain of airfields down from the Yalu to support MiG-15 operations further south and to contest air superiority over the battlefront. Due to strenuous USAF efforts and a limited Communist response, only a few MiGs used airfields in North Korea during the war, and these airfields were quickly attacked and put out of service.

The airmen also launched two effective attacks on Pyongyang in 1952. Fifty-four B-29s along with 1,200 fighter-bombers hit the Communist capital on 11 July 1952. A second strike of 1,400 fighter-bombers followed on 29 August. Although tactically successful, the strategic and political aim of influencing the peace negotiations with these dramatic air attacks failed. Notwithstanding the use of new bombing equipment, electronic counter-measures, and night escort fighters, as well as experiments with guided bombs, the war continued as did aircraft losses.

Despite losses, crew morale problems, and the frustrations of limited war, there were successes. In January 1952, bombing operations by B-29s and B-26s against a number of bridge choke points closed enemy lines of

The crew of a B-26 Invader briefs for another night interdiction mission against rail and road traffic in North Korea. The B-26 flew 60 percent of the night sorties in the war. In so doing the Invader crews logged the most combat time of any USAF aircraft, 224,000 flying hours while the second most was flown by the B-29s, 173,000 flying hours. (USAF)

These North American F-51 Mustangs are loaded with munitions for ground attack missions. The Mustangs accounted for 22 percent of the tonnage of bombs and napalm delivered by USAF fighters, and 64 percent of the rockets. But with a loss rate twice that of the jet-powered fighters, the Mustangs suffered the most losses (300) of any USAF aircraft in the war. (USAF)

The B-26s dropped 29 percent of the bombs dropped by the USAF, second only to the 44 percent unloaded by the much larger B-29, and more than the 25 percent delivered by Air Force fighters. Although employed mainly as a bomber, the B-26s claimed the destruction of seven communist aircraft and damage to seven others in air-to-air combat. The Air Force lost 168 B-26s to operational causes, fifty-six to enemy action. (USAF)

Colonel Ben Preston, 4th Fighter-Interceptor Group commander, congratulates aces Major George A. Davis, (left) and Major Winton W. Marshall, (right) after another victory. (USAF)

communication in a critical area for almost two weeks. The Superfortress attacks on North Korean airfields, power plants, and dams lent considerable weight to the U.N. air offensive and helped the airmen maintain the pressure on the Communists. Overall, planners directed almost 60 percent of the bomber's effort at the Red transportation system. In the end, the B-29s dropped about the same tonnage on North Korea during the war as the Army Air Force had dropped on Japan during World War II, but with far fewer bomber losses. Nevertheless, with few strategic targets and numerous political restrictions, the B-29 crews achieved much less success against Korea than against Japan. The airmen were as frustrated by the limited and stalemated war in Korea as were the ground forces.

Interdiction

About half of the Air Force missions in the Korean War were aimed at the enemy's transportation targets. After quickly defeating the North Korean air force and rudimentary air defenses during the initial mobile phase of the war, USAF aircraft battered Communist supply lines and played a major role in blunting North Korean attacks against the Pusan perimeter.

When the war turned static in the summer of 1951, the interdiction effort became more difficult. The USAF failed to cut off the battlefield for a number of reasons, but not for lack of trying. A major factor in the failure of the USAF interdiction campaign was the Communist reaction. Innovative tactics, improved defenses, deception, but most of all the enemy's minimal supply requirements and stamina defeated the USAF. The Communists increased antiaircraft protection, employed flak traps,

Left: *A pair of F-86 pilots head towards their planes for another mission, having just passed under a sign indicating the distance to the infamous "MiG Alley." Large formations of MiGs would lie in wait on the Manchurian side of the Korean border. When U.N. aircraft entered the airspace that became known as "MiG Alley," MiGs would swoop down from high altitude to attack. Even with the advantage of a sanctuary across the Yalu River, Communist pilots still could not compete against the better-trained Sabre pilots. (USAF)*

Above: *Captain John S. Walmsley, Jr., was shot down over Korea on the night of 14 September 1951 while flying his 25th combat mission. Walmsley expended all ordnance on his B-26 disabling an enemy train then called for another B-26 to finish the job. When the other aircraft arrived, Walmsley circled the train, illuminating it with a searchlight, thus disclosing his own position to enemy gunners who shot Walmsley down. He was awarded the Medal of Honor posthumously. (USAF)*

deployed dummy troops, strung deceptive lights to lure bombers into hills, and used warning sentinels among other measures.

The Air Force also had equipment problems, lacking night vision gear, navigational equipment, and an effective light bomber. It employed the World War II Douglas B-26 Invader, which proved marginal as its limited maneuverability combined with Communist defenses and mountainous terrain made night flying difficult and dangerous. Efforts to illuminate targets with flares dropped by B-29s, C-47s, and B-26s proved no more effective than roofing nails and tetrahedrons dropped on roads to stop trucks, or flechettes employed against ground troops. The Air Force also experimented with guided munitions. The 1,000-pound Razon and 12,000-pound Tarzon bomb, both delivered by B-29s, yielded mixed technical and limited tactical success.

Aircrew skill, dedication, and courage frequently made the difference between success and failure. For example, Captain John Walmsley flew a night mission on 14 September 1951 attacking a train. Walmsley used a searchlight to illuminate the target for other B-26s, and pressed his efforts repeatedly before being downed. For his gallantry, he received the Medal of Honor. Walmsley and other pilots committed to the interdiction campaign hindered the Communists and made their operations more difficult, but despite considerable effort and losses, airpower did not decisively affect enemy operations.

Ground crewmen load 50-caliber ammunition belts into the nose guns of a B-26. (USAF)

An F-80 Shooting Star strafes and bombs a North Korean position in close air support of the 24th Infantry Regiment, north of the Hantan River on 23 April 1951. (USAF)

Above: *One of the innovations of the Korean War was the use of aircraft flying close to the main battle line to direct air support. This World War II trainer, the North American T-6 Texan, served in this role and was nicknamed "mosquito." (USAF)*

Right: *Fully armed, a flight of F-84 Thunderjets from the 49th Fighter-Bomber Wing heads for a target in Korea in April 1952. (USAF)*

Close Air Support

The Korean War can be divided into two clearly defined segments. During the first year, highly mobile warfare swept back and forth across the Korean peninsula. The following two years brought trench warfare and stalemate reminiscent of World War I. As both sides dug in, U.N. forces called for USAF close air support. Of all USAF operations, close air support was the most controversial. Two factors that prompted this controversy were its limited success and a number of regrettable attacks on friendly

forces. Squabbles also erupted between the services as to the most effective manner of close air support, pitting the Marine system against the one used by the USAF.

At first, the airmen took a step backward to fight the air war in Korea by reequipping six jet F-80 squadrons with piston-powered F-51s. This stellar World War II fighter was better suited for the conflict than the F-80 as it was able to use the short and primitive runways in Korea and had superior range and endurance. However, the long-term trend was toward jets that required less maintenance, could carry more ordnance, and were more survivable than prop-powered aircraft. To capitalize on these advantages, the Air Force subsequently transitioned close air support

Above and below: *The Republic F-84 Thunderjet first saw action in Korea in December 1950 and became the primary Air Force fighter-bomber in the conflict. It flew more combat flying hours than any other USAF fighter in the war and went on to great commercial success: Republic built almost 8,000, the largest U.S. jet fighter production run of all time. (USAF)*

Left: *Pilots brief on the wing of one of their aircraft before departing on a fighter-bomber mission against North Korea in December 1950. The Republic F-84 Thunderjets arrived in late 1950 and were effective in daylight ground attack. Interdiction missions were less effective than desired because of nighttime enemy movement and bad weather. The USAF lost 249 Thunderjets on operations. (USAF)*

147

On 5 August 1950, Major Louis J. Sebille, an F-51 Mustang pilot, led an attack against an enemy position threatening United Nations forces in their push toward Pusan. On his first pass against the target, Major Sebille dropped one 500-pound bomb, but his second bomb failed to release. Disregarding the risk associated with a hung bomb, Major Sebille pressed the attack using his .50-caliber machine guns. Hit by ground fire, he crashed into the enemy position destroying it, losing his own life, and earning the Medal of Honor. (USAF)

Above: *Major Charles J. Loring, Jr., led a flight of four F-80s in an attack against an enemy gun position. While pressing the attack, Loring's aircraft was hit by ground fire and he crashed into the gun position under attack by his flight. For this action, he received the Medal of Honor. (USAF)*

Right: *This print depicts a forward operating base for the T-6 Mosquito. Flying low and slow, these dangerous and important missions never received the credit they merited. ("Out on a Limb," by James Dietz)*

units to the F-84 and, in the last months of the war began to reequip with a fighter-bomber version of the F-86.

Military equipment available to close air support units reflected Air Force relegation of this mission to a low priority and post-World War II neglect of military requirements. Radios to link ground troops with pilots proved questionable, and the Air Force encountered problems staffing required liaison positions. Airmen innovated to make the system work. For example, finding jeeps inadequate and discarding the idea of a forward air controller flying an F-51 with inadequate radios, commanders came up with a working solution to the problem. The USAF used the two-seat North American T-6 Texan trainer to fly "low and slow" and provide the platform for an aerial observer to direct close air support. These "Mosquito" missions were dangerous and unglamorous, but important. On occasion, there were strange moments. In September 1950, Lieutenant George W. Nelson spotted a group of retreating North Korean soldiers. He dropped a note demanding their surrender and signed it, "MacArthur." The enemy did just that—surrendering to a nearby U.N. patrol.

The great publicity garnered by F-86 pilots and B-29 crews overshadowed the efforts but not the effectiveness of airmen engaged in close air support. According to captured North Koreans, during the first months of the war, U.N. airpower accounted for about half of the Communist casualties, 70 percent of the equipment destroyed, and a great loss of morale. Close air support fliers also suffered heavier losses than their more acclaimed counterparts. While 186 F-86s were lost to all causes in the war, about 300 F-51s, 280 F-80s, and 250 F-84s were lost, most flying close air support. The losses were not only large in number, but also at a much greater rate than on other Air Force missions.

Two of the USAF's four Medal of Honor recipients in the Korean War flew close air support. On 5 August 1950, Major Louis J. Sebille led a formation of F-51s against enemy positions. Although hampered by a hung-up bomb and enemy fire, he continued driving his attack home. Ground fire hit Sebille's aircraft shortly before it dove into the enemy flak position. Major Charles J. Loring, Jr., earned his Medal of Honor on a close air support mission on 22 November 1952. He was attacking a North Korean gun position when his F-80 was hit and then crashed into the enemy.

Rescue and Special Operations

Unlike World War II when American airmen depended on the British in Europe and on improvisation elsewhere for rescue, the USAF began the Korean War prepared to recover downed fliers. Equipped with a mixture of old and new aircraft including the SB-17 and SB-29—both converted World War II bombers—the SA-16 amphibian, and H-5 and H-19 helicopters, air sea rescue crews established a remarkably successful record. In September 1950, the 3rd Air Rescue Squadron made its first save of an airman from behind enemy lines. By the end of the war, Air Rescue recovered 170 USAF airmen. More than one-third of downed Sabre pilots—including McConnell and three other F-86 aces—were successfully rescued from enemy territory. A number of these rescues were the stuff of Hollywood movies. In one case, a C-47 landed under enemy fire on an island beach off the coast of North Korea to recover eleven B-29 crewmembers.

The USAF also engaged in clandestine activities, sometimes employing the 3rd Air Rescue Squadron in this role. In September 1950, the unit conducted its first recorded special operations mission when it flew a SB-17 into North Korea. The USAF used various aircraft to insert agents into the north, but had considerably more difficulty recovering them. On one mission in early 1951, an H-19 flew about 100 miles behind enemy lines to deliver a team that recovered portions of a crashed MiG-15. The Air Force also used C-47s to broadcast propaganda over enemy territory and deliver propaganda leaflets.

The Sikorsky H-19 Chickasaw returned many downed pilots to fly and fight another day. Of the 170 Air Force airmen rescued by the USAF, forty-one were F-86 pilots including four who already were or soon would be aces: Capt. Joseph C. McConnell (16), Major Frederick C. Bleese (10), Capt Lonnie R. Moore (10), and Capt. Clifford D. Jolley (7). (USAF)

The Grumman SA-16 Albatross, an amphibian, was always a welcome sight to downed airmen, as was the Sikorsky H-5 shown here in flight above the Albatross. During the Korean War, rescue of stranded airmen from behind enemy lines became a standard operating procedure for the Air Force. (USAF)

Airlift: Strategic and Tactical

Air transportation played a prominent role in the war. Korea is almost half way around the world from the United States. Fortunately, the United States had a well-developed infrastructure in Japan, including bases, depots, and a skilled local population that could support the war effort. While most materiel and supplies arrived in Korea by ship, most of the personnel flew to the theater. Commercial aviation supplied the bulk of this support, although military aviation did provide a significant share.

Tactical airlift made early and crucial contributions to the defense of South Korea. At the outbreak of the war, Air Force transports helped evacuate Americans from the war zone. On the first day of the operation, 27 June 1950, twenty-one Air Force transports moved almost 750 people out of Korea. On the 28th, North Korean aircraft destroyed a C-54 on the ground. In those first days of the war, the Air Force also used its small number of transports in the theater to get ammunition to the South Korean army and to move U.S. troops to the conflict. One critical item, first delivered on 12 July, was the new 3.5-inch bazooka that, unlike older bazookas,

could penetrate North Korean T-34 tank armor. Despite difficult conditions, particularly deteriorating airfields, inadequate air traffic control, and lack of lighting for night operations, the airlift went on. The arrival of more and better aircraft, including the C-119 and the C-124, helped the operation. So, too, did the assumption of command by the most famous airlift leader, the commander of both the World War II "Hump" Operation and the Cold War Berlin Airlift, Major General William H. Tunner.

Airlift was particularly important on the drive north in the second half of 1950 because port capacity in Korea was seriously limited. Tunner later observed, "The Inchon landing is one of history's most glaring examples of the use of air transport as a corrector of logistic mistakes." On 20 and 21 October, the United Nations command used airlift to insert paratroopers behind enemy lines, thirty-five miles north of the North Korean capital of Pyongyang, air dropping almost 4,000 men and 600 tons of cargo. Although a great technical success—called by one writer "indisputably the best combat jump the Army had ever staged"—it was of little tactical importance because the bulk of the North Korean forces had already moved north of this position. The airmen supported the rapid advance in an impressive fashion, for example rapidly repairing and extending a North Korean airfield and getting it into use within five days of its capture.

Airlift was also important in the chaotic withdrawal of U.N. forces from North Korea in late November. USAF tactical airlift rushed aid to Army and Marine forces in their retreat from the Chosin Reservoir. USAF C-47s and C-119s air-dropped supplies to the retreating troops, and the old reliable "Gooney Bird" also flew in supplies and evacuated more than 4,000 patients from the short, primitive airstrips at Hagaru-ri and Koto-ri. The most dramatic action was the airdrop of a bridge to the retreating American

This early model Douglas C-124 Globemaster II transport flew strategic airlift missions between the United States and Japan. Entering service with the Military Air Transport Service in May 1950, "old shaky" provided dependable airlift until retirement in 1970. (USAF)

General William H. Tunner, commander of the Hump airlift in World War II and the Berlin Airlift in 1948 assumed command of Combat Cargo Command in 1950 and continued to enhance his reputation as an airlifter. (USAF)

Medical Air Evacuation

Janice Feagin Britton

Army Nurses, recently transferred to the Air Force 801st Medical Air Evacuation Squadron, were still establishing their identity in June l950. Most had not yet received their newly designed blue uniforms when the North Korean People's Army invaded the Republic of Korea (ROK). President Truman directed the U.S. armed forces to assist the ROK. The United Nations Security Council called on all members to aid South Korea. Democracy and communism were in bitter conflict.

The 801st soon relocated from the Philippines to Tachikawa Air Base Japan. Major General William H. Tunner, the Berlin Airlift wonder-boy, took command of Far East Air Forces Combat Cargo Command. Combat Cargo's anything, anywhere, anytime strategy included the 801st and its life-saving mission.

Medical air evacuation (air evac) arrangements were simple. Planes, primarily C-46s, C-47s, and C-54s, flew 50-gallon drums of gasoline, C-rations, or whatever the troops needed from Japan to Korea. After aircraft were off-loaded, those designated for air evac were transformed into hospital wards, loaded with patients,

and flown to Japan. A typical day for a Flight Nurse began at five a.m. with takeoff at eight.

A nurse and medical technician worked as a team. When a patient boarded the plane, his nametag was checked against the manifest and his condition carefully assessed to determine his placement on the aircraft. A person in danger of going into shock was placed with his head lower than his feet. Men with head and chest wounds or those receiving plasma went on middle tier to allow access for frequent checks on respiration and plasma flow. Litter cases with heavy splints were fastened to the floor. Patient comfort, both physical and mental, was top priority. Planes usually flew at 3,000 to 4,000 feet and flights were one or two hours in duration.

Standard medical supplies included a therapeutic oxygen tank, face masks, emesis bags, blankets, urinals (ducks), canvas "straight jackets," coffee, and water. Nurses carried a black bag loaded with intravenous equipment, morphine, Demerol and sodium amytal, bandages, adhesive, and other essentials. Flying from the combat zone had a positive psychological affect, though some patients were frightened to fly. Magazines and funny books helped reduce patient stress. They grabbed these icons of Americana like they were money. Even men who could not read English and held magazines upside down wanted them.

In November, the 801st flew air evac with Marines stationed at Itami Air Base near Osaka. We flew priority air cargo to supply combat troops; patient airlift was secondary. On a typical day, we flew from Itami to

Left: Records are always an important part of comprehensive medical care. Here a flight nurse from the 801st Medical Air Evacuation Squadron takes a few moments on a C-54 flight to catch up with the paper work. (USAF)

Opposite, bottom: This nurse comforts a patient during the flight to medical care in Japan. During December 1950, medical personnel from the 801st helped evacuate more than 4,000 casualties from the Marine Corps and Army units surrounded near the Chosin Reservoir. (Janice Feagin Britton)

airfield near Wonsan, Korea, then headed for Kimpo, picked up ammunition and flew it to Pyongyang. After off-loading the ammunition, the aircraft cabin finally became a hospital for seriously injured patients requiring medical attention in Japan.

Patient evacuation requirements increased sharply when hordes of Chinese flooded into Korea in November 1950. General Tunner sent 801st air evac teams to Sinanju, North Korea. One day, medics flew north in planes loaded with supplies. The next day, supplies were burned and we moved south. Pilots had huge problems landing and taking off from half-built runways of hard, frozen ground. Medical crews focused on the care of patients. This emergency engendered a new sense of togetherness and concern for each other. Litter-bearers,

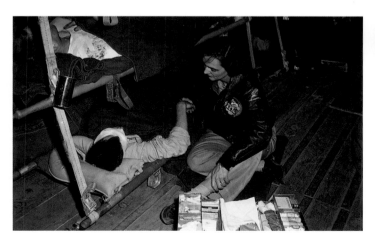

ignoring blisters on their hands, loaded patients and latched down stretchers to every inch of aircraft floor space. Despite a sudden drop in temperature to 30 degrees below zero and numbing cold, we evacuated more than 4,000 casualties—including Chinese and North Korean prisoners.

Then our mission shifted to supporting the First Marine Division surrounded near the Chosin Reservoir. On 5 December, the 801st evacuated 3,925 patients—victims of frostbite and bullets—from Koto-ri and Hagaru-ri. Operating from inadequate airstrips entirely surrounded by enemy troops and subjected to hostile ground fire, 131 flights airlifted patients to safety and medical care.

This dark time in U.S. military history had another face. Air Force nurses measured up, and experience validated the importance and the practicality of medical air evacuation—it is compassionate, it builds morale, and it saves lives.

Top, left: Daily, Air Force nurses flew out of Japan with high-priority cargo for Korea, and flew back with patients. This nurse is assisting a medical technician load a portable oxygen kit on a C-54 before patients arrive at the airplane. (Janice Feagin Britton)

Top, right: This logo of the 801st Medical Air Evacuation Squadron reflected both the mission and the dedication of this unit. (Janice Feagin Britton)

Above: First Lieutenant Janice Feagin and First Lieutenant Lillian Kinkella, both nurses with the 801st Medical Air Evacuation Squadron, take advantage of a quick stop in Pyongyang to warm their toes before loading patients for the return flight to Japan. (Janice Feagin Britton)

A B-29 of the 372 bomber squadron redies for another mission. (USAF)

Aerial reconnaissance was vital to the war effort. Lt. Bryce Poe II flew on the morning of 28 June 1950 in an RF-80A, the first photo reconnaissance mission of the war, and the first USAF jet reconnaissance sortie. (USAF)

The RF-86F provided the extended range required for long-range surveillance missions in China. The RF-86 had superior flying performance to the RF-80. (Clyde Voss)

forces. Along the line of withdrawal, a 16-foot break in a road along the face of a 1,500-foot gorge over Funchilin Pass threatened the loss of all American tanks, vehicles, and heavy equipment. In a spectacular, hastily improvised operation on 7 December 1950, USAF C-119s dropped eight bridge spans, each weighing a ton and a half. Engineers used the spans to successfully bridge the gorge and allow the withdrawal to continue.

While seldom recognized by their service or the public, the efforts of the airlifters were greatly appreciated by the ground forces. During the Korean War, airlift delivered almost 700,000 tons of cargo and over 2.6 million passengers. They also airdropped about 18,000 tons of cargo and airlifted over 300,000 patents. Overall, air transport provided a variety of important services.

Reconnaissance

Similar to other Air Force units stationed in the Far East, the reconnaissance branch was under manned and under equipped. As in World War II, airmen converted aircraft designed for other purposes to the reconnaissance function. Although a shortage of equipment and a shortage of trained photo analysts hindered operations, reconnaissance was there from the very start of the war. Nonetheless, China's covert infiltration of as many as a half million troops into Korea demonstrated the inadequacies of aerial reconnaissance. The value of photoreconnaissance was never in doubt, but limitations of manpower and equipment coupled with a clever foe deployed in difficult terrain hampered reconnaissance efforts.

RF-86 Reconnaissance Missions

Major General Mele Vojvodich, USAF (Ret)

The RF-86A was a modified version of the F-86 fighter, with guns and radar removed to accommodate cameras. Assigned to the 15th Tactical Reconnaissance Squadron based at Kimpo AB, Korea, we pilots who flew these aircraft were highly qualified and all volunteers. We photographed enemy airfields near the Yalu River regularly to update the enemy air order of battle. In addition to missions over North Korea, we also flew reconnaissance missions into China. Those China missions were highly classified and remained so for more than 40 years. F-86 fighters escorted our unarmed reconnaissance aircraft on missions over North Korea, but beyond the Yalu, we were on our own.

The primary threat to U.S. forces in South Korea and Japan was the Russian-built Chinese-operated IL-28 bomber. From unknown bases well north of the Yalu, those Il-28s were capable of striking targets in South Korea and Japan. Fifth Air Force Intelligence needed to know the location of the Il-28 bases, but that mission was beyond the capability of our reconnaissance aircraft. Then, in the spring of 1953, we received new RF-86Fs with about twice the range of the older RF-86A. Unknown to most of the pilots in the squadron, a few of us were selected to look for those IL-28 bases.

Deep penetration missions into China were dangerous and lonely. Survival depended on the reconnaissance pilot seeing the enemy quickly and outrunning him. In March of 1953, I flew one of the longest reconnaissance missions of the war, from Kimpo, Korea, to Harbin, China, a distance of 500 nautical miles. Twenty-four F-86 fighter jets patrolled the Yalu River in support of this mission, but I crossed into China alone. En route to Harbin, I located and photographed several previously unknown airfields, including one of the Il-28 bases. On my return flight, numerous enemy fighter aircraft attacked. I eluded them by diving at high speed to ground level, then remaining at low level until I reached the coastline of the Yellow Sea, where the enemy broke off the chase. I climbed to altitude and landed at Kimpo with minimum fuel after a three-hour flight.

Pilots of the 15th Tactical Reconnaissance Squadron beside an RF-86F at Kimpo Air Base, Korea. (Mele Vojvodich)

The cargo in the foreground has been delivered to an emergency landing field scrapped out by Marine Corps bulldozers at Hagaru-ri near the Chosin Reservoir. Troops outside the aircraft are walking wounded awaiting evacuation from the surrounded airfield. (USAF)

Flying alone and unarmed, the pilot flying this RF-80 reconnaissance aircraft encountered a flight of MiG fighters and sustained near-fatal damage. After somehow managing to shake off his attackers, the pilot nursed his crippled aircraft to a friendly base for landing. (USAF)

Air Force Reserve and Air National Guard

Often overlooked in the Air Force action in the Korean War was the vital importance of Air Force Reserve and National Guard personnel. In all, 146,000 Reservists and 46,000 Air National Guardsmen were mobilized during the war. The Joint Chiefs of Staff authorized the call-up of the first two reserve wings in early July, and one of these, the 452d Bomb Wing, flew its first mission in late October, seventy-seven days after the recall order was issued. Reservists and Guardsmen helped quickly augment the small but rapidly growing active duty force, and served well. Eight Reserve and four National Guard pilots became aces during the Korean War.

This success should not mask significant problems resulting from confused, differing, and often unfair personnel policies, and the involuntary recall of many airmen. Most of these men expected recall to military service only in case of an all-out war such as World War II. Those in organized units expected to serve in those units. In many cases, their expectations were not fulfilled. Recalled Reservists and National Guardsmen resented those regular Air Force personnel who remained in the United States in peacetime billets. They also resented the second-line equipment—such as the B-26—with which they went into combat.

Ill informed about the war and the necessity of their service in it, ill used as replacements rather than cohesive units, and ill equipped with weapons from the last war, the morale of these citizen soldiers suffered. Nevertheless, while the mobilization could have been better managed, it did accomplish its purpose—a rapid buildup of the USAF with experienced and trained personnel in a time of need.

In Conclusion

The Korean War was not a victory for America. At best, the war was a stalemate. The nation was never called to arms for the Korean conflict, thus fostering its perception as a "forgotten war." With the exception of the F-86, the USAF did not send its newest and best aircraft—B-47s and B-36s—to the conflict and delayed using its best electronic countermeasures and tactics. Coupled with restrictive rules of engagement, these factors made the Korean War difficult to fight and frustrating to endure. Nevertheless, airmen performed well under these difficult conditions, clearly demonstrating skill, dedication, and fortitude. As one historian stated, "Air operations deprived the Communists of free movement by day, forced them into a massive program of field engineering, denied them supplies for sustained offensives, and demoralized their troops." This understates the total impact of airpower that also inflicted heavy punishment on the enemy and in a variety of ways helped limit U.N. casualties.

The Korean War demonstrated a number of important lessons to the USAF, including the need for greater aircraft range, more accurate weapons, and better preparation and management of reserve forces. While the Air Force combat tested air-to-air refueling and guided bombs in Korea, and the war aided their development, these new technologies essentially had no impact on the Korean War. During the course of the Korean War, the USAF transitioned from World War II aircraft—F-51s, F-82s, B-26s, and B-29s—to jets. The helicopter also showed its promise for a variety of roles. At the same time, some observations took the Air Force down the wrong road. For example, as a result of Sabre pilot complaints, the USAF sought a dedicated air-to-air fighter and ended up with the high performance, but mission limited F-104. At the same time, the Air Force also went in a counter direction, believing that close in, maneuvering combat was over. As a result, the Air Force opted for an all-missile, no gun, armament package for future fighters. Vietnam subsequently demonstrated the errors of both of these decisions.

In Korea, the USAF flew about 721,000 sorties, lost about 1,500 aircraft to operational causes, and suffered 520 personnel killed in action and 900 listed as missing. The USAF accounted for 85 percent of the 470,000 tons of bombs delivered by U.N. air forces. Beginning the war in June 1950 organized into 48 wings with just over 400,000 personnel, the USAF grew in two years to 106 wings and almost one million men and women.

Although the United States did not win the Korean War, the effort was important. South Korea was saved from communism and went on to become an economic powerhouse and a democracy. And Americans clearly recognized that the United States Air Force would be a major factor in deterring, and if need be, fighting a future war.

Troops unload this C-119 boxcar at Kimpo shortly after the recapture of Seoul in September 1950. (USAF)

This B-29 crewman secures bombs in the bomb bay. (USAF)

A C-119 crew of the 314th Troop Carrier Group head for their plane for another resupply mission to Korea from their base in Japan. The Fairchild C-119 Flying Boxcar gave valuable service throughout the Korean War. (USAF)

THE
Air Force in
Southeast Asia

THE Air Force in Southeast Asia

Bernard C. Nalty

Above: *Colonel Robin Olds and a wingman evade ground fire after a low-level, high-speed attack on the Thai Nguyen steel mills on 30 March 1967. The F-4 Phantoms dropped 500-pound Mark-82 high drag bombs from 200 feet. ("Phantom Strike," Robert Taylor)*

Pages 158–159: *"The first night of Linebacker II we had 350 airplanes over the target for an hour and forty minutes and only thirty-five were Wild Weasels. The job of the Wild Weasel was to protect the B-52. Imagine watching a SAM missile track a B-52 in the middle of the night, bury itself in the bomb bay, and then seeing that huge airplane explode," said Captain Jim Winzell, a Wild Weasel pilot. This print shows two waves of B-52s crossing Hanoi, SAMs lifting off and tracking, flares dropped by the bombers to decoy the SAMs, and a MiG-21 that's just been hit by the tail gunner in the nearest B-52. ("High Road to Hanoi," Jack Fellows)*

The involvement of the U.S. Air Force in Southeast Asia began in 1952 when the United States supported France's attempt to retain possession of Indochina. The Air Force supplied aircraft and mechanics to service them, but not crews to fly them. This gesture and military aid totaling a billion dollars made little difference. The French conceded defeat within two years. The Geneva Accords of July 1954 divided the former colony at 17° north latitude. North of the line, Communist revolutionaries under Ho Chi Minh and General Vo Nguyen Giap assumed control. A demilitarized zone separated Communist North Vietnam from South Vietnam, where Ngo Dinh Diem took charge.

The United States backed President Diem, taking over from France responsibility for organizing, training, and equipping the armed forces of South Vietnam. Since the Americans expected any future conflict to resemble the successful campaign against the French, the United States Military Assistance Advisory Group, Vietnam—precursor of the United States Military Assistance Command, Vietnam—focused on ground combat and relegated its aerial component to a subsidiary role.

A Changing Commitment

Over the years, the United States evolved from advisor to warrior and ultimately chose airpower as the best method of defending South Vietnam. The war expanded in numbers, intensity, and geographic scope until total American strength peaked in 1969 at more than a half-million. The fighting spread to Laos, where another Geneva agreement, designed in 1962 to ensure the kingdom's neutrality, proved as ineffectual at bringing peace as the accords that created the two separate Vietnams. In 1970 hostilities

C-119 transports, made available to France by the United States, were quickly repainted and pressed into service to drop supplies to the beleaguered French forces at Dien Bien Phu. (USAF)

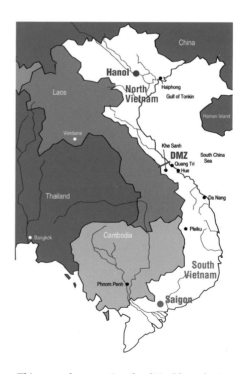

This map shows national political boundaries in Southeast Asia as they existed in 1961.

Above: *Early in the war, modified C-123s, part of the "Mule Train" counterinsurgency force, sprayed defoliant to uncover jungle hiding places from which Viet Cong soldiers might attack. Dubbed "Operation Ranch Hand," defoliation efforts were employed widely in South Vietnam and along the Ho Chi Minh Trail in Laos. (USAF)*

also erupted in Cambodia, where bases and supply lines helped sustain the South Vietnamese Communists, known as the Viet Cong.

Initially, American advisors tried to meet the perceived threat by giving President Diem the large, conventionally equipped ground forces he desired, but the Communist North did not invade as expected. Instead, compact, hard-hitting guerrilla forces attacked villages and government outposts in an increasingly successful attempt to demonstrate that the Saigon regime could not protect its citizens. American advisors urged Diem to concentrate on counterinsurgency operations to protect the security of the populace. He responded with a program of strategic hamlets that would prove more formidable on paper than in reality.

The Air Force and Counterinsurgency

The role of the Air Force in the advisory program reflected the shift away from large conventional forces and tactics toward the new concept of counterinsurgency. When President John F. Kennedy on 11 October 1961 called upon the Air Force, the service turned to the 4400th Combat Crew Training Detachment—nicknamed Jungle Jim after the great white hunter of the comic pages. The Air Force had established the Jungle Jim unit at Eglin Air Force Base, Florida, earlier that year, charging it with developing tactics and techniques for counterinsurgency. Equipped with modified versions of older aircraft—the T-28 trainer, B-26 light bomber, and the C-47 transport—a detachment named Farm Gate deployed to test in South Vietnam the theories developed in Florida.

Farm Gate went into action in South Vietnam by the end of December 1961. Besides flying reconnaissance missions, the detachment supplied distant outposts like those established to reduce the infiltration of men and supplies from the North into the South by way of the Ho Chi Minh Trail through southern Laos. It also supported combat operations by South Vietnamese troops. To integrate training more closely with combat, Farm Gate tried to include South Vietnamese in the crews of its aircraft. Unfortunately, progress remained slow, and the detachment had to fly missions that South Vietnamese fliers could not yet perform. To control Farm Gate's

Above: *Training the Vietnamese armed forces was always an important part of the Air Force mission in South Vietnam. Here, under the wing of their O-1 aircraft, a U.S. Air Force pilot and a South Vietnamese forward air controller discuss the mission they are about to fly. (USAF)*

expanding activity in South Vietnam, Thirteenth Air Force established an advanced headquarters (2d ADVON) at Tan Son Nhut Air Base, near Saigon, under Brigadier General Rollen H. Anthis.

Although concerned because the Diem government moved so sluggishly to exert control over the countryside, the Kennedy Administration faced other more serious problems, including a threat to Berlin in 1961 and the following year's Cuban missile crisis. As a result, the United States chose to intensify the advisory programs rather than dispatch combat troops. For now, American policy called for more of the same rather than some bolder approach.

By choosing more of the same, the Kennedy Administration ignored the views of the Air Force Chief of Staff, General Curtis E. LeMay. A veteran of the strategic bombing of both Germany and Japan during World War II, he believed that the United States should strike at the source of the insurgency that threatened South Vietnam. He maintained that the massive use of airpower against the North could achieve swift and decisive results, whereas killing guerrillas could not.

Reflecting the policy of more of the same, the major Air Force deployment in the spring of 1962, Mule Train, consisted of sixteen C-123 transports, six of them fitted to spray defoliants and kill the vegetation that concealed the Viet Cong. The Air Force also sent a few jet aircraft— F-102 interceptors to protect Tan Son Nhut and RF-101s for aerial reconnaissance. The South Vietnamese, moreover, received additional T-28s from the Air Force and A-1 attack bombers from the Navy. Meanwhile, the 2d ADVON's initial complement of B-26s and T-28s was wearing out.

Above: *This Air Force mobile air traffic control team has just facilitated the safe landing of a C-123 Provider on a small and remote airstrip at Dau Tieng in South Vietnam. An important element in the network of command, control, and communications assets, these mobile air traffic control teams moved with the action. (USAF)*

Opposite, top: *In South Vietnam, the Air Force "Farm Gate" counterinsurgency detachment used the twin-engine B-26 and single-engine T-28 for both training and operations in 1962 and 1963. These and other World War II-era aircraft were particularly adaptable to the primitive airfield conditions throughout most of South Vietnam. (USAF)*

U.S. Air Force and South Vietnamese forward air controllers used the O-1, seen here, to conduct reconnaissance and fire marking rockets to designate targets for air strikes. These small, slow aircraft were the eyes of the air effort to interdict enemy supply lines or troop concentrations. (USAF)

Above: *This A-1E sits armed and ready on the ramp at Qui Nhon. Both the Americans and the South Vietnamese flew this rugged attack plane in the early days of the war in Southeast Asia before jet aircraft were introduced. As American jets began to arrive, surplus A-1s were transferred to the South Vietnamese Air Force. (USAF)*

While the airmen waited for replacements, they had to avoid subjecting their war-weary planes to dangerously stressful maneuvers.

The limited aerial campaign continued. By mid-1963, Air Force numbers increased to 5,000—roughly a third of aggregate American strength. Reflecting this growing American commitment and requirements

Right: *Lieutenant Billy G. Priddy, a male flight nurse with the 9th Aeromedical Evacuation Squadron administers aide to a wounded serviceman being evacuated from a forward location. Depending on the nature of their injuries, casualties in South Vietnam were quickly and efficiently evacuated to American hospitals in South Vietnam, Clark Air Base in the Philippines, Japan, or the United States. (USAF)*

Opposite, bottom: *The Air Force C-130 served as the workhorse for tactical airlift operations in Southeast Asia. Assigned to bases in Taiwan or the Philippines, C-130s shuttled supplies into South Vietnam daily, and provided a logistical channel for the distribution of troops and supplies throughout South Vietnam. This transport has redeployed troops from the central highlands of South Vietnam to the coastal plain. (USAF)*

Right: *As the war intensified, Air Force transports like this Fairchild C-123 Provider delivered men and cargo to outlying bases. The short-field takeoff and landing characteristics of this aircraft were fully exploited in South Vietnam. (USAF)*

for improved command and control, 2d Air Division superseded 2d ADVON. President Diem failed, however, to carry out an ambitious campaign plan urged on him by his American advisors to reverse Communist gains in the countryside. While the Viet Cong extended its control over rural areas, ethnic and religious clashes weakened Diem's hold on the cities. Concerned that a descent into anarchy would aid the Communists, the Kennedy Administration endorsed a coup planned by South Vietnamese generals. The dissidents toppled Diem on 1 November 1963, and on the following day killed him.

Three weeks after Diem's death, President Kennedy was assassinated. Vice President Lyndon B. Johnson became Commander in Chief and sought to continue fighting a limited war in Southeast Asia, even accepting a short-lived reduction in American strength there. President Johnson, however, proved more willing than his predecessor to punish North Vietnam. In August 1964, after a clash between American destroyers patrolling in the Tonkin Gulf and North Vietnamese torpedo boats, the President approved air strikes against military targets in the North.

The Tonkin Gulf incident resulted in a rapid buildup of Air Force strength. Aircraft deployed included F-100 and F-105 jet fighters, KC-135 aerial tankers, and C-130 transports. The Air Force also transferred to the South Vietnamese a squadron of A-1s received from the Navy. Besides triggering the increase in aerial strength, the naval skirmish in the Tonkin

Above: *Nemo, a USAF sentry dog stands with his handler, Airman First Class Robert A. Thorneburg, after both have recovered from combat wounds. While patrolling on Tan Son Nhut Air Base in July 1967, Nemo detected four Viet Cong infiltrators. Although both Nemo and Thorneburg were wounded, Thorneburg commanded Nemo to charge. The sentry dog killed two of the intruders. (USAF)*

Gunners in the cargo compartment of an AC-130H insert another round in the 105-mm howitzer of the Spectre gunship. With an intricate system of sensors that could detect and track targets on the ground, a programmable fire control system, and an electronic gun sight, these C-130 gunships were deadly against trucks on the Ho Chi Minh Trail. (USAF)

The Commanding General, 7th Air Force, Lieutenant General Joseph H. Moore, confers in June 1966 with his deputy, Major General Gilbert L. Meyers, about the expanding air war in South Vietnam. (USAF)

Gulf enabled President Johnson to obtain from Congress a joint resolution authorizing retaliation against North Vietnam for any future provocation. He proved reluctant, however, to exercise the newly conferred power because a presidential election was scheduled for 3 November 1964, and he planned to be the less warlike candidate.

The immediate response to the Tonkin Gulf incident included the transfer of B-57 light bombers from Japan to South Vietnam to take up the slack until the arrival of A-26s—modernized attack versions of the B-26. The B-57s became the target of Viet Cong mortar crews who, on the night of 1 November 1964, damaged or destroyed eighteen of the bombers, three American helicopters, and eight South Vietnamese aircraft. American casualties totaled four killed and seventy-two wounded. Because the presidential election was just hours away, the Johnson Administration ignored the attack. Despite a landslide electoral victory, the President refused to retaliate when the Viet Cong detonated a bomb that killed two American officers in Saigon.

The President's patience had limits, however. Early in 1965, he approved intensified operations in South Vietnam and air strikes against the Ho Chi Minh Trail in southern Laos. In February, he retaliated for attacks against Pleiku and Qui Nhon with strikes against military installations in North Vietnam. Instead of continuing to retaliate for individual provocations, President Johnson on 13 February approved Operation Rolling Thunder, a sustained though limited air campaign against North Vietnam. Political unrest in Saigon and bad weather over the North delayed the launching of Rolling Thunder until 2 March.

Rolling Thunder

Rolling Thunder became the third air campaign that the Air Force fought simultaneously in Southeast Asia, joining those in Laos and South Vietnam. The 2d Air Division, expanding in size to fulfill its greater responsibilities, became the Seventh Air Force on 1 April 1966. The Commanding General, Seventh Air Force—initially Lieutenant General Joseph H. Moore—doubled as deputy for air operations to the Commanding General, U.S. Military Assistance Command, Vietnam, then General William C. Westmoreland, United States Army. Although Westmoreland, through his deputy for air operations, directed the air campaign in South Vietnam and those operations just north of the 17th parallel, he had to coordinate activity in Laos with the U.S. Ambassador at Vientiane.

The Commander in Chief, Pacific, Admiral Ulysses Grant Sharp, exercised overall control of Rolling Thunder. For purposes of coordination, North Vietnam was divided into six so-called Route Packages, each assigned to the Navy or the Air Force. Attacking the Air Force route packages became the task of the Thailand-based squadrons of the Seventh/Thirteenth Air Force, an awkward title chosen because the Seventh Air Force provided operational direction and the Thirteenth Air Force administrative support.

When Rolling Thunder began, the Joint Chiefs of Staff prepared a list of ninety-four targets in North Vietnam, but Secretary of Defense Robert S. McNamara chose not to destroy them quickly, as the Air Force urged. Instead of striking a sudden blow, or relentlessly increasing pres-

Ground crewmen hustle a maintenance cart between Republic F-105 Thunderchiefs as munitions loaders await the opportunity to begin loading bombs for the next strike mission. Although seldom in the limelight, the long hours and dedication of these men and women always meant the difference between mission success or failure—and sometimes the difference between life and death for the aircrew. (USAF)

Onboard a Lockheed RC-121 Constellation flying over the Tonkin Gulf, A2C Douglas C. Christensen plots the location of enemy aircraft over North Vietnam. The RC-121, forerunner of AWACS, provided critical information to American airmen engaged in strike missions. (USAF)

Top, left: *The crew of a Soviet-supplied heavy antiaircraft gun prepares to fire on American aircraft attacking North Vietnam. Along with surface-to-air missiles, radar directed 85-mm and 100-mm guns forced Rolling Thunder formations to attack at low altitudes where 37-mm and 57-mm weapons proved deadly. (USAF)*

Top, right:: *Reconnaissance pilots usually flew alone, collecting intelligence photos, and relying on speed and surprise for survival. The pilot of this RF-101 Voodoo has succeeded on both counts, capturing the shadow of his aircraft over unmanned enemy antiaircraft guns somewhere in North Vietnam. (USAF)*

Above: *Colonel Charles A. Gabriel, commander of the 432nd Tactical Fighter Wing, prepared for another combat mission in 1971. Colonel Gabriel went on to earn four stars and serve as the Air Force chief of staff from 1982 to 1986. (USAF)*

sure, Rolling Thunder escalated unevenly. From time to time, the bombing stopped briefly, as the Johnson Administration strained to hear signals that Hanoi was calling off the war in the South. When no signal came, Rolling Thunder resumed, striking some new target or revisiting an old one. Persuasion thus replaced destruction as the goal of an air war, and Rolling Thunder therefore spared the government machinery that might choose to call off the fighting.

The F-4s and F-105s that carried out Rolling Thunder encountered both interceptors and antiaircraft weapons. The Soviet Union supplied MiG-17s, a few MiG-19s, and finally MiG-21s. Until airfields became available in North Vietnam, the fighters remained in China, and during Rolling Thunder, whenever American pressure became too great, they could gain refuge beyond the border. Enemy pilots found that approaching from the rear, as though making an attack, could sometimes force a strike formation to jettison its bombs to increase maneuverability for a dogfight. The antiaircraft arsenal, which proved more dangerous than the interceptors, included visually aimed automatic weapons, along with radar-directed guns and surface-to-air missiles.

When Rolling Thunder began, radar seemed to hold the key to North Vietnamese air defenses, warning of approaching American aircraft and isolating targets for surface-to-air missiles or antiaircraft guns. The Air Force adopted several countermeasures against radar. Specially equipped fighter-bombers known as Wild Weasels could detect radar signals and launch anti-radiation missiles that homed on the transmitters. Other F-4s and F-105s mounted jamming transmitters in wing pods. By maintaining a formation that enhanced the effect of the pods, the attackers could confuse the hostile radars with electronic noise.

Rolling Thunder proceeded spasmodically, attacking roads, rail lines, bridges, warehouses, oil storage facilities, power plants, and North Vietnam's few industries. Ports like Haiphong were spared because of

Tanker to the Rescue

Colonel Drue L. DeBerry, USAF (Ret)

For Major John H. Casteel, pilot; Captain Richard L. Trail, copilot; Captain Dean L. Hoar, navigator; and Master Sergeant Nathan C. Campbell, boom operator, 31 May 1967 began as a routine day. Regularly, KC-135 tanker crews from the 4258th Strategic Wing at U Tapao Air Base, Thailand, flew "anchor" missions over the Gulf of Tonkin or over northern Laos. The tankers flew a racetrack pattern, always retracing their path over some specific reference point—some "anchor"—while waiting to refuel strike aircraft returning from missions over North Vietnam. On 31 May, Major Casteel's crew was assigned to the Tonkin Gulf.

Soon after establishing their track, Major Casteel's crew received a call requesting fuel for two Air Force F-104s. While refueling those aircraft, Captain Trail, working the radios, received another call. Two Navy KA-3 tanker aircraft with only minutes of fuel remaining needed to hookup to the tanker. The F-104s completed a partial download of fuel and made way for the Navy

KA-3s. The first KA-3 took on minimum fuel, than backed off so boom operator Campbell could begin fueling the second KA-3. With all the activity, the F-104s were asked to remain nearby to defend against possible MiG activity. The morning was quickly becoming anything but routine.

Then Trail heard two Navy F-8s requesting emergency fuel. Navigator Dean Hoar gave the fighters a vector to intercept the tanker, still refueling the second KA-3. The first F-8 arrived so low on fuel that the pilot could not wait for the KA-3 to complete taking on minimum fuel. In desperation, the Navy pilot hooked up to the KA-3 that was still taking fuel from the KC-135 in what is believed to be the first triple hook-up in aviation history. The first KA-3 began refueling the second F-8. While this operation continued, two Navy F-4s arrived with insufficient fuel to reach their carrier.

By shuffling aircraft onto the refueling boom long enough to pass some fuel to the one most in need, Major Casteel and his crew eventually managed to transfer sufficient fuel to all eight aircraft so the Navy planes could return to their carrier and the two Air Force F-104s could return to Tan Son Nhut Air Base near Saigon. Now also short of fuel, Major Casteel landed in South Vietnam to refuel before returning to U Tapao Air Base, Thailand. For their suburb airmanship, professionalism, and dedication, Major Casteel's crew was awarded the Mackay Trophy for the most meritorious Air Force flight of the year.

In-flight refueling assured strike aircraft maximum tactical flexibility for low-level high-speed attack profiles. These F-105s refuel over Laos before heading for North Vietnam. (USAF)

A Republic F-105 Thunderchief, known by its crews as the Thud, attacks a target in North Vietnam. Designed to deliver nuclear weapons and rely for protection more on speed than on armor, this fighter-bomber proved particularly vulnerable to antiaircraft fire. Thud Ridge, a location in North Vietnam, takes its name from the number of these aircraft that crashed there. (USAF)

possible damage not only to Soviet ships, but also to ships of those friendly nations that had remained neutral in the conflict. The careful selection of targets for Rolling Thunder may have spared many North Vietnamese non-combatants, but caution did not ensure steadfast support by the American public. A lack of measurable progress, despite continuing American casualties, fed the dissatisfaction.

The Tet Offensive and its Consequences

On 30 and 31 January 1968, taking advantage of the celebration of Tet, the holiday marking the lunar New Year, the North Vietnamese and Viet Cong launched a series of attacks throughout South Vietnam. Enemy forces penetrated the U.S. Embassy compound in Saigon, laid siege to the historic city of Hue, and attacked other cities and most major bases. The Tet Offensive contradicted official reports of steady progress and predictions of imminent victory. Surprised American officials requested more men for strategic reserve as well as for service in Vietnam. The request leaked onto the pages of the nation's newspapers and deepened the gloom caused by the attacks. President Johnson responded by approving only a small increase in strength in Southeast Asia. He also accepted the recommendations of his most trusted advisors to impose a ceiling on the American effort and to seek a negotiated end to the fighting.

Rolling Thunder soon became a casualty of the Tet Offensive. Ho Chi Minh continued to wage war in South Vietnam despite bombing that battered his nation's infrastructure. Inflicting this apparently acceptable damage cost 726 airmen killed or captured and more than 500 Air Force planes destroyed. The price in lives and aircraft—together with the dismay caused by the Tet Offensive—persuaded the President to restrict the bombing

An F-105 shoots down a MiG-17 during a June 1967 Rolling Thunder attack. (USAF)

of the North and, effective 1 November 1968, to end Rolling Thunder. The limitations on attacks against the North lasted until the spring of 1972, although aerial reconnaissance continued. The United States insisted that Hanoi, when entering cease-fire negotiations, had agreed at least tacitly to the reconnaissance flights. Whenever North Vietnamese gunners fired on the planes, American aircraft could retaliate.

The Air War in South Vietnam

Aerial operations in South Vietnam—whether strikes against hostile troops, reconnaissance, air transport, rescue operations, or administrative flights—kept pace with the buildup of American forces, as the United States, beginning in the spring of 1965, took over fighting the war. The first contingent of U.S. Marines landed on 8 March, six days after the first Rolling Thunder strikes, and an Army brigade followed in May. By year's end, American strength reached 181,000 building to 385,000 in December 1966 and 486,000 in December 1967. In January 1965, before the massive buildup began, the Air Force flew some 6,200 sorties of all sorts in South Vietnam. By December 1965, the monthly total surpassed 17,000 in a steady increase that exceeded 37,000 in December 1966 and reached 60,000 in October 1967, that year's most active month.

The increasing demand for aerial firepower persuaded General John P. McConnell, who had succeeded LeMay as Air Force Chief of Staff, to employ B-52s of the Strategic Air Command against targets in South Vietnam. Modified to drop high explosive rather than nuclear bombs, the

SSgt William E. Collins, chief observer of the weather detachment at Phu Cat Air Base, South Vietnam, examines a surface prognostication and prepares to brief an aircrew for another mission. Because of monsoonal patterns in Southeast Asia, weather varied considerably between North Vietnam, South Vietnam, Laos, and Thailand. (USAF)

Ground crewmen hustle to remove arming pins from ordnance on a McDonnell Douglass F-4 awaiting takeoff clearance at Phu Cat Air Base, South Vietnam. (USAF)

Above: *Colonel Devol Brett, vice commander of the 12th Tactical Fighter Wing, has just been rescued from the Gulf of Tonkin by the pararescueman kneeling barefoot beside him in the troop compartment of a Sikorsky HH-3E helicopter. Colonel Brett's F-4C was hit by enemy fire over North Vietnam. The look in his eyes says much about the experience. (USAF)*

huge aircraft attacked hostile troop concentrations and supply dumps. Ground-based radar—either beacons that served as offset aiming points or the Combat Skyspot system formerly used to determine the accuracy of practice bombing—guided the aircraft to their release points.

The first of the B-52 missions in South Vietnam, named Arc Light strikes, produced mixed results. On 18 June 1965, twenty-eight of the aircraft dropped some 1,300 bombs, more than half of which exploded in a target box measuring one-by-two miles. South Vietnamese troops entered the area and found abandoned camps and supplies, but no dead or wounded. Locating profitable targets and assessing Arc Light results remained difficult throughout the war.

Besides bombing distant troop concentrations and supply dumps, the B-52s joined tactical aircraft in supporting American and South Vietnamese troops in combat against the enemy. During the fight for Khe Sanh, a Marine strong point in northwestern South Vietnam near the Laotian border, airpower broke the enemy's back. On 21 January 1968, as the hour approached for the Tet Offensive, a North Vietnamese attack on one of Khe Sanh's outposts signaled the beginning of a seventy-eight-day encirclement of the Marine Corps base. The enemy shelled the plateau where the Marines had dug in and spun a web of trenches around it, convincing General Westmoreland that a decisive battle would be fought at Khe Sanh and persuading him to mass airpower to defend the base.

Since North Vietnamese troops had cut the road to Khe Sanh, Air Force transports and Marine helicopters had to deliver supplies, evacuate casualties, and bring in reinforcements. Air Force, Navy, and Marine fighter-bombers and attack planes suppressed hostile antiaircraft fire as the helicopters and transports approached. To minimize exposure to enemy artillery, supply missions spent as little time as possible at the airstrip atop the plateau. Helicopters hovered just long enough to lower cargo-laden nets, and transports unloaded within one minute. The Air Force parachuted some supplies, but to improve accuracy and deliver bulky items, it used either of two extraction systems. The aircraft might skim low over the airstrip and release a parachute that pulled the cargo pallet through the opening at the rear of the cargo compartment, or deploy a hook attached to the pallet that snagged a cable stretched across the runway and extracted the cargo.

B-52s joined in battering the North Vietnamese, benefiting like tactical aircraft and artillery from electronic sensors deployed along the enemy's likely avenues of approach. Signals from the sensors were relayed to a computerized control center at Nakhon Phanom, Thailand, where analysts interpreted them and identified key targets. Airpower and artillery

Daytime truck traffic on the Ho Chi Minh Trail. The enemy eventually realized that the hours just after daybreak and shortly before sunset afforded the best protection from marauding aircraft—shadows interfered with visual observation, and the ambient light imposed limits on infrared and other night vision devices. (USAF)

Opposite, top: B-52s bombed troop concentrations and supply dumps, battered enemy forces attacking friendly outposts, and in 1972 concentrated their firepower against the North Vietnamese heartland during Operation Linebacker II. (USAF)

Above: *South Vietnamese units (without any American advisors) advanced toward Tchepone during the Lam Son 719 operation in 1971. The South Vietnamese encountered heavily wooded terrain that slowed their advance and lent itself to ambush. With massive U.S. air support, the South Vietnamese units reached Tchepone, destroyed enemy supplies stored there, and withdrew hastily in the face of mounting resistance. (USAF)*

Top, right: *A C-130 employs low-altitude parachute extraction to deliver bulky cargo during the expansion of the Khe Sanh airstrip in 1967. The same technique saw service during the North Vietnamese encirclement of the base in the following year. (USAF)*

Opposite, top: *The C-130 parachuted supplies to embattled troops in South Vietnam and Cambodia. Here one of the transports helps sustain Operation Junction City, carried out in 1967 northwest of Saigon near the Cambodian border. (USAF)*

A South Vietnamese pilot is learning to fly an F-5 jet fighter delivered to South Vietnam during the Nixon Administration's Vietnamization program. The lightweight plane, though fast and comparatively easy to maintain, could not replace the firepower of the American F-4 aircraft being withdrawn from Southeast Asia. (USAF)

174

cut loose with devastating effect, and the enemy did not storm the base. Possibly, they were less interested in fighting a decisive battle there than in pinning down manpower and aircraft that otherwise could have helped suppress the Tet offensive.

Vietnamization

After the Tet Offensive, the nature of the war in South Vietnam changed as President Johnson and especially his successor, Richard M. Nixon, embarked on a policy of withdrawing American combat troops and making the South Vietnamese increasingly responsible for fighting the war. According to this strategy, which President Nixon called Vietnamization, airpower provided a shield behind which American ground forces could withdraw as the South Vietnamese trained and took over the conflict.

Vietnamization required stronger efforts to arm, train, and advise the South Vietnamese armed forces, but results proved uneven. The Vietnamese air arm rapidly expanded in manpower and number of aircraft, but the U.S. Air Force never provided the Vietnamese Air Force an aerial weapon even remotely comparable to the B-52. Nor were the South Vietnamese flying F-4s, the latest C-130 transports, or AC-130 gunships, the transports fitted with side-firing cannon and electronic sensors for target acquisition. Moreover, the South Vietnamese Air Force lacked a rescue service like the one that enabled the Air Force to recover downed airmen from all but the most heavily defended areas, and the Air Force command and control system had yet to be Vietnamized. If South Vietnam were to survive an invasion, American airpower would have to intervene.

The most ambitious operation undertaken by the Vietnamese armed forces, Lam Son 719, began on 8 February 1971. South Vietnamese troops, supported by American aircraft and long-range artillery, advanced into southern Laos toward Tchepone, an important way station on the Ho Chi Minh Trail. The attackers established a succession of fire

bases, reached Tchepone, and destroyed the supplies stored there, but the North Vietnamese pinched off the salient. Despite a massive surge in the sortie rate by U.S. Air Force squadrons supporting the invasion, North Vietnamese pressure forced the South Vietnamese to retreat in disorder, leaving behind their armor and artillery. President Nixon hailed the operation as a victory despite the narrow escape of the invasion force, which might well have been destroyed except for American airpower.

The Air War in Laos

The war in Laos evolved into two distinct campaigns. In the northern part of the kingdom, an army composed largely of American-supported irregulars tied down a force of Pathet Lao—the Laotian Communist faction— that was strengthened by North Vietnamese troops who otherwise might have been fighting in South Vietnam. The anticommunist forces did best when the weather permitted airpower to hammer the enemy. B-52s proved especially effective, as did the new OV-10s, twin-engine turboprop aircraft capable of directing strikes or conducting armed reconnaissance and observation missions. Another new aircraft, the all-weather F-111 fighter-bomber, also saw action. T-28s of the minuscule Royal Laotian Air Force played a minor role. Airpower helped the irregulars, and the Laotian army units fighting alongside them, to survive until 1972 when North Vietnam focused on conquering the South.

Above: *During Lam Son 719, South Vietnamese soldiers on the ground in Laos moved through thick tropical vegetation, sometimes triple canopy jungle to uncover enemy suply depots and protective bunkers. (USAF)*

Above: *The Lockheed RC-121 Constellation provided airborne early detection and warning of enemy aircraft to U.S. strike forces operating over North Vietnam. (USAF)*

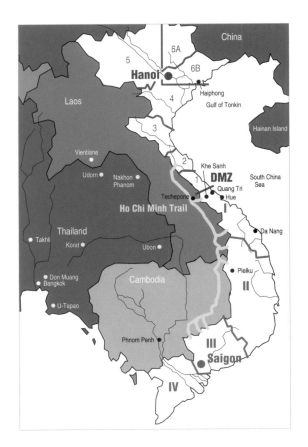

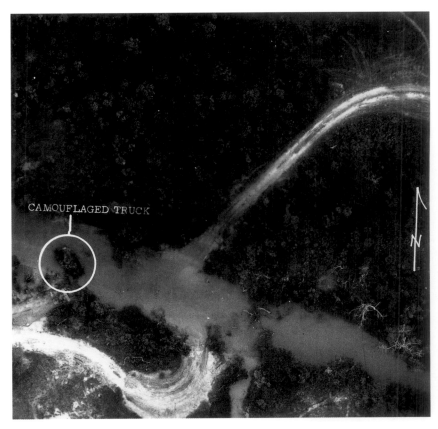

CAMOUFLAGED TRUCK

Top, left: *The Ho Chi Minh Trail—really a system of trails—ran through mountain passes separating North Vietnam and Laos, through southern Laos, and into Cambodia. North Vietnamese army units maintained and defended the trail and established caches of supplies for the Viet Cong guerrillas—and later, the North Vietnamese army—operating in South Vietnam. American forces slowed but never stopped the flow of supplies and reinforcements entering South Vietnam from the Ho Chi Minh Trail. (USAF)*

Top, right: *The Ho Chi Minh Trail was not a single trail, but a network of roads through Laos and Cambodia. Trucks, porters pushing bicycles loaded with large bags of rice, boats, and even elephants were employed by the North Vietnamese, generally at night, to move troops and supplies south. The Trail was heavily protected by antiaircraft guns, guarded, and maintained by North Vietnamese regular forces. (USAF)*

To American eyes, the skirmishes in northern Laos seemed less important than systematically attacking the roads, trails, and waterways of the Ho Chi Minh Trail, the so called Steel Tiger area, which wound among the jungle-covered ridges of southern Laos. As early as April 1965, a strike by B-52s against Mu Gia Pass, which channeled supplies and reinforcements from North Vietnam onto the Ho Chi Minh Trail, foreshadowed American interest. At about the same time, fighter-bombers began hitting areas where the trail entered South Vietnam.

The air attacks against the trail evolved into Commando Hunt, a sequence of related campaigns designed to impede North Vietnamese infiltration of men and supplies through southern Laos. The seven Commando Hunt operations conducted from the fall of 1968 until the spring of 1972 pitted American technology against weather, darkness, jungle, mountains, and a clever and determined enemy. Radar, night vision devices, and trail-watch teams—along with a network of sensors reporting to the

Right: *The AC-130 Spectre gunship was the most effective American weapon against the North Vietnamese trucks moving down the Ho Chi Minh Trail. Shown here parked at Ubon Air Base in Thailand, is aircraft 56-0490, Thor. This aircraft and all thirteen crewmen aboard were lost near Pakse, Laos, on 21 December 1972. (USAF)*

computerized surveillance center at Nakhon Phanom, Thailand—sought to penetrate camouflage and natural cover to find targets for laser-guided bombs and other weapons. The North Vietnamese concealed their movements, scheduling them for dawn or dusk when airborne sensors were less effective and even setting fires to mimic burning trucks and blind infrared devices. Ultimately, the enemy would prevail, not only sustaining the war within South Vietnam, but also massing forces to invade the country from southern Laos.

Into Cambodia

By 1969, a series of North Vietnamese bases had sprung up in eastern Cambodia to store and distribute supplies and provide rest areas for Communist troops fighting the Saigon regime. On 18 March 1969, President Nixon unleashed the B-52s against these targets. To conceal this expansion of the scope of the war, official reports falsely described the missions as raids inside South Vietnam. The secret bombing totaled some 3,500 sorties, lasted fourteen months, and did not become public knowledge until 1973.

In April 1970, during the secret air attacks, American and South Vietnamese troops crossed into Cambodia and advanced on the bases. This operation, described as a temporary incursion rather than an invasion, destroyed or captured a vast amount of military stores, but it also enlarged the scope of the war and aroused domestic opposition. Indeed, Congress refused to provide funds to continue the ground campaign beyond 30 June. As a result, the American incursion ended on that date, but South Vietnamese troops continued their operations, with the support of their own and American aircraft. The United States, moreover, committed itself to sustain a weak revolutionary Cambodian government and an ill-organized army that proved no match for the growing strength of the Communist Khmer Rouge.

Invasion, 1972

When the Tet holiday of 1972 passed without a repetition of the January offensive of four years earlier, American intelligence analysts assumed that the enemy would pass up the opportunity to undercut public support for the Nixon Administration's policy of Vietnamization as the November presidential election approached. Signs of smaller-scale North Vietnamese attacks appeared, but the pattern did not portend a decisive challenge to Saigon's Vietnamized armed forces. On 30 March, however, startled American aerial observers patrolling the demilitarized zone peered through gaps in the cloud cover and saw massive enemy formations advancing southward.

The United States rushed airpower to Southeast Asia, reversing the withdrawals that during Vietnamization had reduced the total number of Air Force aircraft in South Vietnam and Thailand by some 40 percent. By June 30, the equivalent of fifteen Air Force squadrons had deployed to Southeast Asia, strengthening an armada that now included 119 B-52s and 110 KC-135s.

Technicians load a 2,000-pound laser-guided bomb on an F-4 during tests at Eglin Air Force Base. Introduced as Rolling Thunder ended, laser-guided weapons of various sizes proved their worth on the Ho Chi Minh Trail, in South Vietnam, and in both Linebacker and Linebacker II. (USAF)

Air Force F-4s, carrying laser-guided weapons, head north during Operation Linebacker. (USAF)

After completing 100 combat missions, a smiling pilot presents a case of cold beer to his crew chief. The pace of operations in the air war could not have been maintained without the skilled and dedicated support of hard-working maintenance professionals. (USAF)

The Medal

Colonel Drue L. DeBerry, USAF (Ret)

Airman John L. Levitow, on his 180th combat mission over Vietnam, reeled and slammed against the floor of the cargo compartment in an AC-47 "Spooky" gunship. The aircraft and its occupants absorbed the shrapnel from an enemy 82-mm mortar shell exploding in the old airplane's right wing. As the pilot, Major Ken Carpenter, fought to control the damaged and partially out-of-control aircraft, Airman Levitow struggled to his feet. The explosion had wounded all four occupants of the cargo compartment. Levitow himself would later learn that he carried forty fragments from the explosion in his back and legs. Bleeding and stunned by the concussion, he began assisting Airman Ellis C. Owen, a gunner on the aircraft who had been wounded and was bleeding profusely.

Then Levitow saw the flare.

The AC-47 was flying a night mission in support of U.S. forces at Long Binh Army Post, dropping flares to illuminate the defensive perimeter. The gunship would then attack enemy forces disclosed on the ground by the flare's illumination. The Mark 24 flares used on this mission consisted of powdered magnesium and other chemicals that burned at 4,000 degrees Fahrenheit and emitted a brilliant light. When the safety pin on the 27-pound flare was

pulled, the flare would ignite in about 20 seconds. Before the gunship was hit, Airman Owen had attached the firing lanyard of a Mark 24 to the aircraft, hooked his finger through the flare's safety pin ring, and was awaiting Major Carpenter's command to toss the flare out the open cargo door of the gunship. When the mortar exploded in the wing of the aircraft, wounding Owen and throwing him to the floor, the flare was pulled from his hands, his finger still through the safety pin ring, arming the flare.

Levitow saw the three-foot-long flare roll across the cabin floor. Unable to grab the rolling canister because of the pitching aircraft, he threw himself on the flare, dragged it to the open cargo door, and threw it out. The flare ignited almost immediately. Levitow collapsed in the open door, a trail of blood behind him on the floor of the cargo compartment.

Major Carpenter landed the badly damaged aircraft successfully. Airman Levitow, Airman Owen, and the other two men in the cargo compartment received medical attention and recovered from their wounds. Had the flare ignited inside the aircraft, the aircraft and all aboard would have been lost.

For his actions on this mission, on 14 May 1970 Airman John L. Levitow was awarded the Medal of Honor by President Richard M. Nixon in ceremonies at the White House.

Top: Airman John L. Levitow proudly wears the nation's highest award for valor, the Medal of Honor. (USAF)

Left: This illustration shows a wounded A1C John Levitow dragging a smoking Mark-24 flare toward the open doorway of an AC-47 gunship. (Professional Loadmaster Association)

An AC-47 "Spooky" gunship and an AC-130 "Spectre" patrol above the dusk-shrouded countryside of South Vietnam. ("Bloodline," Ronald Wong)

Major Bernard Fisher (left) and Lieutenant Colonel Dafford Myers celebrate at Pleiku airfield, South Vietnam. In March 1966 after Myers's aircraft was hit and forced down on a field being overrun by the Viet Cong, Fisher, under intense ground fire, landed his A-1E Skyraider on the field long enough for Meyers to scramble aboard. For this heroic act, Fisher was awarded the Medal of Honor. (USAF)

Marine aircraft, withdrawn in April 1971, began returning a week after the invasion. They would support the overall air campaign, since Marine ground forces—the last of whom departed in July 1971—were not reintroduced. The Navy responded to the invasion by increasing the number of aircraft carriers off Vietnam from two to six, each with some sixty aircraft. Meanwhile, the scheduled withdrawal of American ground forces continued.

Airpower faced the difficult task of cutting the supply lines sustaining the North Vietnamese offensive and at the same time shattering the enemy forces menacing Quang Tri City, Kontum City, and An Loc. To protect the advancing troops, the North Vietnamese deployed their radar-directed surface-to-air missiles as far forward as feasible and issued shoulder-fired, heat-seeking antiaircraft missiles to the assault units. The MiGs, however, continued to concentrate on defending North Vietnam's heartland.

B-52s joined the interdiction campaign, attacking targets in southern North Vietnam and in June bombing oil storage facilities at Haiphong. Meanwhile, they also hammered the troops trying to overrun An Loc and Kontum City. AC-130 gunships, some of them mounting a side-firing 105mm howitzer, pounded hostile troops besieging the towns, and C-130 transports parachuted supplies when it became impossible to use the airstrips. Fighter-bombers ranged over the North in Operation Linebacker, even severing the rail link with China, and Navy aircraft planted mines in Haiphong harbor. Although attacks against Hanoi and Haiphong required presidential approval, Linebacker planners had the authority to strike a greater variety of targets than during Rolling Thunder.

By employing tanks, infantry, and artillery and advancing along roads that also served as supply arteries, the North Vietnamese high command presented lucrative targets for airpower. To neutralize the heat-seeking mis-siles carried by North Vietnamese soldiers, attacking airmen released flares that provided a heat source to lure the weapon away from the hot engine of an airplane or helicopter. To make the decoys more effective, technicians

Combat aircrew regarded the pararescueman in Southeast Asia as the bravest-of-the-brave. On many occasions, when due to injury a downed crewman was unable to secure himself to a rescue hoist, a pararescueman would descend on the hoist and secure the downed crewman and himself to the rescue device. This photo shows one of these brave men bringing a downed pilot into a rescue helicopter. (USAF)

Colonel Robin Olds, commander of the 8th Tactical Fighter Wing, took advantage of North Vietnamese routine tactics to plan Operation Bolo, a successful aerial ambush in January 1967. Olds' F-4s, using a flight profile normally employed by F-105 strike aircraft, enticed North Vietnamese MiGs to attack. Before the MiG pilots escaped the ruse, the F-4s shot down as many as seven MiGs. (USAF)

Above: *The wreckage of a warehouse near Hanoi after an attack during Linebacker by F-4s armed with laser-guided bombs. (USAF)*

Right: *A North Vietnamese pilot climbs into the cockpit of his MiG 21. (USAF)*

added shielding around aircraft engines, and pilots maneuvered to avoid giving gunners a clear shot at the engine or its exhaust plume.

The Soviet-built tanks that spearheaded the invasion outgunned the lighter types provided under Vietnamization. As a result, the Air Force loaded heavier U.S. Army tanks in C-5A transports and flew them to bases like Da Nang. In an attempt to prepare South Vietnam for renewed attacks, the airlift of military supplies and equipment continued after the ground fighting ebbed.

The offensive overran Quang Tri City at the outset, but South Vietnamese troops recaptured it, even though the enemy still held the territory to the west and north. Thanks to savage and accurate aerial attack, An Loc held out, barring the way to Saigon; and the defenders of Kontum City, where the B-52s proved decisive, frustrated an attempt to cut South Vietnam in half. The South survived, but the enemy had gained control of a strategic crescent from the demilitarized zone southward through the western highlands, thus ensuring the security of the Ho Chi Minh Trail and providing bases for future attacks.

As the fighting slowed on the ground, the negotiations at Paris, under way since January 1969, finally seemed on the verge of shaping a truce acceptable to the United States. Secretary of State Henry A. Kissinger declared that peace was at hand, and President Nixon, who had visited Beijing in February 1972 and Moscow in May, showed willingness to cut back, though not end, Operation Linebacker. Peace proved elusive, however, for both North and South Vietnam raised last-minute objections.

The South Vietnamese government of Nguyen Van Thieu demanded ironclad guarantees of American aid to counterbalance the continued presence of North Vietnamese troops south of the 17th parallel. President Nixon succeeded, however, in satisfying the Saigon regime with his "absolute assurance" that he would take "swift and severe retaliatory action" if North Vietnam violated a cease-fire agreement. The Nixon Administration's reaction to the 1972 invasion may well have persuaded South Vietnam to accept this personal pledge in lieu of a more formal pact. Once Saigon agreed, President Nixon had to convince North Vietnam to cooperate, a goal he proposed to attain with airpower.

Linebacker II

North Vietnam balked, perhaps to see what President Nixon might yield besides accepting the continued presence of its troops in the South. If so, events overwhelmed Hanoi. The President, easily reelected, obtained greater freedom to do what he believed necessary to end the war. The college campuses, where opposition to his policies flourished, had grown quiet, in part because draftees were no longer needed in Vietnam as American ground forces withdrew. In addition, the Christmas break complicated the task of organizing student protests. The newly elected Congress, another possible source of opposition, had yet to convene.

The Commander in Chief decided that airpower could force North Vietnam to accept a cease-fire. He therefore launched Linebacker II on December 18, an operation that sent B-52s against Hanoi and Haiphong. The huge bombers could not, however, match the accuracy

During Linebacker II, mechanics struggled to keep the B-52s flying, whether from Guam (as shown here) or U-Tapao in Thailand. In the eleven days of Linebacker II, B-52s flew 729 sorties over North Vietnam, expending over 15,000 tons of ordnance. (USAF)

Above: *The EB-66 provided electronic warfare support for Air Force operations against North Vietnam. (USAF)*

Left: *A C-130 transport taxis on the ramp during the fighting at Khe Sanh as aerial port personnel prepare to unload the aircraft. Aircraft ground times were kept to a minimum due to the threat of mortar attacks on the Marine Corps base. Note how shell fragments have damaged the structure in the foreground. (USAF)*

Linebacker II

Brigadier General James R. McCarthy, USAF (Ret)

In December 1972, one hundred and fifty B-52's, the greatest number ever gathered at one location, assembled at Andersen AFB, Guam. For the first time during the Vietnam War, Washington had decided to unleash strategic airpower to strike the enemy's capacity and will to wage war.

Late on the afternoon of 18 December, Major Bill Stocker's black-bellied B-52D lumbered onto the runway, accelerated, and lifted off from Andersen. In the course of the evening, eighty-six more B-52D's and G's from the 43rd and 72nd Bomb Wings followed. Forty-two B-52D's of the 307th Bomb Wing at U-Tapao, Thailand would soon join the Andersen force. Their target was downtown Hanoi. At a dozen other bases, KC-135 tankers, F-4's, B-66's, F-105's, and other support forces were preparing for the night's work. Each had a part to play in this air operation. Operation Linebacker II had begun and except for 25 December, would continue for 11 days.

I remember flying toward the target on the second night of Linebacker II, watching SAMs lift off. After a flash on the ground the size of a city block, the missile would begin climbing. Looking down at it, a SAM looked like a black basketball surrounded by a ring of silver fire. As the warhead came directly at us, it took on the appearance of a lighted silver doughnut. Crews nicknamed that sight the "deadly doughnut." The silver doughnuts that maintained their shape and relative position on the cockpit windows were the ones you worried about the most. They were tracking you.

Our crew saw several of those silver doughnuts during our bomb run on that night. Three SAMs exploded nearby at our altitude. Two passed us and exploded overhead. Then, our B-52 began to shudder as twenty-two tons of ordnance cleared the bomb bay. We turned steeply and a second later, a SAM exploded where our right wing had been. The gunner reported more SAMs on the way, but free of our ordnance, we successfully evaded them and headed back to Andersen.

During the eleven days of Linebacker II, we launched 729 B-52 sorties against the Hanoi-Haiphong area, delivering fifteen thousand tons of bombs on thirty-four military targets. Because several countries denied overflight rights for B-52s, some Andersen-based missions required post-strike refueling and took sixteen hours for the 8,000 mile round trip. These were historically long and dangerous missions. We lost fifteen B-52s during Linebacker II, but it was the most successful air campaign of the Vietnam War because we forced the North Vietnamese to negotiate a settlement and to release our prisoners of war.

Three B-52s taxi out for takeoff while ground crewmen arm and fuel other Stratofortresses for the next wave of bombers during Operation Linebacker II in December 1972. (USAF)

GIA LAM RR YARD & SHOPS

18 PIECES ROLLING STOCK DAMAGED/DESTROYED

CRANEWAY DAMAGED

6 SUPPORT BUILDINGS DESTROYED

16 DAMAGED BUILDINGS

→ DAMAGED BUILDING
ↄ DESTROYED BUILDIN
◯ TRACK INTERDICTION

27 DEC 72

Left: *North Vietnam's rail net came under heavy attack during Linebacker II. Using radar bombing offset points, B-52s achieved good targeting accuracy from high altitudes. (USAF)*

Above: *General John D. Lavelle, whose broad interpretation of protective reaction resulted in his being replaced as Commanding General, 7th Air Force. (USAF)*

achieved against targets farther south. Combat Skyspot radar provided uneven coverage this far north, forcing bombardiers to rely on their airborne radar.

The deadliness of the radar-controlled surface-to-air missiles and guns required the use of extensive countermeasures throughout Linebacker II. These included fighter-bombers armed with anti-radiation missiles, jamming transmitters mounted in pods carried by fighters or installed in EB-66s and B-52s, and radar-reflecting chaff. Although the same countermeasures remained in use, the techniques of employment changed.

From the first Linebacker II mission until the suspension of B-52 strikes for the Christmas holiday, the bomber stream followed a corridor of chaff that unexpectedly made the bombers more vulnerable. The corridors, as they formed, alerted missile crews to the approaching B-52s and enabled the defenders to salvo their missiles, depending not on radar but on proximity fuses set for altitudes determined by the pilots of MiGs shadowing the formation. Winds, moreover, tended to fray the chaff corridor, exposing the B-52s nearest the end of the stream. After dropping their bombs, the B-52s turned so sharply that their jamming signal could no longer focus on the transmitters below, thus opening a window of opportunity for the radar operators and their missiles.

General John Vogt (on the right), who replaced General Lavelle, received a pep talk from President Nixon, urging greater aggressiveness, the very trait that had led to Lavelle's recall. Vogt is getting a first hand account from a pilot after a combat mission. (USAF)

183

American POWs in Vietnam

Colonel Fred Kiley, USAF (Ret)

Lieutenant Colonel Robinson Risner, banged up and exhausted, stood in a cell of "The Hanoi Hilton" prison in September 1965, two days after being captured. Risner, a Korean War ace and recipient of the Air Force Cross, had been featured on the cover of Time magazine for a mission he flew earlier in 1965. The Vietnamese knew who he was and that he was their senior POW. He would pay a terrible price for that.

Beyond his own personal concerns, Risner wondered whether the POWs had organized resistance, a chain of command, and a method of communication. The answers came quickly. Before he went to sleep that night, he had learned the tap code—the lifeblood of POW communication.

It was an alphabet arranged in a 5 x 5 matrix, omitting the letter "k." Risner was 4-2, 2-4, 4-3, 3-3, 1-5, 4-2.

A	B	C	D	E
F	G	H	I	J
L	M	N	O	P
Q	R	S	T	U
V	W	X	Y	Z

Risner soon communicated with Ray Merritt, Ron Byrne, and Wes Schierman, pilots from his own squadron. To the tune of "McNamara's Band," he quietly sang:

MY NAME IS ROBBIE RISNER—I'M THE LEADER OF THE GROUP
LISTEN TO MY STORY AND—I'LL GIVE YOU ALL THE POOP.

Two days later, Risner gave his first order: "Memorize the tap code and use it wherever you are sent"—one of the most vital orders issued during the entire period of captivity. When Risner was moved to Hanoi's other large prison,

"The Zoo," he soon had a resistance program humming until guards found a list of his policies and dragged him back to the Hilton for a siege of torture and punishment. Like others who endured similar barbarisms, he determined that the Code of Conduct—intended for traditional POW camps—had to be interpreted not as a law but as an ethical ideal. So while encouraging strong resistance, admitting as little as possible, then recovering to resist again, he also recommended that the men not resist past the point of losing a limb or their sanity. In retrospect, the overall resistance based on these guidelines was remarkable and inventive. For many POWs, Robbie Risner stood as their exemplar.

As fellow POW Jerry Coffee said, "Robbie lost battles—we all would—but he never lost the war." When forced to meet American anti-war visitors or attend the release of POWs for propaganda, he negated his captors' efforts. When he was forced to read a "newscast" on the camp radio, he swallowed lye soap to injure his voice thereby misreading the statement rendering it useless. He paid a heavy price but knew he had won a "little victory."

Most POWs found ways to cope with the daily grind and to pass time inventively. Risner learned to "run" long distances in solitary and to work square root problems in his mind. Others designed homes, played imaginary golf courses, or "wrote" stories, and one—Charlie Plumb—nearly created a radio from wires, spools, tin foil, waxed paper, razor blades, and nails before guards caught him. If communication was the lifeblood of resistance, such coping was the bridge to sanity. Colonel John Flynn, the senior officer during the final years of captivity, wisely encouraged such mental and physical activity. Flynn also organized the "4th Allied POW Wing" and led the POWs home under the motto "Return with Honor," which has come to represent to the American people not only the POWs' remarkable achievement but also their heroic place in history.

Left: In the hands of their North Vietnamese captors, American airmen faced torture and loneliness. ("At the Hanoi Hilton," Maxine McCaffrey, U.S. Air Force Art Collection)

Frequent Wind

Lieutenant Colonel John F. Guilmartin, Jr., USAF (Ret)

After the 1973 Paris Peace Accords, the Air Force kept two HH-53 squadrons in Thailand. Our mission was to evacuate Phnom Penh, when and if Cambodia fell. The primary evacuation force was two carrier-based Marine CH-53 squadrons. If there wasn't enough time to pre-position the carriers, the mission was ours; otherwise, we were backup. In the event, there was plenty of warning. Phnom Penh was evacuated on 12 April and the Marines did the job.

While our attention was on Cambodia, South Vietnam collapsed. By the time it became apparent that the fall of Saigon was imminent, the Cambodian evacuation task force had dispersed, and one of the Marine CH-53 squadrons was back in Hawaii, cutting lift capacity by roughly one-third. We were mobilized to fill the gap, deploying south to U Tapao Royal Thai Navy Base on 19 April, then rounding South Vietnam to land aboard USS Midway on 20 April. Our eight special operations '53s, radio call sign Knife, and two rescue '53s, call sign Jolly Green, brought the evacuation force to forty-four CH-53s and HH-53s, and about as many smaller Marine H-46s.

This was the first-ever operational Air Force helicopter carrier deployment and the Navy was under-standably nervous. First off, our blades didn't fold, so we blocked the flight deck. More critically, we were unfamiliar with shipboard procedures, a problem solved by a brief but intense course in deck handling.

The Saigon evacuation, Operation Frequent Wind, began on 29 April at 11:30 a.m.. I led the last element in the first extraction wave, two Jolly Greens and a Knife. As we made landfall, we heard radio chatter indicating an active 57-mm anti-aircraft battery to the north, broken by a voice on Guard channel yelling, "Protective reaction! Protective reaction!" As I later learned, Air Force "Iron Hand" F-4 pilot Captain Jay Suggs had taken out the battery and just may have saved our bacon. Our Jolly Greens had radar-warning receivers and on the initial run-in, they showed three active SAM batteries well within range; they never fired.

That day we flew three sorties into the old MACV compound on Tan Son Nhut Airport. We had crisscrossed the cabin floor with cargo straps. We loaded evacuees and told them to hang on. On our final run-in, our two Jolly Greens took out two 12.7-mm machine gun sites with minigun fire. The operation was chaotic, particularly after dark, and it speaks well for the airmanship of all concerned that there were no crashes or midairs. On our last trip, we loaded over a hundred evacuees; the helicopter was over grossed and I hit every transient torque limit climbing out. A few minutes later, my bird drew an SA-7 shoulder-fired heat-seeking missile that the ramp gunners decoyed with hand-fired Mk 50 flares. It missed by 20 feet. We recovered aboard Midway at 11:00 p.m. Navy intelligence officers told us that our two Jolly Greens put in 80 percent of all reported return fire. I'd like to think it made a difference.

As the military situation in South Vietnam deteriorated, Air Force transports helped evacuate refugees. In April 1975, this C-141 flew women and children to Clark Air Base on Luzon in the Philippines. (USAF)

An improved version of the AC-47, mounting three multi-barrel machine guns, fires against Viet Cong forces. (USAF)

Smoke rises from a burning oil storage tank as the Khmer Rouge imposes its authority on Phnom Penh after the American evacuation in 1975. (USAF)

This 105mm howitzer was the most powerful weapon carried by AC-130E gunships. (USAF)

Intense fighting resumed in South Vietnam in 1975. On 10 March, North Vietnam attacked in the central highlands, forcing President Thieu to order a retreat. His troops started toward the coastal plain, their families joined them, and the retreat became a rout. Compounding the disaster, other North Vietnamese units attacked southward along the coast, overrunning Hue and Da Nang, ending evacuation flights from these cities, and drawing ever closer to Saigon.

U.S. Air Force transports and chartered commercial airliners began evacuating Americans and selected Vietnamese citizens, including a number of orphans, from Saigon. On 4 April 1975 dependent wives of American servicemen stationed at Clark AB in the Philippines volunteered to fly into Saigon on an Air Force C-5 transport and assist in the evacuation of the youngest Vietnamese orphans. As the C-5 climbed to cruising altitude for the return to Clark, it experienced a structural failure requiring an immediate emergency landing. The C-5 crashed short of the runway at Saigon, killing most aboard, including thirty-eight of the American women volunteers.

The Ford Administration debated whether to send emergency military aid, but the first American combat aircraft to appear escorted helicopters assigned to withdraw the last Americans from the embassy at Saigon. Evacuation flights from Saigon continued as North Vietnamese army units advanced on the capital. Hysteria swept the city. By 29 April, with the Saigon airport closed by the advancing North Vietnamese, Air Force, Marine, and Central Intelligence Agency helicopters began the final evacuation of more than 6,000 people from the American Embassy.

When helicopters began picking up evacuees on the grounds, and ultimately the roof, of the American embassy, they encountered hostile fire from North Vietnamese troops and South Vietnamese crowds. Unlike the passive crowd at Phnom Penh, panic-stricken civilians and soldiers tried to force their way onto the helicopters. The evacuation continued, however, until the last helicopter lifted the U.S. Marine security force from the roof of the American Embassy at 0730 on the morning of 30 April. By the end of the day, South Vietnam collapsed.

In the last action of the Southeast Asia conflict, the Air Force supported the recovery of the SS *Mayaguez*, an American-registered containership, seized on 12 May 1975 by naval units of Pol Pot's Cambodian government. Air Force crews flying CH-53 special operations helicopters and HH-53 rescue helicopters inserted a U.S. Marine landing force on Koh Tang Island to accomplish the recovery. Of the fifteen Air Force helicopters in action that day, four were shot down and nine damaged. The action at Koh Tang ended the Air Force involvement in America's Southeast Asia conflict.

No More Vietnams

The lessons learned by the armed forces from their experience in Southeast Asia might be summarized in a single phrase—No More Vietnams—but other limited wars seemed inevitable. To prevent future struggles from dragging on, as had the fighting in Southeast Asia, Air Force planners

A C-130 takes off from Kham Duc, South Vietnam, and begins an abrupt climb to avoid enemy fire. (USAF)

proposed adopting the advice of General Curtis LeMay, finally carried out in Operation Linebacker II, to strike decisively at the enemy's heartland. Indeed, after Iraq invaded Kuwait in August 1990, Air Force units subsequently launched an air campaign directed at the Iraqi leadership, along with the machinery of government and military infrastructure, using improved versions of the guided weapons employed so effectively during Linebacker II.

The contrast was stark between the two limited wars, each at their height engaging roughly 500,000 American service personnel. In Southeast Asia, Air Force combat operations lasted nearly fourteen years—from the arrival of Jungle Jim counterinsurgency forces in December 1961 to the *Mayaguez* incident in May 1975—and cost the lives of 2,583 Air Force men and women. Operation Desert Storm lasted forty-three days—from 17 January to 28 February 1991—and cost the lives of thirty-four Air Force personnel.

F-4s loaded with 750-lb bombs and sparrow air-to-air missiles refuel from a KC-135 on their way to a combat mission in March 1966. (USAF)

THE
Air Force
Renaissance

THE
Air Force
Renaissance

Benjamin S. Lambeth

Above: *Northrop F-5E Aggressors sit at the ready at Nellis AFB, Nevada, with Sunrise Mountain providing an appropriately dramatic backdrop. In Red Flag large-force training exercises, they will simulate Soviet-flown MiG-21s as dissimilar adversary threats against U.S. combat aircraft participating in the exercise. (USAF)*

Pages 190–191: *Four General Dynamics F-16Cs sporting self-protection jammers and LANTIRN navigation and targeting pods—and armed with two GBU-10 2,000-pound laser-guided bombs and four air-to-air missiles—display the latest Air Force combat aircraft, avionics, and munitions to telling effect. Among the unprecedented performance attributes of these fourth-generation fighters are track-while-scan radars, thrust-to-weight ratios permitting both rapid acceleration and good vertical performance, and unmatched maneuverability for close-in aerial combat. ("Viper Venom," Robert Taylor)*

America's failure in Vietnam was a defining experience for U.S. airpower. Although the nation's defeat in Southeast Asia was mainly a product of flawed strategy and lack of sufficient leadership commitment, deficiencies in the air weapon and in the ability of its users to make the most of it also played a part. Until Operation Linebacker II finally overcame North Vietnam's air defenses at a considerable cost in downed U.S. aircraft, enemy surface-to-air missiles (SAMs) and antiaircraft artillery (AAA) posed a constant threat to offensive operations. Night and all-weather missions likewise remained extremely difficult, and the risks associated with attacking heavily defended targets in the northernmost Route Packages remained high enough to preclude the effective use of airpower.

If the Vietnam experience starkly highlighted disturbing shortcomings in American airpower, the concurrent Soviet military buildup opposite NATO provided more than enough incentive to acquire a sharper edge. During the years the United States was bogged down in Southeast Asia—between 1965 and 1972—the USSR expanded its conventional forces into a daunting juggernaut overshadowing Western Europe. On top of that, less than a year after America's combat involvement in Southeast Asia ended, a sobering encounter between Israel and its Arab opponents in the 1973 Yom Kippur War further underscored the need for being ready to fight outnumbered against a well-equipped and determined enemy. Israel, overwhelmed by the Egyptian and Syrian surprise attack, lost more than a third of its air force—ninety-seven aircraft—to enemy surface-to-air fire before eventual victory.

For USAF leaders still burdened by fresh memories of America's defeat in Southeast Asia, the Yom Kippur War offered yet another lesson in the lethality of modern air defenses. The combat debut of the SA-6 radar-guided SAM foreclosed operations by the Israeli Air Force at higher

The first preproduction F-16, its speed brakes still extended for landing, touches down at Edwards AFB, California, to join the F-16 Combined Test Force. Incorporating microelectronic rather than electromechanical technology, the F-16 quickly demonstrated a sortie rate 65 percent higher than that of the F-4 of the previous generation, with only some twenty maintenance man-hours required per flying hour compared to more than twice that number for the F-4. (USAF)

The introduction of the Soviet MiG-23 fighter (shown here in Czechoslovakian Air Force markings) with improved radar range and a forward-hemisphere air-to-air missile capability gradually replaced the "check-six" emphasis of Vietnam-era air combat with an awareness of the growing all-aspect air-to-air missile threat. (USAF)

A Boeing E-3 Sentry airborne warning and control system (AWACS) aircraft turns away from the tanker after completing an in-flight refueling. The aircraft carries long-range pulse-Doppler surveillance radar capable of detecting and tracking fighter-sized targets in all directions out to a distance of around 250 miles. The antenna for the radar is contained within the large rotating dome mounted atop the fuselage. (Ted Carlson)

Above: *A McDonnell Douglas KC-10 hooks up with a Lockheed C-5 Galaxy heavy transport over Edwards AFB in the first test refueling by the tanker and the first test of its advanced aerial refueling boom. (USAF)*

Right: *A McDonnell Douglas F-15A chase aircraft out of Edwards AFB takes on fuel from a Boeing KC-135 tanker as an early flight-test Rockwell B-1A bomber flies formation on the wing. (USAF)*

altitudes and forced Israeli fighters down into the equally deadly envelope of shorter-range antiaircraft weapons. That proxy test of Soviet and American equipment offered an arresting preview of how an allied showdown with Soviet forces arrayed against NATO might evolve.

In response to the combined wake-up calls of Vietnam, the Soviet buildup, and the Yom Kippur War, the Air Force set in motion multiple efforts to acquire the wherewithal needed to fend off a Soviet attack against Western Europe or anywhere else the United States had core interests at stake. Far-reaching innovations in training, strategy and tactics, organization, equipage, technology exploitation, and concepts of operations—all grounded in lessons learned the hard way from a war the nation lost—focused the Air Force to fight the *next* war rather than the last one. The ensuing improvements left no facet of the Air Force untouched. Among other things, they included extending the service

life and increasing the reach of the Air Force airlifter fleet by rewinging the C-5 and providing the C-141 with an in-flight refueling capability. Reengining the KC-135 tanker and introducing new KC-10s further extended the reach and sustainability of U.S. conventional striking power, as did releasing Air Force strategic bombers from commitment to the nuclear mission and giving them a conventional capability. Streamlining and consolidating provisions for maintenance and logistics also increased the efficiency and sortie generation capacity of the entire Air Force.

Yet the most dynamic and consequential changes in the USAF during the first decade and a half after Vietnam occurred at the sharp end—in the air superiority and theater ground-attack mission areas where American airpower faced its most demanding challenges. Among the many areas in which significant gains were made, the most important were concepts of operations, equipment capability, personnel proficiency, and organization and preparation for tomorrow's needs. Improvements in these four areas ranged from greatly enhanced training and tactics through new and better platforms, munitions, and other hardware to more effective force employment and management. Many of the measures undertaken, especially in the realm of leveraging high technology, spawned legions of critics in and out of government who staunchly opposed them on the alleged ground that such complex weapons would "never work." In 1991, however, the spectacularly successful application of allied airpower in the Persian Gulf war attested resoundingly to the validity of the new vision that lay at the heart of the Air Force's rebirth in the wake of Vietnam.

Above and below: A KC-10 Extender sporting a combat camouflage paint scheme reels out its three hose-mounted refueling drogues (above). Another KC-10 refuels a C-141 transport using its fuselage-mounted boom (below). With its combined boom and drogue features, the KC-10 is capable of refueling USAF aircraft as well as Navy, Marine, and allied aircraft that employ the probe-and-drogue system in lieu of a refueling boom. (USAF)

Above: The Fairchild Republic A-10 was expressly designed to attack enemy tanks and other armored vehicles with great effectiveness and lethality. It mounts a GAU-8 seven-barrel Gatling gun which fires 30mm armor-piercing cannon shells made of depleted uranium at a rate of up to 6,000 rounds a minute. (USAF)

195

Right: This Aggressor F-5E from the 57th Fighter Weapons Wing at Nellis AFB is shown in a Soviet camouflage paint scheme and mounting captive AIM-9L heat-seeking air-to-air missiles. Dissimilar air combat training pitting the Aggressors against line USAF fighter aircrews during the 1970s and 1980s progressed from 1 vs. 1 to 2 vs. 1, 2 vs. 2, and eventually more complex multiaircraft engagement scenarios. (USAF)

Below: General Robert J. Dixon, commander of Tactical Air Command during the early formative years of the Air Force's post-Vietnam renaissance, is shown climbing into the cockpit of an early-model F-15 wearing a torso harness and G-suit in preparation for an air-to-air training sortie. (USAF.)

Bottom, left: The MiG-21MF (shown here in Czechoslovakian Air Force markings) was the principal air-to-air fighter of Soviet and Warsaw Pact air forces during the 1970s. (USAF)

Bottom, right: An F-5E Aggressor on the ramp at Nellis AFB undergoes final preflight checks before taxiing for takeoff. As early as 1971, Air Force innovators had begun to challenge the rigid "welded-wing" tactics of the Vietnam era and to espouse a more flexible approach to maneuvering air combat which permitted free and engaged roles for fighters in a two-ship element, along with tactical role reversals as necessary to provide mutual support. (USAF)

Improving Training and Concepts of Operations

The first initiative undertaken was the establishment of a serious program of exposing USAF fighter aircrews to enemy tactics and the gradual beginnings of dissimilar air combat training for USAF tactical air forces worldwide. That long-overdue move was rooted in recognition that simulated air combat between fighters of the same type was unrealistic and only identified the more capable pilot. In contrast, training against fighters of different size and with different performance features in such key areas as acceleration and turn rate not only gave Air Force aircrews better preparation for real air combat, but also honed skills at leveraging their aircraft's advantages against an enemy's weaknesses. Toward that end, the 64th Fighter Weapons Squadron, the Air Force's inaugural Aggressor squadron, became operational at Nellis AFB, Nevada, in June 1973. Shortly thereafter, it was followed by a sister unit in the 65th Fighter Weapons

Squadron at Nellis and by similar units in Europe and the Pacific. Initial Aggressor training, aimed at emulating known Soviet operating practices, employed the T-38 supersonic trainer that was later replaced by the radar-equipped and more maneuverable F-5E to provide a slightly faster and more realistic MiG-21 threat simulator.

Three years after the initiation of the Aggressor program, the commander of Tactical Air Command (TAC), General Robert Dixon, approved the proposal of a remarkably ingenious USAF fighter pilot, Lieutenant Colonel Moody Suter, for a recurring exercise aimed at providing heightened training realism under peacetime conditions. Both the Vietnam War and earlier aerial warfare experiences had shown that the first ten combat sorties flown by a pilot are likely to be the main determinants of his subsequent wartime survival. The intent was to give aircrews the functional equivalent of their first ten combat missions in a realistic, yet supervised and safe, peacetime environment.

What was at first called Operation Red Flag began at Nellis in late 1975. Engaging tactical air forces from throughout the United States, it entailed a mock war aimed at providing realistic training to participating units. A designated "core squadron" wrote the exercise scenario, did the overall mission planning, and developed strategy and tactics. The Blue Force consisted of Air Force F-4s, A-7s, and F-111s and Air National Guard F-100s launched in realistic packages to attack tactical targets, electronically simulated SAM sites, and AAA emplacements. The Blue Force also included OV-10 forward air controllers, RF-4C reconnaissance aircraft, and F-105G Wild Weasel defense-suppression support.

Above: The packed flight line at Nellis during a typical Red Flag exercise shows participating Navy Grumman A-6 medium bombers in addition to the usual gamut of Air Force aircraft. Air Force planners began getting serious about large-force employment tactics during the early 1980s, with a view toward integrating maintenance and support, intelligence, communications, planning, and tactical application. The experience gained from these undertakings showed that the organization, execution, and control of such large-force packages entailed unprecedented complexities. (USAF)

Below: An A-10 ripples off a string of Mk 82 general-purpose bombs at low altitude. High-drag devices ensure safe aircraft separation from the fragmentation pattern of the bombs. Although slow and ungainly compared to the more elegant F-15 and F-16, the A-10 offered an impressive force multiplier against the Warsaw Pact's numerically superior legions of tanks. (USAF)

Red Flag

Colonel James G. "Snake" Clark, USAF (Ret)

While our four F-5E Aggressor aircraft cruised in formation, I checked in with range control. "Baron Flight, ready to play."

"Roger, Baron Flight. Bogeys bearing 090, 28 miles, at 20,000 feet. Strikers are five miles back at 15,000."

"Baron One will take the escorts. Baron Three, blow through the escorts and take out the strikers."

The deadly air-to-air combat maneuvering begins. Pilots perform intense high-G turns, defensive breaks, and vertical scissors trying to position for a shot. The engagement lasts only a few minutes. It seems like a lifetime. The debriefing is even tougher right up there on the big screen. The ACMI (Air Combat Maneuvering Instrumentation) 3-D computer recreates the battle, documenting my mistakes. Monitors replay every move to the amusement of my squadron mates—until it's their turn in the gunsight. That is how my first Red Flag began in 1978. The training was realistic and demanding and pushed me to my limits. Accidents happened. We lost an F-4 and crew that first day. Since then, a lot has changed. It isn't a fighter-only show anymore. Red Flag now incorporates the entire spectrum of air and space power. The intensity in the skies over Nellis hasn't changed. Red Flag is the closest thing to combat that aircrew can experience without real bullets.

The concept for Red Flag was born deep in the basement of the Pentagon in the 1970s within a group known as the "fighter mafia." Pilots knew that the first ten combat missions were the most dangerous. Air-to-air combat training during the Vietnam War consisted of "canned scenarios" with F-4s training against other F-4s, using U.S. tactics. The result over North Vietnam was an appalling one-to-one kill ratio. The fighter mafia knew this had to change. They conceived the idea of realistic training with young pilots flying against a dedicated "aggressor" force that flew dissimilar aircraft and used enemy tactics in a SAM/AAA-rich environment. Christened "Red Flag," the concept was refined at the Officers Club, documented on bar napkins, and eventually transformed into a briefing that led to implementation. Lieutenant Colonel Moody Suter became the chief visionary and salesman.

In 1975, the first exercise, involving 561 people and thirty-seven aircraft, demonstrated revolutionary change in tactical training, as well as greater risk of training accidents. General Robert J. Dixon, then commander of Tactical Air Command, believed the benefits outweighed the risks—a belief now validated by experience. In the past quarter century, almost half a million warriors from all four services and twenty-three allied nations have benefited from Red Flag exercises. Since that first Red Flag, American and Allied pilots have dominated skies over Iraq, Bosnia, Kosovo, and Afghanistan, and no U.S. aircraft has been lost in air-to-air combat.

Top: The question at the debriefing will not be did this F-4 (seen here through an F-5E gunsight) escape from the Aggressor attack, but how could the F-4 pilot avoid this circumstance in combat? (USAF)

Left: These Northrop F-5Es and T-38s play the role of enemy aggressors during Red Flag exercises, engage the Blue forces, and employ tactics expected from prospective enemy air forces. (USAF)

A-7s provided close air support. HH-53 combat search and rescue forces participated, along with a four-man team of survival experts. Pilots designated as "downed" by simulated enemy fire were heliborne into the desert to conduct an individual escape-and-evasion exercise, using only the equipment in their survival kits. The opposing Red Force consisted of Aggressor T-38s and F-5Es using Soviet-style ground-controlled intercept support.

Not long thereafter, under the leadership of Dixon's successor, General Bill Creech, Red Flag was greatly expanded in both scope and operational realism. Canadian, British, German, and other allied air-crews were invited to participate out of recognition that U.S. aircrews would inevitably fight in a coalition in any future war. At the same time, Red Flag spawned a number of related offshoots. To note but two, Blue Flag, a nonflying activity conducted at Eglin AFB, Florida, concentrated on the myriad details of large-force mission employment planning. In addition, Checkered Flag became an exercise in which each fighter unit periodically planned for its real-world contingency tasking and then deployed overseas in an actual rehearsal of that tasking.

At first, the predominant emphasis in Red Flag was placed on low-level penetration out of a belief that enemy SAM envelopes could not be safely transited at higher altitudes where the missiles were most effective.

A B-1B releases a string of high-drag munitions over a weapons test range while General Dynamics FB-111 and McDonnell Douglas F-4E chase aircraft fly alongside in close formation. During the 1990s, the B-1 was reconfigured to carry conventional weapons and was equipped with the ALE-50 towed decoy to improve its survivability in light to moderate SAM environments. As a result, a B-1 with a payload more than five times that of an F-15E can fly at fighter-equivalent airspeeds more than 4,200 miles unrefueled to attack soft targets such as enemy troop concentrations. (USAF)

Derelict 1950s-vintage Republic F-84F fighter-bombers serve as simulated revetted enemy MiG-17s in the Nellis AFB tactical range complex. (USAF)

An F-4 pulls off hard immediately after a low-level release of live ordnance. To cope with the unforgiving demands of the low-altitude environment, the Air Force developed a step-down approach based on the "comfort-level" theme, gradually acclimating a pilot to high-speed, low-level operations by ramping down his permitted low-altitude limit first to 500, then to 300, and finally to 100 feet, where most mission segments near heavily-defended targets would be flown. The Air Force further developed stringent rules regarding each pilot's low-level qualifications, dictating how low he was permitted to fly at any time. (USAF)

Right: An enlisted controller follows flight activities in the Nellis range complex during a Red Flag exercise in the mid-1980s, by which time the Red Flag Mission Debriefing System, with its advanced data fusion capability, had been fully installed and activated. (USAF)

Far right: This controller monitors transponder returns of all aircraft, as many as 50 or more, operating within the diverse restricted areas of the Nellis AFB range complex delimited by the lines on his display screen. Even more elaborate than Red Flag, the USAF Fighter Weapons School's twice-yearly Mission Employment phase entailed a highly intense and realistic graduation exercise for students and instructors alike simulating a major air operation in a high-threat environment. (USAF)

Threat avoidance techniques included terrain masking to reduce the chance of being detected by enemy radar and aggressive maneuvering in close proximity to the ground during target egress to complicate any attempted enemy AAA or man-portable infrared missile shots. The challenge presented by this risky practice was not only terrain avoidance, but also complex mission management in a merciless environment. Compounding that challenge was the high likelihood of being shot down by pervasive enemy AAA while trying to evade SAMs.

Recognizing the multiple demands associated with surviving and performing effectively in the low-altitude environment, TAC's leadership sought an appropriate blend of technology and tactics that might help pilots return to higher altitudes where they could escape the dangers of

the low-level regime and improve their chances of mission success. During earlier Red Flags, all daily starting scenarios presumed that it was the first minute of the first hour of a war against undegraded Warsaw Pact air defenses. No kill removal was provided to account for SAMs destroyed during previous days. Low-level penetration to target was invariably the standard practice, on the premise that radar-guided SAMs could not be negated from higher altitudes. Not only did the resulting simulated loss rate to enemy AAA and short-range infrared SAMs soar to a point where many pilots concluded that they could not survive in combat, the actual aircraft accident rate rose dramatically as a consequence of the unforgiving nature of the training environment.

This situation underscored what General Creech came to call "go-low disease," motivated by concern that stress on low-altitude ingress was not only causing a needlessly high accident rate, but also jeopardizing aircrew survivability and flexibility in future combat while constraining TAC's appreciation of the equipment needed to perform the ground-attack mission. In response, Creech insisted on developing and applying new tactics aimed at making defense rollback the first order of business. Since the most lethal Soviet SAMs could not be successfully underflown, emphasis swung to devising alternative techniques for opening safer operating altitudes above the lethal reach of AAA. Taking out or neutralizing enemy SAMs became the most urgent campaign priority.

At the same time, determined to insert not just greater tactical but also strategic and campaign-level realism into Red Flag, General Creech eliminated the initial "core squadron" mission planning practice, in which relatively junior captains and majors played the lead role, and instead put TAC's general-officer air division commanders in charge of scenarios on a rotating basis. At the same time, he emphasized acquiring the needed wherewithal for rendering medium-altitude tactics both possible and effective. Out of this new emphasis came the EF-111 electronic jammer, advanced antiradiation missiles, and a variety of electro-optical and laser-guided precision munitions. TAC spent more than $600 million to increase the scope and realism of the enemy threat simulators fielded throughout

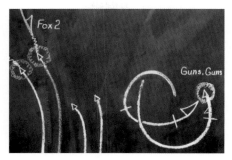

Bottom, left: The latest generation of USAF combat aircraft typified by the F-15, shown here as a pilot straps in for an air-to-air training mission, offered substantially improved in-commission rates thanks to the increased durability of their avionics and the greater ease of repair permitted by exchanging line-replaceable modular units. Much of that heightened reliability resulted from the shift from an electromechanical era to a microelectronics era. (USAF)

Bottom, right: This Lockheed EC-130 Compass Call electronic warfare aircraft from Davis-Monthan AFB, Arizona, features state-of-the-art jammers to disrupt enemy voice communications to airborne fighters. That development reflected a belated recognition that a key Soviet vulnerability was the heavy dependence of Soviet fighter pilots on directives from ground controllers to perform their mission successfully. (USAF)

the Nellis range complex, along with improved range measurement instrumentation which allowed a detailed real-time monitoring and subsequent reconstruction of each event performed by each participating aircraft. At the same time, new capabilities and tactics for operating at night were pushed aggressively and ultimately validated at Red Flag.

Closely connected to this emphasis on the suppression of enemy air defenses was a need to introduce the complexities of electronic warfare into peacetime tactical training, especially in scenarios simulating a heavy communications-jamming environment. In 1981, TAC initiated Green Flag, a Red Flag–like exercise conducted biennially at Nellis, with special emphasis on electronic warfare and SAM suppression. During the first Green Flag exercise, communications jamming began at the outset and continued throughout the operation, just as the Soviets would have done in actual combat. The EC-130 Compass Call system, an airborne electronic warfare platform that had been fielded to jam enemy voice transmissions to airborne fighters, was used for this purpose. As a result, 82

percent of the Blue Force sorties proved ineffective. That ended the naive belief that one could overcome enemy jamming merely by manually changing radio frequencies in a timely manner.

Because of the Green Flag experience, it quickly became clear that fast-hopping enemy jammers would identify the new frequency almost instantly and begin jamming it as well. That realization confirmed the need for antijam radios. In short order, Have Quick and improved Have Quick II UHF radios were installed on all USAF combat aircraft to counter enemy comm-jamming attempts with high-speed automatic random frequency hopping.

Thanks to these and other innovations, the character of Red Flag evolved to approximate more realistic large-force employment against an enemy whose SAM defenses could be degraded in actual combat. By 1984, Red Flag training had expanded far beyond its modest beginnings. The first Red Flag in late 1975 involved only thirty-seven aircraft. By 1988, a mass exercise called Big Flag was conducted in the Red Flag manner, with more than 375 aircraft involved—ten times the size of the original exercise and now aimed at testing concepts far more sophisticated than anything that figured in the original Red Flags. All told, such initiatives eventually produced a new generation of Air Force combat crews whose skills could be honestly described as second to none.

Above: *The Air Combat Maneuvering Instrumentation (ACMI) system revolutionized air-to-air training at Nellis AFB and elsewhere during the 1970s by providing a fully instrumented electronic range. Each participating aircraft mounted a pod for transmitting flight data to downlinks throughout the range complex, feeding a comprehensive, real-time, all-aspect picture of the ongoing training exercise to a ground station, as is shown here   ACMI opened up an entirely new medium for air-to-air combat training, permitting mass debriefings with total recall of all aircraft performance and weapons firing data. (USAF)*

Opposite, top: *This photo-op formation of the USAF's stable of post-Vietnam combat aircraft features, from left to right, the F-16, F-15E, A-10, F-15C, and F-4G. Equipped with rebuilt smokeless J-79 engines to reduce the aircraft's visual signature to ground gunners, the F-4G SAM killer was designed to carry the new Standard ARM and AGM-88 HARM (high-speed antiradiation missile). The heart of its defense suppression capability was the APR-38 threat sensor, which offered both azimuth and range information on the location of enemy SAM acquisition and tracking radars. (USAF)*

As TAC's commander from 1978 to 1984, General Bill Creech presided over much of the maturation of the USAF's post-Vietnam renaissance. Beyond his innovations in the realm of training and tactics, he sought a tone of command based on trust and respect, such that coherence and control might be maintained through incentive rather than through top-down authoritarianism. (USAF)

Above: *General David C. Jones, the USAF's influential chief of staff during the first years of its transformation, empowered General Creech to institute his radical reforms in TAC as described above. He later was selected as chairman of the Joint Chiefs of Staff at about the time the Air Force's renaissance entered full swing. (USAF)*

Right: *The Soviet MiG-29 fighter first flew in October 1977 and entered line service with Soviet Frontal Aviation units during the early 1980s. That long-expected development finally gave the Soviets a credible air-to-air counterpart to the F-15 and F-16. (USAF)*

A New Approach to Organization and Management

Along with these training advances, an important parallel improvement took place in TAC's organizational efficiency during General Creech's six and a half years as commander. Earlier during the 1970s, upward of half of TAC's aircraft were not mission-ready at any given moment due to maintenance deficiencies and a shortage of spare parts. Moreover, pilots who required a minimum of twenty hours of flying time a month to remain operationally ready were getting only half that amount in most cases. Unwilling to reduce its force structure to absorb the deep funding cuts of the Carter administration, the Air Force instead opted to accommodate this financial crunch by raiding its operations and maintenance accounts. All of this was heavily driven by the top-down management style that had become entrenched the previous decade because of Defense Secretary Robert McNamara's strict dogma of centralization imported from the business world.

With the full support of Air Force Chief of Staff General David Jones, Creech replaced TAC's traditional top-down centralization with a new bottom-up approach to management, forcing both authority and responsibility down to the lowest levels possible. At the same time, he replaced the former tone of leadership intimidation with what he called "reasoned command." The new watchword became management through motivation rather than through decree, on the premise that professionals would willingly assume greater responsibility if they were treated with dignity and respect.

Creech's approach, while clearly cognizant of the fact that military organizations are not democracies, was a common-sense variation on the golden rule, based on recognition that loyalty was a two-way street. It was profoundly intolerant of autocratic practices and recognized that an organization can only be as successful as those at the bottom are willing to make it. Toward that end, Creech sought to minimize excess regulation, which he believed stifled motivation, and he worked hard to replace inhibitions on communication with full openness. Above all, he sought to instill at all levels an appreciation of the difference between quality *control* and quality *creation* and to focus overwhelmingly on the latter.

In short order, these reforms gave a sharper focus to authority and accountability and got unit-level peer pressure working in positive rather than negative directions by giving everyone in the system both pride

of involvement and a personal stake in the product. Each squadron became responsible for its own assigned aircraft, with all disciplines working together within the squadron in small teams to get the job done. The net result was a genuine personalizing of a once-impersonal system that soon thereafter produced a doubling of the number of peacetime sorties per training period with no increase in required funding allocations. In an enduring legacy of what came to be known as the "TAC turnaround," this team-based, decentralized approach to organizational management later spread throughout the rest of the Air Force as Creech's subordinates in TAC went on to rise in rank and head other major commands.

Modernizing the Aircraft Inventory

The decade that followed the end of the Vietnam War was also a time of great dynamism in the strengthening of the Air Force's hardware assets. Leading the modernization of the fighter inventory was the introduction of the F-15 air combat fighter and F-16 multirole fighter, each of which offered performance capabilities well beyond anything available in then-existing Soviet fighters. The A-10 was also introduced as a dedicated anti-armor platform to provide friendly ground forces with direct fire support by means of Maverick air-to-surface missiles and a 30mm cannon firing high-velocity rounds of depleted uranium capable of penetrating the aft portion of a tank turret. For defense suppression, the F-4G was fielded in

Above: Three dual-role F-15E Strike Eagles attached to the USAF Fighter Weapons School at Nellis show the fuselage-mounted conformal fuel tanks and LANTIRN pods which permit the aircraft to conduct long-range night and adverse-weather missions. Developed to supplement and ultimately supplant the F-111, the F-15E attained initial operational capability in 1989. Its conformal tanks nearly double its internal fuel-carrying capacity, offering greatly extended range-payload performance and the ability to conduct many strike missions with reduced or no tanker support. (USAF)

Page 206: This F-15E mission simulator shows the cockpit multifunction displays to good effect as the pilot and weapons systems operator prepare to roll in on a simulated element of MiG-23s projected on an over-head dome. Not only were the new fighters of this generation more combat-capable than their predecessors, they were more user-friendly to their aircrews. (USAF)

Page 207: The unique design of Lockheed's F-117 stealth attack aircraft minimizes the aircraft's detectability by enemy radar. That effect was achieved with special coatings and a flat-plate design that exacted an aero-dynamic penalty yet rendered the F-117 all but unobservable by any existing enemy radar-based defenses. (USAF)

1978 as a planned replacement for the F-105G Wild Weasel. For night and adverse-weather interdiction, a decision was announced in early 1984 that the F-15E would become the Air Force's new dual-role fighter, following a flight evaluation of F-15 and F-16 derivatives.

A final platform of truly revolutionary impact that made its debut during this period of Air Force equipment enhancement was one that did not even figure in public discussion at the time because of the extreme secrecy that shrouded its development from the very outset. The F-117 stealth attack aircraft was designed and produced by the Lockheed Corporation's renowned "Skunk Works," which earlier had developed the radically innovative U-2 and SR-71 high-flying reconnaissance jets. The development of stealth, like the other defense-suppression initiatives discussed above, was prompted by growing concern over the mounting difficulty of penetrating the increasingly formidable array of Soviet radar-guided SAMs which provided an overlapping threat envelope from near-ground level to as high as 125,000 ft.

Lockheed earlier had pioneered low observability to radar through the shaping and skin treatments imparted to the Mach 3 SR-71, a remarkable aircraft roughly the size of a B-58 bomber yet with a radar cross-section no larger than that of a Piper Cub. A subsequent discovery enabled the development of fighter-sized aircraft with a radar cross-section between ten and a hundred times lower than that of any existing American or Soviet fighter. With modest funding, Lockeed successfully flew the first technology demonstrator on December 1, 1977, and quickly learned that it had indeed achieved a fundamental breakthrough. The first production variant was delivered to the Air Force in 1982, and the F-117 went operational the following year. Operated solely at night either in pairs or autonomously, the aircraft was built to carry two 2,000-lb. laser-guided bombs internally and to provide its own laser target designation. In all, fifty-nine were produced.

Even as the aircraft was exposed in ever more tantalizing detail following its initial disclosure in November 1988, not until its bravura performance during the opening night of Operation Desert Storm against Saddam Hussein's Iraq more than two years later would its unique

US Air Force Thunderbirds

General Fig Newton, USAF (Ret)

When the fighting stopped in Korea, the United States Air Force was six years old, families still went to airports just to see planes takeoff and land, and the sound of military jets overhead caused people to look up, shade their eyes, and wonder. How could a young Air Force tell the citizens about its capabilities and skills? You didn't tell them, you showed them. And when you showed them, you really showed them.

Low from the far horizon sped a formation of red, white, and blue jets, the USAF aerial demonstration squadron—better known as the Thunderbirds. The pilots flew their airplanes above assembled crowds and engaged in an aerial dance of thunder and grace. The people watched. They applauded. A tear or two flowed because of the majesty before them. When the show ended, they still did not understand the technical world and jargon of the United States Air Force, but they understood its meaning. It meant freedom.

From that first air show in 1953, the Thunderbirds have taken their unique and powerful brand of the American spirit to fifty states. As America's Ambassadors in Blue, they have traveled to sixty foreign nations. In all they have flown the flag at more than 3,700 air shows before more than 325 million people. Heads of state and aboriginal tribesmen have shared common emotion during the same thirty minutes while they watched the team take machines of thunder, tie them together with talent and dedication, and then pitch them through a calling sky.

The Thunderbird experience affected those who flew as well as those who watched. Just over 1,700 Americans have served on this glorious team in the past half-century. For those fortunate few, their time as a Thunderbird changed their lives forever. For each member of our team, only the lens of maturity and time brings the experience into focus, and it takes a lifetime to appreciate that our Thunderbird days tower above all others. When we came aboard, we were only the best of those who applied. As we moved on to other Air Force assignments, we realized that we never left the Thunderbirds because those indelible red, white, and blues that flourish with such splendor are implanted forever in our souls. It explains our motto: Once a Thunderbird, Always a Thunderbird.

Bottom, left: Thunderbird lead and opposed solo pilots pass assembled air show spectators canopy to canopy, with the lead pilot flying inverted and the opposed pilot tucked in close on his wing. (USAF)

Botttom, right: Five Thunderbird F-16s end an air show performance dramatically with a horizontal bomb burst maneuver just before joining up again in loose trail formation for landing. (USAF)

Opposite: Four Thunderbird F-16s form up in close trail over New Mexico on their way to a base to perform in an air show. The Thunderbirds have long been instrumental in sustaining public interest in the Air Force and as a recruiting tool. (Ted Carlson)

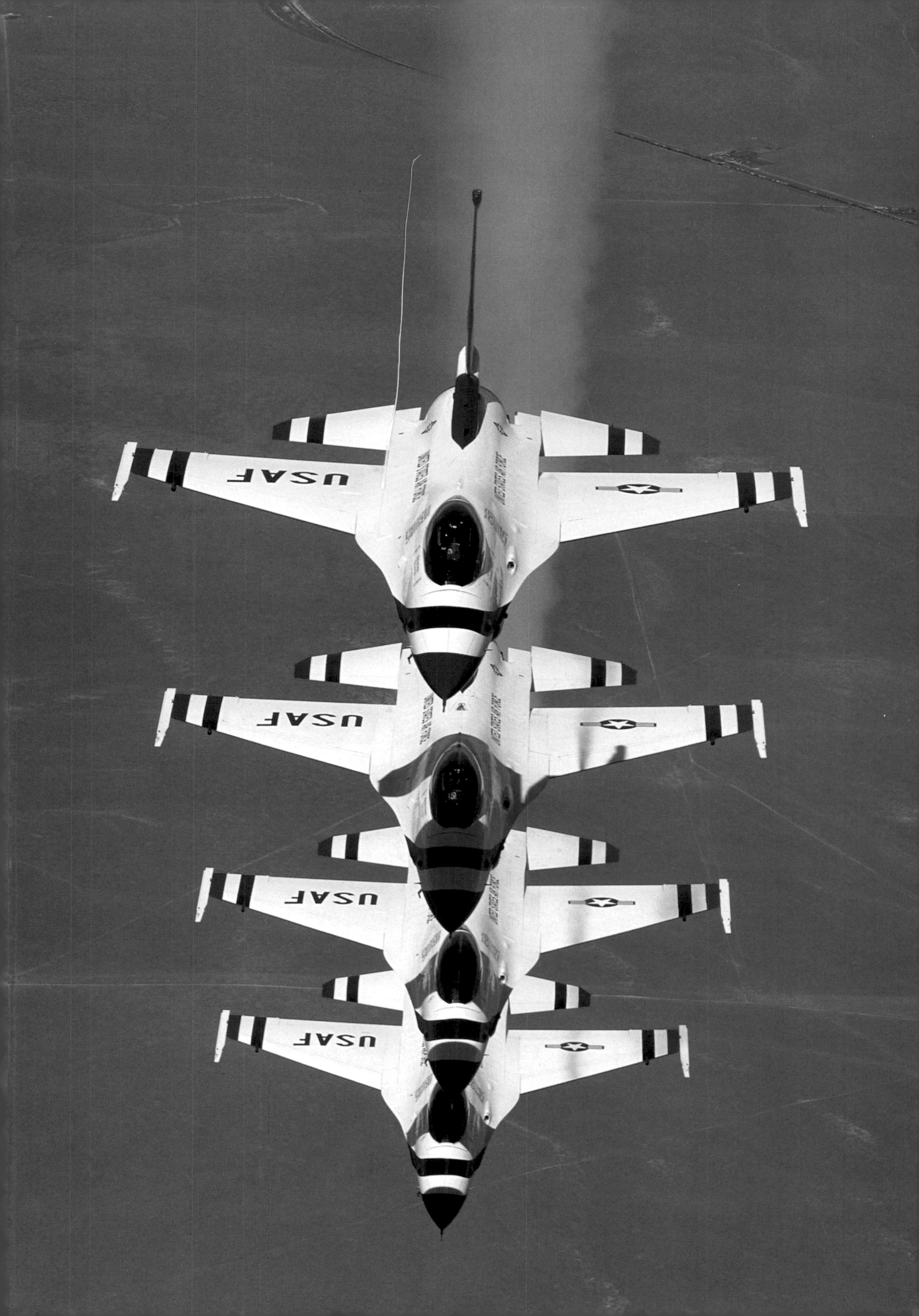
USAF
USAF
USAF
USAF

First-generation stealth technology pioneered by the F-117 was improved significantly in Northrop's long-range B-2 stealth bomber, shown here taking off from Edwards AFB. Essentially a high-technology flying wing, the aircraft was unveiled in 1988 after more than a decade of development in great secrecy. It gave the United States the ability to conduct precision attacks with surprise against the most heavily defended targets anywhere in the world. (USAF)

Ever since the retirement of the USAF's EF-111 after the 1991 Persian Gulf war, the U.S. Navy has operated its EA-6B Prowler squadrons with mixed Navy and Air Force flight crews. This EA-6B crew from VAQ-128 is shown en route to Nellis to participate in Red Flag. (Ted Carlson)

capabilities be fully appreciated by airpower professionals, let alone by the defense establishment as a whole. Viewed in hindsight, the F-117 was probably the single most pivotal contribution of the 1980s to the revolution in the effectiveness of American airpower.

Low-observable technology took another advance with the subsequent development and testing of the long-range B-2 stealth bomber. That aircraft, essentially a high-technology flying wing, was unveiled in 1988 after more than a decade of development in great secrecy. Its introduction into the bomber force gave the United States, for the first time, the ability to conduct surprise precision attacks against the most heavily defended targets anywhere in the world. Originally developed as a means of penetrating highly echeloned air defenses and attacking key targets in the Soviet Union with nuclear weapons, the B-2 was later configured to carry the full spectrum of the latest-generation conventional munitions as well.

With its greatly extended reach, the B-2 portended the ability to carry more than ten times the payload of the F-117 to five times the latter's unrefueled range. As its first combat application eventually demonstrated in NATO's air war for Kosovo, the B-2 advanced USAF airpower to a point where one could now speak routinely of the number of targets that might be successfully engaged during a single sortie rather than how many sorties would be needed to destroy a single target.

This enhancement of the USAF's force structure was further accelerated by the substantial growth in defense funds made available to all

services by the Reagan Administration beginning with the 1981 appropriation. Thanks to that long-overdue increase in U.S. defense expenditure, the 1980s became a decade in which the post-Vietnam drawdown of forces was finally reversed and when critically important operations and maintenance accounts were restored to their proper level, bringing an end to the hollow force of the Carter years. In addition, during that decade the Air National Guard and Air Force Reserve, hitherto all but dismissed as weekend warriors consigned to make do with obsolescent hand-me-down aircraft given up by the active Air Force, were finally integrated into the total force. The nation's defense leadership actively sought to embrace and assimilate its citizen soldiers, assigning them new front-line equipment straight off the production line concurrently with active units, training Guard and Reserve units to the same proficiency and readiness standards that applied to the active force, and making them a vital part of Air Force combat capability.

In addition to developing and fielding these successor-generation aircraft, the Air Force renaissance years also saw a surge of long-overdue attention toward the unglamorous but essential needs of readiness and sustainability. Toward that end, determined efforts were made in the latest generation of fighters to make aircraft less dependent on an elaborate logistics infrastructure by reducing the number of parts, increasing the accessibility of critical components, using line-replaceable avionics modules, and providing onboard systems that reduced the need for

By 1988, the tightly-closed F-117 community had developed a mature combat capability with its secret and mysterious aircraft. Accordingly, the Air Force determined that the time had come to expand training activities to include other units and to begin working the F-117 into existing contingency plans. Since that would necessitate at least a partial lifting of the security wall that had thus far kept the program hidden from all but a few, the Defense Department reluctantly disclosed the aircraft's existence so that such efforts could get under way. (USAF)

USAF airmen deployed to Kuwait in support of Operation Southern Watch to help enforce the no-fly zone over southern Iraq gather at a military airfield for an informal address. (USAF)

211

The introduction of LANTIRN, shown here on an F-15E operated by the USAF's armament test wing at Eglin AFB, Florida, made it possible to conduct night and under-the-weather manual and automatic terrain following down to 200 feet and at speeds of 500 knots and above. It promised to impart to the F-15E and F-16C the same night terrain avoidance capability possessed at that time only by the Air Force's F-111. It further promised a capability for night bombing, at least against some target types, as good as that only available before for daytime missions. (USAF)

A weapons load team member watches the launch of the aircraft he just helped arm with precision strike weapons. (USAF)

ground servicing. Because of such efforts, besides increased concentration of firepower, the new platforms promised to offer more sustained force application through improved reliability and maintainability.

This enhanced maintainability and reliability contributed significantly to the confidence of commanders that their high-technology equipment would perform as expected when needed. In the case of Vietnam-era aircraft, the reliability of the overall weapon system, defined as the mean time between failure of various essential on-board subsystems, was often shorter than the average duration of a combat sortie. That meant that a certain percentage of scheduled aircraft would never make it to the target because something critical to the mission, such as the radar, would fail en route, forcing mission planners to build a margin of additional aircraft into a strike package simply to ensure that enough aircraft would be available to get the job done. With the reliability and maintainability improvements designed into the latest generation of fighters, combat aircraft were likely to land after a sortie in Code One condition, namely, with all systems in proper working order and the aircraft ready to launch again upon being refueled and reloaded with weapons.

Munitions and Avionics

A parallel growth in the variety and quality of munitions for aerial combat and surface attack accompanied these trends in aircraft modernization. For air-to-air combat, the principal improvement was the introduction of the AIM-7F and AIM-9L, upgrades of the basic Sparrow and Sidewinder missiles used in Vietnam. The first of these was guided by semi-active radar and offered beyond visual-range capability. The latter was an infrared-guided weapon for close-in combat. Both could be fired at a

target from any aspect within the missile's lethal parameters. They out-performed by a considerable margin any counterparts then available to Soviet and Warsaw Pact air forces. The AIM-9L, in particular, occasioned a quantum change in the lethality of infrared air-to-air missiles. Its all-aspect capability made it effectively a point-and-shoot weapon, capable of being fired head-on prior to the point at which converging friendly and enemy fighters closed to dogfight range. That meant that any fighter equipped with AIM-9L no longer needed to maneuver behind an enemy aircraft to achieve a kill.

In the surface-attack arena, the predominant weight of effort centered on continued improvements in weapons accuracy and lethality,

Until the F-117's existence was finally revealed officially in 1988, both the aircraft's appearance and its numerical designator had remained tightly guarded secrets, with public discussion of "stealth" consigned almost entirely to the realm of speculation among aviation buffs and novelists. (USAF)

Above: *A GBU-12 Paveway II laser-guided bomb guides unerringly only moments before impacting directly on a moving vehicle. This weapon is a revolutionary improvement of the Mk 82 500-pound general-purpose bomb. (USAF)*

Left: *Weapons handlers prepare a CBU-87 combined-effects munition for loading onto an F-16. The munition's canister contains more than 200 fragmentation bomblets designed for use against enemy troop concentrations and other soft area targets. (USAF)*

both in powered and unpowered precision-guided munitions (PGMs) and in wide-area submunitions. The mid-1980s also saw the development of the GBU-24 penetrator weapon, which consisted of a 2,000-lb. bomb core with an attached laser seeker for attacking and destroying buried enemy command posts, aircraft shelters, and other hardened facilities.

A major improvement in the ability of USAF aircraft to deliver free-fall weapons more accurately complemented these advances in precision

The unprecedented maneuvering advantage of the latest generation of USAF air combat fighters is graphically shown in this comparison of the turn performance of the F-16 and an older F-4E. The F-16, forming the inner contrail, completed a maximum-performance 360-degree turn in about half the radius and three-fourths the time required by the F-4E. (USAF)

ground-attack munitions. The head-up display in the F-16 presented the pilot with a continuously computed impact point for gravity bombs whenever that mode was selected, enabling almost any pilot with a steady hand to place bombs consistently close to the target. For example, F-16 pilots rated combat-ready routinely attained an overall circular error average of twelve meters in all scored conventional bombing events in annual weapons meets, about ten times better than F-4 pilots achieved on comparable missions involving low-altitude weapons release during the Vietnam era.

New surveillance and battle management platforms in the form of the E-3 airborne warning and control system (AWACS) and the E-8 joint surveillance target attack radar system (Joint STARS) provided better off-board targeting information. After some initial growing pains, AWACS eventually came to be considered a de facto "third wingman" for fighter pilots, and Joint STARS promised to provide accurate real-time location and targeting information on moving enemy armor and vehicular traffic. An important related improvement was the deep battlefield surveillance and data-link capability offered by the TR-1 reconnaissance aircraft, an upgraded U-2, as well as improved radar warning receivers intended to provide information on threat radar types, operating modes, and range and bearing.

Finally in the realm of avionics innovations, a novel system called LANTIRN—an acronym for low-altitude navigation and targeting infrared for night—denied Warsaw Pact forces a night or weather sanctuary. Ultimately mated with the F-16C and F-15E, the system incorporated two externally mounted pods. The first, a navigation pod, contained terrain-following radar and a forward-looking infrared (FLIR) sensor that projected a daylight-quality image of the world out in front onto a wide field-of-view head-up display. The second, a targeting pod, contained a more narrowly focused FLIR for target identification, plus a self-contained laser designator for precision delivery of conventional guided munitions. This new capability opened up a greatly expanded operating envelope for the combat

The synthetic aperture radar (SAR) and ground moving target indicator (GMTI) sensor displays aboard the E-8 Joint STARS, as depicted here, offer sufficiently fine resolution to enable senior air commanders to locate and count fixed and moving vehicles on a battlefield and execute lethal attacks against enemy ground force targets day or night. (USAF)

Of all the fourth-generation fighters fielded by the USAF during its post-Vietnam renaissance, the F-15E, its front and aft cockpit instrument panels shown above, was by far the most advanced in its incorporation of sophisticated and user-friendly digital displays. Those included, among other things, a horizontal situation indicator, a stores status panel, a moving map display, and a radar display, all accessible on interchangeable color screens in both cockpits. (USAF)

The ungainly but effective A-10 fires an AGM-65 Maverick electro-optically guided missile at a simulated enemy tank. The combined Soviet and Warsaw Pact ground threat opposite Central Europe by the end of the 1970s added up to a clear NATO inability to match the enemy tank for tank and a consequent need to acquire force multipliers aimed at denying the Warsaw Pact any advantage from its numerical edge and offensive doctrine. (USAF)

air forces, which, in turn, portended greater leverage from any given number of aircraft and a reduced requirement for total numbers of aircraft in a theater of operations.

Above and below: *A view through the head-up display of a LANTIRN-equipped F-16 during a low-level daytime flight, shown above, and a similar view through the HUD at night, shown below. (USAF)*

A New Vision

Many of the improvements outlined above were set in motion during the first decade after Vietnam by mid-career officers armed with a "never-again" mindset, who eventually rose to positions of senior Air Force leadership determined to eliminate American airpower shortcomings revealed during their Korean and Vietnam War experiences. Although the new hardware acquisitions ensuing from this effort were crucially important to the Air Force's renaissance, more crucial yet was the over-arching vision that lay behind them. That vision was based in substantial part on an appreciation that any future high-intensity conventional war would require deep and sustained air interdiction and that enemy air defenses *had* to be negated to get the job done.

As best reflected in the way Red Flag evolved from its modest start in 1975 into a far more realistic and operationally meaningful training exercise a decade later, there was also a realization of the greater efficiencies to be had by engaging enemy air threats not only in the air but also on the ground. Moreover, the new vision of air warfare stressed the need to apply pressure not just from the outset of a campaign but around the clock, which necessarily meant operating effectively both under the weather and at night in order to deny the enemy a night and weather sanctuary. Finally, the new vision recognized and placed unprecedented stress on the importance of disrupting enemy command, control, and communications from the very first moments of combat. It marked the beginning of what has since come to be routinely understood as thinking and planning not only at the tactical but also the operational and strategic levels of war.

This new vision led in time to such fielded capabilities as the dual-role F-15E strike fighter, antijam communications, LANTIRN, target location systems like AWACS and Joint STARS, improved weapons capable of suppressing and rolling back enemy surface-to-air defenses, hard-structure munitions that could destroy enemy command bunkers and sheltered fighters, and two revolutionary new stealth aircraft—the F-117 and B-2. The significant commitment to improve mobility through airlift improvements and development of the C-17 reflected the increased importance of rapid deployment. These and related developments put the Air Force on a steady course toward transforming itself into a winning combination of high-technology weapons, improved operator skill, and smarter ways of organizing and fighting. That legacy of an otherwise lamentable chapter in the history of U.S. airpower during the nation's ten-year embroilment in Southeast Asia was the dominant hallmark of the Air Force's long-awaited coming of age during the two decades between Vietnam and Desert Storm.

Above: A USAF B-2 drops a satellite-guided GBU-31 Joint Direct Attack Munition (JDAM) in a weapons test. A preview of the much-improved combat leverage portended by this lethal combination was provided in a demonstration over the Nellis AFB ranges in 1996 by three B-2s, in which the aircraft delivered 16 satellite-guided munitions against 16 dispersed targets, destroying or disabling each. That confirmed that American airpower has now reached a point where one can routinely speak of the number of aim points that can be engaged by a single aircraft on a single mission rather than, as was the case until recently, how many aircraft would be needed to service a single target with confidence. (USAF)

Opposite, top: An E-3 AWACS takes off to provide a continuous real-time air situation picture for the regional joint-force commander. Its onboard sensors and information processing systems are capable of providing comprehensive coverage of both friendly and enemy air activity in a theater of operations. (USAF)

Left: A two-seat F-16B sports LANTIRN navigation and targeting pods affixed on either side of its air inlet between its wing-mounted external fuel tanks. A major advantage offered by the generation of avionics typified by LANTIRN was that "multi-mission" finally became a realistically attainable goal. In earlier years, fighters like the F-4 with both air-to-air and ground-attack mission tasking generally allowed pilots to maintain well-honed skills in only one area or the other because of the heavy training demands associated with each. With the arrival of the F-16 and targeting systems like LANTIRN, air-to-ground proficiency became that much easier to acquire and maintain, which meant that multirole pilots could spend more time polishing their techniques for the no less demanding air-to-air arena, with a consequent increase in their proficiency at both missions. (USAF)

THE
Air Force
in Space

THE
Air Force
in Space

Dr. David N. Spires

Pages 218–219: *Air Force Lieutenant Colonel Edward H. White II, pilot of the Gemini-Titan 4 spacecraft in 1965, was the first astronaut to "walk" in space. In this photo, White floats freely, tethered to the Gemini spacecraft. Two years later while practicing for the Apollo 1 mission, White, USAF Lieutenant Colonel Virgil I. Grissom, and Navy Lieutenant Commander Roger B. Chaffee lost their lives in a flash fire that consumed the spacecraft. (NASA)*

Above: *Captain Joe H. Engle lands his North American Aviation Corporation X-15 on 29 June 1965 at Edwards Air Force Base, California, at the blistering speed of 300 miles per hour as a Lockheed F-104 chase plane prepares to go around. Engle is returning from a flight that reached an altitude of more than fifty miles above the earth's surface, earning his qualification as an astronaut. ("First Re-Entry," Mike Machat)*

Opposite, top: *This photo shows a captured German V-2 rocket launched after World War II from the American Southwest. The V-2 was the first ballistic missile to traverse space. (USAF)*

A ir Force interest in space emerged at the close of the Second World War when Henry H. "Hap" Arnold, Commanding General of the Army Air Forces, and Franklin Collbohm of the Douglas Aircraft Company established the service-sponsored RAND Corporation. RAND's initial report, "Preliminary Design of an Experimental World Circling Spaceship," predicted that an artificial Earth observation satellite could be developed and launched within five years.

Arnold charged Theodore von Kármán, chairman of the Army Air Forces Scientific Advisory Group, to provide the scientific foundation for the Air Force course ahead. With publication of von Kármán's *Toward New Horizons* in late 1945, the service received a sound research and development focus and an agenda that envisioned both missiles and satellites.

Yet, the Air Force had no interest in pursuing a major satellite development program in an era of frugal budgets and an air-atomic defense strategy. The latter meant supporting the bomber as the nation's first line of defense rather than missile and space systems that seemed futuristic and foreign to the aviation-oriented Air Force. Nevertheless, Air Force leaders asserted "exclusive rights in space," to forestall Navy and Army claims. In 1948, Air Force Chief of Staff General Hoyt Vandenberg declared, "The USAF, as the service dealing primarily with air weapons—especially strategic—has logical responsibility for the satellite."

From Vandenberg's policy statement forward, the Air Force role in space proceeded along two broad tracks. One track involved repeated efforts to convince national leaders that the Air Force should be designated

Above: *General Henry "Hap" Arnold championed Air Force interests in the new postwar missile and space age and shaped the future Air Force's scientific focus. In the Fall of 1944, he charged his newly appointed director of the Army Air Forces Scientific Advisory Group, Theodore von Karman, to assess the current state of technical progress and provide a blueprint for future Air Force research and development programs. (USAF)*

221

Above: *In late 1945, Dr. Theodore von Karman's team of civilian and military experts produced thirty-three reports, entitled* Toward New Horizons, *that established the importance of science and long-range forecasting and set the agenda for future Air Force research and development. In 1947, the Air Force reconstituted the AAF Scientific Advisory Group as the Air Force Scientific Advisory Board, with Theodore von Karman its first chairman. (USAF)*

Above: *Air Force Chief of Staff General Hoyt Vandenberg's policy statement on space reflected the Air Force's intention to establish exclusive rights in space based on the argument that it was the logical service for satellite development responsibilities. (USAF)*

Right: *Discoverer VII prepared for launch from Vandenberg AFB, California. The Agena satellite vehicle used in Project Discoverer was boosted into polar orbit by an Air Force Thor intermediate range ballistic missile. Project Discoverer was executed by the Air Force Ballistic Missile Division for the Advanced Research Projects Agency of the Department of Defense. (USAF)*

the service responsible for military space activities, including deploying weapons and flying pilots in outer space.

The other broad track centered on institutionalizing space throughout the armed forces by transferring space activities from the realm of research and development to operations. Space advocates believed that "normalizing" and "operationalizing" space would also help the Air Force achieve leadership of the national military space program.

The Air Force Agenda for Space

In early 1954, President Eisenhower, seeking strategic intelligence on Soviet military capabilities, established a Technological Capabilities Panel, chaired by Massachusetts Institute of Technology President James Killian. Meanwhile, ongoing RAND satellite studies culminated with the publication of Project Feed Back, which convinced the Air Force to initiate WS 117L, a reconnaissance satellite project. That same year, Air Force Secretary Harold Talbott approved recommendations of John von

Neumann's Strategic Missiles Evaluation Committee—known as the "Teapot Committee"—for a high-priority development program to produce intercontinental ballistic missiles (ICBMs) in six years. In February 1955, the Killian panel issued its report calling for development of the Lockheed U-2 reconnaissance plane, an accelerated ICBM program, and rapid development of intermediate-range ballistic missiles.

Brigadier General Bernard Schriever, selected to organize and command the Western Development Division, became, in effect, the space pioneer most responsible for developing the nation's missile and space programs. (USAF)

Far left: *Trevor Gardner, Special Assistant for Research and Development, convened the Strategic Missiles Evaluation Committee and convinced government leaders to establish the Western Development Division to manage the crash Atlas missile development program using streamlined management procedures. (Jay Ashurst, Air Force Space Command)*

Left *Renowned mathematician John von Neumann chaired the Strategic Missiles Evaluation Committee. Its 1954 report determined the measures necessary to accelerate development of the Atlas missile and helped convince President Eisenhower to accord the ICBM and IRBM programs the highest development priority. (Jay Ashurst, Air Force Space Command)*

223

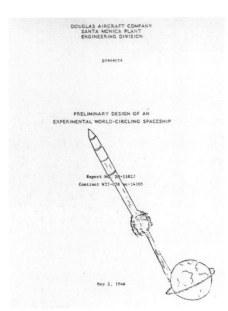

Above: *Douglas Aircraft's 1946 Project RAND study predicted that the United States could launch a 500-pound satellite into a 300-mile orbit within five years at a cost of $150 million; and it described potential satellite uses for reconnaissance, communications, meteorology, scientific research, interplanetary travel, and space-based weapons operations. The RAND report was the first comprehensive analysis of satellite feasibility, and it served as the foundation for the numerous studies on missiles and satellites to follow. (RAND Corporation)*

Led by the dynamic Trevor Gardner, Assistant Secretary for Research and Development, the Air Force intensified development of a Convair ICBM proposal named Atlas, placing it under the direction of hard-charging Brigadier General Bernard A. Schriever. By 1957, Schriever's crash program encompassed the Atlas ICBM, the Titan ICBM, the Thor intermediate-range ballistic missile, and the military reconnaissance satellite project. The latter would lead to the first early warning infrared satellite and reconnaissance satellites under the auspices of the Air Force and the National Reconnaissance Office, respectively.

At the same time, the Eisenhower Administration established a freedom of space policy that promoted unimpeded overflight in outer space. That meant emphasizing civilian space flight and Project Vanguard, the Administration's scientific satellite to be launched during the 1957–58 International Geophysical Year. It also meant a self-imposed restriction on the deployment of space-based weapons. Under no circumstances would the Administration allow a military satellite to precede Vanguard into space.

Air Force leaders vigorously opposed these restrictions. Preferring to guard against potential threats, they viewed the Administration policy as dangerous. Yet, space-based weapons remained restricted to studies only. Air Force space efforts would center on satellites for what came to be called defense support functions—reconnaissance and surveillance, early warning, navigation, communications, and meteorology. These activities, and the Eisenhower space policy that framed them, endured for the next thirty years.

Left: *A technician at the Langley NASA Research Center checks a full-scale Mercury capsule before testing in a thirty-by-sixty foot wind tunnel. (NASA)*

Above: *Air Force Chief of Staff General Thomas D. White established the aerospace concept that served as the basis for every Air Force effort to establish its leading role in military space and also provided the rationale for opposing a joint military command for space operations. (USAF)*

Opposite, top: *Lockheed's U-2 reconnaissance aircraft provided photo coverage of Soviet strategic targets until superceded by Project CORONA satellites. The same CIA-Air Force management team responsible for developing and operating the U-2 would direct CORONA. (USAF)*

Air Force Primacy in the National Space Program

The launch of Sputnik in 1957 intensified an already heated service contest for leadership of the national space program. Before Sputnik, the Air Staff and civilian leaders had not accorded space the support General Schriever and his team of "space cadets" believed their efforts deserved. Following Sputnik, however, Air Force leaders, like Chief of Staff General Thomas D. White, coined the term "aerospace" to justify Schriever's claims. White's first objective was Air Force leadership of the national space effort. Then, when it became clear that national policy preferred two programs, one a civilian-led effort dependent on military support, the Air Force campaigned to be designated the "executive agent" for military space.

The Air Force confronted a host of competitors. The creation of the National Air and Space Administration (NASA) in 1958, for example, proved a mixed blessing. On the one hand, NASA acquired its most important space assets from the Army and Navy, which, by 1960, left the Air Force the dominant military space service and NASA dependent on the Air Force for support. Although NASA would chart the nation's civilian space flight future and compete for space funding, the Air Force sought to create a strong partnership with the new civilian agency. The single-seat hypersonic orbital bomber, designated Dyna-Soar, for dynamic soaring, became central to this cooperative relationship. For many in the Air Force space community, Dyna-Soar represented the ideal weapons system to fly Air Force pilots in space, and thereby gain support from the traditional flying element in the service.

Apart from NASA, in the military sphere the Air Force found itself subordinated first to the Pentagon's Advanced Research Projects Agency, then later to the Director, Defense Research and Engineering. Then, in 1958 another competitor appeared when the Administration sanctioned

On the morning of 4 October 1957, the Soviet Union launched Sputnik I, a 184-pound instrumented satellite, into orbit. The rocket booster for this launch weighed nearly 4 tons. Sputnik established the precedent, freedom of space, and its "Pearl Harbor" effect on public opinion led to massive increases in funding for American missile and space programs. (Smithsonian Air and Space Museum)

After the formation of NASA, the X-20 Dyna-Soar spaceplane, scheduled to be lofted into space atop a Titan IIIC, represented the Air Force's only manned space program. This artist's rendition includes photos of the X-20 pilots: Captain Albert H. Crews, Major Henry C. Gordon, Captain William J. Knight, Major Russell L. Rogers, Major James W. Wood, and NASA's Milton O. Thomas. (USAF)

This artist's concept shows a launch of the Dyna-Soar space plane atop a Titan IIIC. To reflect the requirements of the Air Force's first "aerospace" vehicle, engineers designed the Dyna-Soar as a manned, delta-winged vehicle capable of being boosted into orbit yet retaining reentry and controlled landing maneuverability. As such, Dyna-Soar satisfied multiple mission requirements and could be supported by a vast network of existing ground facilities. (USAF)

Project CORONA, a reconnaissance satellite program managed by the future National Reconnaissance Office (NRO).

Under Eisenhower, the Air Force did not achieve an "independent" leadership position, but could point to an impressive list of achievements including space booster and infrastructure support as well as management responsibility for the early warning satellite and the ground-based space surveillance network. Air Force leaders also fought off two attempts by their Army and Navy rivals, led by the Chief of Naval Operations, Admiral Arleigh Burke, to create a unified command for military space activities.

White and Schriever remained convinced that space must support traditional military operations. This would be an important legacy for the future, when space would become an increasingly vital medium for both strategic and tactical operations. That, in turn, would serve to help institutionalize space within the Air Force.

At the close of the Eisenhower Administration, the Air Force found itself responsible for nearly 80 percent of the military space budget. Air Force space enthusiasts, however, remained frustrated with a "space for peace" policy that restricted space-based weapons. They expected greater support from the incoming Kennedy Administration that promised an integrated, national space program designed to surpass the Soviet lead.

The Air Force interpreted the new administration's approach as an opportunity to convince government leaders that national security required an expanded military space program. Optimism rose in the spring of 1961 when Secretary of Defense Robert McNamara designated the Air Force as the service for space development. Although the Army and Navy would continue with existing satellite projects and conduct preliminary space research, the Air Force became responsible for future programs with exceptions authorized only by the Secretary of Defense.

As part of the arrangement, the Air Force reorganized to accommodate the space mission, vesting all research, development, and acquisition of space and missile systems in Air Force Systems Command, a new command under General Schriever. As the service's most aggressive advocate for Air Force leadership of the national space community, Schriever expected to manage research and development for space projects in the years ahead. Unrecognized at the time, however, the central role of Systems Command would retard the process of moving space systems from the research and development community to operational commands.

The Air Force agenda in the 1960s included making permanent NASA's early dependence on the service and receiving formal DOD designation of the Air Force as the executive agent for NASA support. As early as 1962, the Air Force provided NASA the boosters for Projects Mercury, Gemini, and Apollo as well as launch and range facilities at Cape Canaveral, communication and tracking networks, funding, and personnel. The service had achieved executive agent status for NASA support in all but name.

Other elements on the Air Force agenda proved unachievable. Despite established national space policy, the Air Force lobbied for space-based anti-satellite weapons. Yet, attempts to move space-based weapons projects beyond the drawing board proved fruitless because DOD officials were unconvinced that the military had a legitimate requirement for a manned space mission. By the end of 1963, McNamara canceled two Air Force projects for flying pilots into space: the Blue Gemini interim space station and the Dyna-Soar space plane. At the same time, he authorized initial development of a Manned Orbiting Laboratory (MOL).

In the latter half of the decade, the escalating financial burdens of Vietnam and the domestic "Great Society" social agenda reduced support for the national space program. Critics argued that the MOL duplicated

Unlike its predecessor, this third-generation DSCS III satellite is 3-axis stabilized, considerably heavier at 2,475 pounds in orbit, and rectangular rather than cylindrical in shape, with dimensions of 6 x 6 x by 10 feet and a 38-foot span when the solar arrays are deployed. Designed to function for ten years, it is also the first operational satellite to use electronically switched super-high-frequency multiple-beam antennas. (Air Force Space Command)

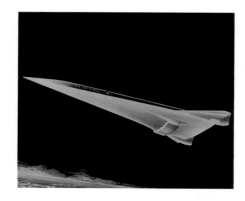

An artist's concept of a Dyna-Soar Aerospace plane. Such a plane would have the capability to routinely cruise and maneuver into and out of the atmosphere, to gain rapid responsiveness for low-earth orbit missions, or to attain very rapid transport between earth destinations from conventional airfields. (USAF)

Opposite, top left: *Apollo 11 mission officials are shown here in the Kennedy Space Center's Launch Control Center following successful liftoff. From left to right are: Charles W. Mathews, Dr. Wernher von Braun, Dr. George E. Mueller, and General Samuel C. Phillips. General Phillips, the most prominent Air Force officer seconded to NASA, joined the civilian agency in 1962 to manage Project Apollo. (NASA photo)*

Opposite, top right: *The Air Force Manned Orbiting Laboratory (MOL) pilots pose with a model of the laboratory atop a Titan IIIC. From left to right are: Lieutenant Colonel Robert Herres, Major Robert H. Lawrence, Major Donald H. Peterson, and Major James A. Abrahamson. Herres would become the first commander-in-chief of U.S. Space Command, and Abrahamson would head the Strategic Defense Initiative program. (USAF)*

Above: *The Augmented Target Docking Adapter seen here from the Gemini 9 spacecraft reminded astronaut Thomas Stafford of an "angry alligator." (NASA)*

Right: *NASA relied on considerable Air Force support for its manned spaceflight programs. Here an Air Force Titan II launches Gemini 7 astronauts Frank Borman and James Lovell from Cape Canaveral on 4 December 1965. The Gemini 7 crew established an endurance record for the Gemini program by completing 206 orbits in 330 hours and 36 minutes. (NASA photo)*

human space flight and exploration missions already assigned to NASA and the reconnaissance mission of the National Reconnaissance Office.

When the Nixon Administration canceled the MOL, the Air Force lost its best means of generating support for space within the service. Space was far from institutionalized in the traditional Air Force. The service would continue to cooperate with NASA, but Air Force leaders no longer saw military manned space flight as the centerpiece of the Air Force space program.

With the larger Air Force space agenda unrealized, by default, Systems Command assumed operational responsibility for space. This set the stage for a future contest between the research and development community and operational elements. Meanwhile, Air Force leaders downplayed space and spoke instead about traditional Air Force missions. It was the escalating operational importance of unmanned, instrumented spacecraft and the advent of the Space Shuttle that reinvigorated the Air Force space program.

The Air Force Space Mission Matures

Communications, navigation, weather, and surveillance and reconnaissance spacecraft came of age during the late 1960s and early 1970s. With solid-state microelectronics, satellites could collect vast amounts of data by means of increasingly powerful sensors. That data, rapidly transmitted to ground stations, became available to global users on a near-real-time basis. Equally important, developments in rocket boosters produced a standardized launcher fleet of reliable space boosters with greater lifting capacity. Larger, increasingly complex satellites carried multiple payloads and performed a wide range of operational functions.

At the same time, engineers succeeded in extending the lifetimes of satellites in orbit, thereby reducing the number of spacecraft needed. To support expanding satellite and booster capabilities, the Air Force created an elaborate space infrastructure of launch facilities, tracking and control networks, and research and development laboratories.

Space reconnaissance, missile detection, and early warning represented the most important military space functions during the Cold War.

Above: *An Air Force Titan III-C rocket placed eight satellites into orbit 21,000 miles above the equator on 16 June 1966. This artist's recreation illustrates the protective shroud falling away, exposing seven communications satellites and an experimental gravity gradient satellite carried in the transgate of the booster. The multiple-launch technique provided an economical means for establishing a military communication satellite system. (USAF)*

Above: *At the White House, President Dwight D. Eisenhower and Air Force Chief of Staff General Thomas White (center) view the Discoverer 13 capsule, the first object recovered from space. The capsule, which carried an American flag, was later exhibited to the public at the Smithsonian Institution. (USAF)*

Top: *On 19 August 1960, Air Force Captain Harold E. Mitchell, piloting a C-119 "Flying Boxcar," and trailing a special nylon cable with retrieval hooks, made the first successful midair recovery of a CORONA satellite film capsule over the Pacific Ocean on his third pass. (Jay Ashurst, Air Force Space Command)*

Space reconnaissance involved highly classified activities managed by the NRO. Initially, officials considered CORONA only an interim project until the Air Force's more ambitious Samos Atlas-Agena reconnaissance project became operational. However, CORONA's camera development assured the higher resolution stereoscopic photography desired by intelligence analysts for accurate assessment of Soviet ICBMs and other military targets. On 19 August 1960, Discoverer XIV, the first successful CORONA mission, produced more film of Soviet targets than all the U-2 flights of the previous four years.

Increasingly successful, CORONA provided vital intelligence data until 1972, when more capable reconnaissance camera systems replaced it. In September 1961, an agreement between the CIA and the DOD established the highly classified NRO to consolidate and manage all overhead strategic reconnaissance programs. From this time forward, Samos and CORONA became national reconnaissance projects managed by civilian rather than uniformed Air Force personnel. The Undersecretary of the Air Force became the Director of the NRO. The Air Force continued reconnaissance satellite flights under NRO direction well into the 1980s.

In addition to its central role in reconnaissance, the Air Force was responsible for two important space surveillance programs. One, Vela

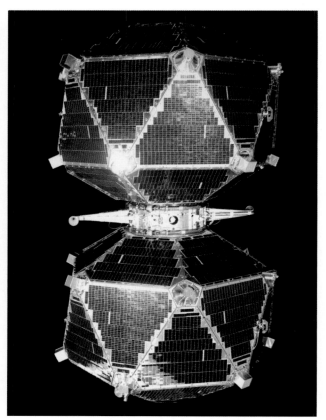

Hotel, comprised a space-based nuclear detection system to ensure compliance with the nuclear test ban treaty of 1963. The other, the Missile Detection and Alarm System (referred to as MIDAS)—was an early warning satellite that detected the launch of ballistic rockets using infrared radiometers. The latter's high costs and technical problems, however, led Pentagon officials to cancel the program in 1966 in favor of the larger, more capable Defense Support Program (DSP) satellites. Vela Hotel satellites also gave way in the early 1970s to the Integrated Operational Nuclear Detonation Detection System (IONDS). As part of the movement toward larger, multi-purpose satellites, IONDS nuclear detectors were lofted into space aboard Global Positioning System (GPS) navigation and DSP early warning satellites.

Representing the only operational satellite system wholly controlled by the Air Force, the DSP strategic system consists of three operational infrared satellites and two spares in geostationary orbit. The ground station at Buckley Air Force Base near Denver, Colorado, provides data transmission and space control. Data transmitted to the ground stations is simultaneously relayed to the North American Aerospace Defense Command and other users. First launched in late 1970, DSP satellites still provide strategic warning of ballistic missile launches as well as nuclear detonations for test ban treaty monitoring purposes.

DSP satellites are complemented by Air Force ground-based radar systems that have been providing missile warning data and the tracking of space objects since the early 1960s. By 1963, the Air Force had activated three Ballistic Missile Early Warning System radar sites, located at Thule Air Base, Greenland; Clear Air Force Station, Alaska; and RAF Fylingdales Moor in Great Britain. These sites complement the Cobra Dane phased array radar site at Shemya, Alaska, and the two Phased

Top, left: Workers are installing the MIDAS 6 Series III Infrared Sensor Payload atop the Agena B in November 1962 at Vandenberg Air Force Base in preparation for launch. Although MIDAS remained a test program, it had shown conclusively that infrared satellites could provide early warning of a missile attack by detecting and tracking missiles of all sizes. (USAF)

Top, right: First launched in 1963, the 500-pound icosahedron-shaped twin Vela Hotel nuclear detection satellites performed flawlessly as "treaty monitors" until the 1970s, when they gave way to nuclear detectors placed on other Air Force satellites. Shown here are Vela 11 and Vela 12, the last Vela satellites to be launched, on 8 April 1970. (USAF)

Opposite, bottom: A specially adapted C-119 Packet modified to recover space capsules in mid-air is put through its paces by members of the 6593rd Test Squadron, stationed at Hickham AFB, Hawaii. In trials over the Pacific, a captured practice capsule is reeled into the open end of the C-119. (USAF)

Above: *This initial DSP satellite weighed 2,000 pounds and measured 23 feet in length and 10 feet across. Mounting a 12-foot telescope with an array of over 2,000 lead sulfide infrared detectors, the DSP satellite itself rotated so that its telescope scanned the face of the Earth and returned to its selected starting point six times each minute. By 1974, the three operating satellites had detected nearly 1,300 missile launches. (USAF)*

Right: *DMSP Block 5D satellites are shown here in various stages of testing. Weighing 1,140 pounds and measuring four feet in diameter and twenty feet long, the 5D satellites tripled the size of the earlier spacecraft. Cloud cover imagery and other weather data could be stored for later transmission or immediately downlinked to ground stations and tactical terminals deployed worldwide. (USAF)*

Opposite, center right: *The Cobra Dane phased array radar site on Shemya Island in Alaska's Aleutian chain has been operational since 1977. Simultaneous tracking of multiple targets is provided by electronic controlling of the phase, or timing, of incoming as well as outgoing signals. (USAF)*

Opposite, bottom right: *A Thor booster prepares to launch the first DMSP Block 5D satellite from the Western Test Range on 11 September 1976. Although the launch was successful, the satellite lost stability and began to tumble shortly after attaining orbit. Representing a major technological leap over previous models, DMSP satellites suffered technical and managerial problems throughout the late 1970s. (USAF)*

Array Warning Systems—known as PAVE PAWS—at Cape Cod Air Force Station, Massachusetts, and Beale Air Force Base, California. These two coastal sites provide warning of potential submarine-launched ballistic missile attacks. Phased array antennas are part of the exterior building walls and make it possible to simultaneously track multiple targets without loss of the system's surveillance capability.

Weather satellites represent another important element of support for tactical and strategic military operations. The Air Force meteorological satellite program began as a classified NRO project with the mission of providing specific weather data on targets in the Soviet Union. Although the first military weather satellites were relatively unsophisticated, their data provided accurate hurricane warnings and facilitated Apollo recovery operations in the Pacific Ocean. Planners in Vietnam relied extensively on meteorological satellite data for combat operations. From an altitude of

232

450 NM, the satellites furnished day and night, visual and infrared imagery consistently at 0700, 1200, 1900, and 2400 hours local time.

The program transferred from NRO to Air Force Systems Command in the mid-1960s and became known as the Defense Meteorological Satellite Program (DMSP). By the early 1970s, the Air Force had launched a series of weather satellites, each more capable than its predecessor. In the middle of the decade, the Air Force launched the first of a new generation of polar orbiting satellites designed to provide very high quality weather pictures both day and night.

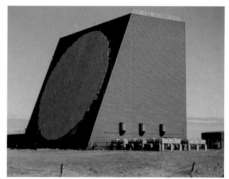

In the 1960s the Air Force became the executive agent for the Global Positioning System (GPS), a DOD program intended to furnish accurate, all-weather position data to an unlimited number of users anywhere on or near the surface of the Earth. The unified program adopted Air Force signal structures and frequencies and Navy atomic clocks and satellite orbits. Planners sought a 24-hour-a-day capability for global, three-dimensional positioning within 15 meters 50 percent of the time and 27 meters 90 percent of the time. Budget shortfalls, technical problems, military reluctance to accept the system, and the *Challenger* accident delayed launch of the first five operational satellites. At the time of the Gulf war, the GPS constellation numbered sixteen satellites, and provided 24-hour two-dimensional and 19-hour three-dimensional coverage of operations.

For over three decades the Air Force led efforts to expand satellite communications capabilities for defense needs by providing launch vehicles, supporting infrastructure, and communications satellites. In 1964, DOD authorized an Air Force–proposed system of up to eight satellites in

Above: *Eight first generation DSCS I communications satellites are placed in a dispenser for mounting atop a Titan IIIC booster for launch into near-synchronous equatorial orbit. Operating in the super high frequency bandwidth, weighing about 100 pounds, and measuring only 3 feet in diameter and nearly 3 feet in height, these spin-stabilized satellites had only a basic telemetry capability for monitoring purposes. (USAF)*

Right: *A Thor-Able 5 launches from Cape Canaveral on 1 April 1960 with its Television Infrared Observation Satellite payload. The Douglas Aircraft Thor, measuring 65 feet in length and 8 feet in diameter, relied on liquid oxygen and kerosene to produce 150,000 pounds of thrust from its single main engine. (NASA)*

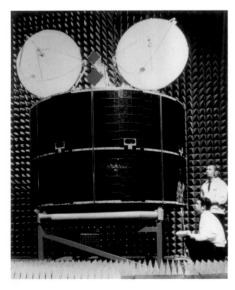

Above: *This DSCS II satellite undergoes testing in a specialized test chamber during the 1970s. With each DSCS II satellite measuring 9 feet in diameter, 13 feet in height with antennas extended, weighing 1,300 pounds, and being dual-spun for stability, its 5-year design life nearly doubled that of DSCS I, while providing redundancy, multi-channel and multiple-access features, and increased capability to communicate with smaller, more mobile ground stations. (USAF)*

a near-synchronous equatorial configuration. The first seven satellites went aloft in June 1966. Vietnam tested satellite communications from a real-world theater of operations. That experience established the military practice of relying on commercial space systems for routine administrative and logistical needs while trusting more sensitive command and control communications to the dedicated military system.

While the satellites provided good service for nearly ten years, this first phase of what became known as Defense Satellite Communications System (DSCS) remained limited in terms of channel capacity, user access, and coverage. The much-improved DSCS II constellation, with four active satellites in geosynchronous orbit, supported by two orbiting spares, overcame these deficiencies by the early 1980s. That decade the Air Force began deploying the more capable DSCS III satellite, which possessed greater survivability and increased communications capacity, especially for mobile terminal users.

While satellites provided important information for operational commanders, system performance remained dependent upon boosters and upper-stage vehicles capable of achieving the desired orbit. Thor, Atlas, and Titan boosters enabled the Air Force to achieve early recognition as the "booster service" and guaranteed its central space role throughout the Cold War era.

During the 1960s, the Thor booster began its impressive flight history with the initial December 1959 Project CORONA launch and achieved a remarkable performance record that included only three failures among 154 launches from 1962 to 1972. In addition, the Air Force designated the Thor to launch its weather satellites in the 1970s. The more capable Atlas ICBM began its booster career launching heavier payloads from the Eastern Test Range at Cape Canaveral, and served as the basic booster for NASA's Mercury and Gemini programs and the GPS constellation.

In the 1960s, the Air Force augmented its booster fleet with the Titan IIIC, consisting of a two-stage liquid-propellant Titan II rocket core with two enormous solid-propellant strap-on motors, together with a third "Transtage." With Titan, the Air Force possessed a booster of vastly increased size, capable of launching a wide range of satellites into higher, geosynchronous orbits. Between 1964 and 1979, 111 of the 119 Titan III launches proved successful. Those successes vindicated proponents who sought to create a "DC-3 of the space age."

These boosters supported a variety of upper stages and provided needed mission flexibility. Among the many upper-stage vehicles, the Air Force preferred Agena. By the 1970s, the Agena and other space launch vehicles had matured to the point where Air Force planners could consistently count on available standard boosters for launching substantial payloads, placing them into complex orbits, and demonstrating reliable performance.

Cold War concerns compelled the nation's leaders to develop surveillance capabilities for detecting, tracking, and monitoring satellites and space debris. Known as the Space Detection and Tracking System (SPADATS), this ground-based network initially comprised the Navy's Space Surveillance sensors and data processing facility in Dahlgren, Virginia, and the Air Force's Spacetrack sensor network. The latter began in the late 1950s with a variety of radars and Baker-Nunn satellite-tracking cameras for deep space surveillance. This system underwent continual

This Mercury-Atlas 5 lifts off from the Kennedy Space Center on 19 November 1961 with the space chimp Enos aboard. This successful flight was the dress rehearsal for the 20 February 1962 Mercury launch that made Lieutenant Colonel John Glenn the first American to orbit the Earth. The 71-foot long, 10-foot wide stage-and-one-half Atlas booster, built by General Dynamics-Astronautics, could produce 387,000 pounds of thrust from its three main and two vernier engines. (NASA)

Above: *Early Air Force space advocates dreamed of manned vehicles going into orbit then returning to land on Earth. Some of those men lived to see their dreams become reality in the space shuttle. In this artist's illustration,* Enterprise *is launched from a modified Boeing 747 in a critical test to evaluate the space shuttle's approach and landing characteristics. ("Free Enterprise," Mike Machat)*

Left: *Shown here is the General Dynamics Atlas assembly plant on Kearny Mesa near San Diego, California. (USAF)*

improvements to detect, track, and monitor a space population that by 1969 found North American Air Defense Command's Space Defense Center in Cheyenne Mountain observing 20,000 objects daily.

Over the next two decades, operators activated additional, improved sensor sites, including five facilities designed to provide near-real-time detection and observation of objects in deep space. The Space Defense Operations Center in Cheyenne Mountain handled the growing SPADATS challenges of operational warning, anti-satellite operations, space surveillance, and control of integrated ground stations.

Two major Air Force launch centers supported the nation's satellite program from its inception. One, the Eastern Test Range at Cape Canaveral, Florida, proved ideal for testing cruise missiles and, later, for launching ballistic missiles and space flights. The Eastern Test Range became the center for Vela and communications satellite launches and all American manned spacecraft, including NASA's Mercury, Gemini, and Apollo, which were launched eastward into low-inclination equatorial orbits.

The Western Test Site at Vandenberg Air Force Base, California, also began operating as a missile test base. Officials selected the California site for launching NRO and DMSP satellites and others that required near polar orbits. After 1971, Vandenberg also became the designated location for near polar-orbit Space Shuttle operations. Like its eastern counterpart, the western range depended on a long line of space tracking stations spread across the Pacific from California to the South and Southeast Asian coasts.

A second group of space facilities comprised the tracking network and its control center that made possible the crucial integration of satellites, launch sites, and processing centers. Designated the Satellite

Control Facility, it included a global system of remote tracking, telemetry, and command stations. A central control center originally located in Sunnyvale, California, and associated communications links bound together all the equipment and software needed to track and control spacecraft during launch, orbit, descent, and recovery.

The importance of impending Shuttle operations led planners in the 1980s to create an additional component, the Consolidated Space Operations Center at Falcon Air Force Station, Colorado, to serve as the primary mission control operational element in the Air Force Satellite Control Network. Taken together, by the early 1970s, the tremendous growth of space systems and supporting infrastructure increasingly propelled unmanned space systems from the realm of research and development to the broader arena of operational applications.

The east coast launch site for space shuttles, Cape Kennedy is well suited with its multiple launch pads and large capacity hangars and facilities. (NASA)

The "Blue Cube" at Onizuka Air Force Base, California, has been a major element in the Satellite Control Facility since the late 1960s. Originally scheduled to handle Manned Orbiting Laboratory flights, the 10-story windowless "Advanced Satellite Test Center" provided controllers vastly increased capabilities for supporting 24 hours per day, 7 days per week, of real-time operations for instrumented satellite missions. (USAF)

Space Shuttle

The other important development that encouraged Air Force space enthusiasts was the advent of the Space Shuttle. Civilian Air Force leaders saw in the Shuttle the promise of routine access to space, especially for larger, heavier satellites like the NRO's strategic reconnaissance spacecraft. The uniformed Air Force, however, proved more reluctant to accept a multipurpose reusable vehicle that NASA expected would become the sole means of launching all civilian and military satellites. Under pressure to use the Shuttle in place of expendable boosters, the Air Force agreed to assist with development costs, produce an upper stage vehicle, and construct a West Coast launch facility.

For its support, the Air Force demanded a vehicle capable of launching its largest, heaviest payloads into polar orbit from Vandenberg Air Force Base and, under emergency conditions, returning to the California launch site. Rather than the NASA-proposed straight-winged orbiter with a cargo bay measuring 12 feet in diameter by 40 feet in length, the approved version was delta-winged, with cargo bay dimensions of 15 feet by 60 feet. These requirements led to greater technical problems and development costs that would eventually jeopardize the initial projections of 60 flights per year at half the cost of expendable boosters.

By the mid-1970s, the attitude of Air Force leaders had evolved from "resigned acceptance" to "cautious optimism." Although in 1977 the Shuttle gained a strong ally in Dr. Hans Mark, Undersecretary of the Air

Air Force Astronauts

Colonel Frederick D. Gregory, USAF (Ret)

Space has no end. It is black like velvet with diamonds sprinkled generously all about. It challenges the curious to explore its risky depths. Some few have traveled within it a short distance and come back in wonder.

Many of us joined the Air Force not just to serve our country, but because we loved to fly. Our early experiences pushing the limits in the atmosphere excited us to go a bit higher. Air Force officers like Gus Grissom, Ed White, Buzz Aldrin, Gordon Cooper, Tom Stafford, and Frank Borman, just to name a few, did just that. I could see amazement in their eyes when they talked of their adventure. Their descriptions always ended in questions about what was next.

In 1985, I got my chance to fly in the most complex flight vehicle ever built. Even though I had trained to fly the Space Shuttle for many years, I was not emotionally prepared for the sensations of launch, the on-orbit revelations, or the solitude of re-entry and landing. Each space flight that I took after that convinced me that our future should not be limited by a shortsighted vision. It is hard to explain what it's like to fly in space, but what is most astounding, at least to me, is the view of Earth. On the Shuttle, you orbit Earth from about 190 miles above its surface. It takes approximately 90 minutes to complete

an orbit, so you have ample opportunity to take it all in. From low Earth orbit, you can't really see boundaries and borders; everything looks unified and orderly.

Our next adventure is an international partnership aboard the International Space Station "Alpha." Perhaps it could provide working volume for great scientists to discover cures for human ailments. Perhaps it will be a rest stop en route to L1, the location between moon and Earth where the gravitational attractions of the two bodies are equal. Perhaps it will be a platform for a revolutionary observation instrument or a departure point for a probe that is in search of new life. Perhaps it will be the foundation for the robotic and human technology necessary to travel farther beyond the influence of Earth's magnetic pull.

The United States Air Force will always be a part of the future of this great Earth, asking and providing answers about what is next and where we go from here.

Above: The crew of STS-33 Discovery posing before the American flag and their mission logo includes (seated) Commander Frederick D. Gregory, center with Mission Specialists Kathryn C. Thornton, left, and Story Musgrave, right. Standing are Pilot John E. Blaha, left, and Mission Specialist Manley L. Carter. (NASA)

This Earth observation is of China and the Earth's limb. It was taken mid-afternoon, local time, near Canton, China. (NASA)

Above: *Undersecretary of the Air Force Dr. Hans Mark became a passionate champion of the Space Shuttle and favored the reusable Shuttle becoming the nation's launch vehicle for all military and civilian space flights. (Department of Defense)*

Right: *On 12 April 1981, NASA launched its first Space Shuttle mission from the Kennedy Space Center with astronauts John Young and Robert Crippen aboard. The successful, 54-hour mission ended with an unpowered landing at Edwards Air Force Base in California. (NASA)*

Air Force Chief of Staff General Lew Allen, under pressure from elements within and outside the Air Force, guided the decision-making process that resulted in creation of an Air Force operational Space Command. (USAF)

Force and Director of the NRO, DOD and Air Force leaders grew increasingly worried about the Shuttle's high costs, production delays, reduced flight schedules, and the growing pressure to phase out the service's expendable launch fleet.

In the early 1980s, these concerns led the Air Force to a "mixed fleet" strategy, complementing the Shuttle with expendable launch vehicles. On the eve of the *Challenger* disaster, Air Force support had been tempered by diminished expectations and hope that a "mixed fleet" of expendable Titan and Atlas boosters would help realize the Shuttle's lofty expectations.

Meanwhile, artificial satellites and the approach of Shuttle operations precipitated a major shift in Air Force thinking on organizational issues. Traditionally, the Air Force and DOD assigned space systems on a functional basis to the command or agency with the greatest need. Systems like GPS and the Shuttle, possessing multiple capabilities, promised to blur functional lines. Indeed, the Shuttle generated intense competition for operational responsibility among four Air Force commands, each considering itself the logical choice for operational command of space systems.

Renewed interest in space also appeared at the national level, where both critics and opponents of arms control agreements increasingly relied on space systems to provide surveillance and verification. The potential impact of space systems prompted Air Force leaders to reassess the importance of space for operational commanders. The growing debate focused on whether the research and development community should continue to launch and control space systems, or relinquish these responsibilities to the operational side of the Air Force. If the latter, would Air Force space requirements be better served by creating a new, major operational command for space?

Several champions of operational space appeared to lead the way forward. Complementing Hans Mark on the civilian side, for example, Lieutenant General Jerome F. O'Malley, Air Force Deputy Chief of Staff for Operations, Plans and Readiness, became a tireless advocate for normalizing space operations through the creation of a major Air Force command for space. That goal was realized in 1982 with the activation of Air Force Space Command under the command of General James V. Hartinger.

Lieutenant General Jerome F. O'Malley and Undersecretary of the Air Force Edward C. "Pete" Aldridge played a central role in the creation of Space Command. Here they are shown observing General James V. Hartinger signing the order authorizing his assumption of command. (USAF)

Space Command

Possessing few resources, General Hartinger's new command had to acquire space systems scattered among various Air Force commands, gain experience, and convince the wider Air Force of the operational importance of space for traditional missions. Effective command relationships had to be forged between Space Command, other services, and unenthusiastic Air Force research and development commands. Not until 1993, for example, did the research and development community relinquish complete responsibility for satellite control and space launch.

The new unified space command established in September 1985 also presented a challenge. When the Air Force formed Space Command in 1982, Air Force officials referred to a unified operational command for military space activities as the "next logical step." General Hartinger and his staff developed procedures and a rationale for a unified space command built around his Air Force command as the "core" component of the new unified command. As such, the Air Force would take the lead in coordinating all American military space operations, and his successor would serve as commander of both as well as commander of the North American Aerospace Defense Command.

Planning and support for a unified space command received a crucial boost from President Reagan's Strategic Defense Initiative (SDI) because SDI would clearly be dependent on space-based systems. SDI compelled officials to review the entire role of space in military operations and proceed with a unified space command as the sensible alternative for SDI planning and operations. Yet, roles and missions controversies would bedevil the relationship between Air Force Space Command and United States Space Command into the 1990s.

Air Force Space Command also had to deal with the crisis following the *Challenger* accident in January 1986. By the time NASA resumed Shuttle operations on a conservative schedule after a 31-month delay, the Air Force had reprogrammed eighteen of thirty-six previously manifested Shuttle payloads for expendable launchers. After 1992, the DOD would use the Shuttle only for SDI or research and development missions. In effect, the Air Force chose to abandon the standardized Shuttle, the "airliner to space," for the diversification represented by expendable boosters.

A Titan IV launches from Cape Canaveral Air Force Station on 14 June 1989. Even before the Challenger *accident, the Air Force had decided to retain its main heavy-lift expendable Titan IV booster, which proved capable of launching 10,000 pounds into geostationary orbit. (USAF)*

Space Launch Operations

Lieutenant General Forrest McCartney, USAF (Ret)

I arose from the console, stretched, and walked outside to watch dawn break. Clear skies and light winds favored the launch of the Titan IV towering 20 stories above Complex 40 at Cape Canaveral. Even after 40 years, I still tingle with excitement after a long night working shoulder-to-shoulder with Air Force and contractor teams preparing for a complex launch. Countdown had progressed smoothly—not always the case when fueling the Centaur upper stage with liquid oxygen and liquid hydrogen.

If everything goes as planned, the 11,000-pound Milstar communication satellite atop the Titan IV will soon enter orbit 22,000 miles above the equator. Milstar is big and heavy—and very expensive. We lost the last Milstar in a rare launch failure. The launch business is unforgiving. You get one bite at the apple. A launch either succeeds or fails. I had experienced both, and the failures remain vivid in my mind.

I returned to my console, feeling tension build as the countdown continued. At T minus 60 seconds, the computer took control of the launch sequence leading to ignition of two solid-fuel booster rockets. Ten feet in diameter and 112 feet tall, the boosters will generate over three million pounds of thrust.

Three, two, one, T minus zero seconds—and ignition. The Titan leaps from the pad. Once again, I am amazed at our ability to control and direct the enormous energy released during a launch. I watch telemetry data for anomalies. If problems occur, they occur in the blink of an eye—and it is all over.

Two minutes after lift off, the Titan engines ignite as booster rocket motors burn out, separate from the Titan, and fall toward the Atlantic Ocean. Long-range cameras catch the event—one major milestone now successfully behind us. Data streams into launch control, revealing every detail of the Titan's flight. After another seven minutes, the Titan core falls away and Centaur's two engines ignite—the first of three burns needed to carry Milstar into the desired orbit.

I follow telemetry data for the next six hours through the final burn, engine shutdown, and Milstar release from the Centaur. A loud cheer breaks out as we realize we have succeeded. This time the operation unfolded without a hitch, the result not of luck, but experience and team effort developed over years of hard work by Air Force and contractor personnel.

Top: The workhorse Titan III is shown here with its Centaur upper stage vehicle launching Jupiter-bound *Voyager 1* from the Kennedy Space Center on 5 September 1977. Measuring 108 feet long by 10 feet in diameter. the Titan III generated nearly 3,000,000 pounds of thrust and could place up to 33,400 pounds into low-earth orbit and nearly 4,000 pounds into a synchronous equatorial orbit. (NASA photo)

Left: Astronaut Donald K. Slayton looks on in Mission Control at Cape Kennedy as technicians monitor the progress *Gemini 5* moments after liftoff. (NASA)

The Shuttle problem also compelled reexamination of the Air Force commitment to space. By the end of the 1980s, Air Force leaders referred to the Air Force as the "lead service for military space" and accepted responsibility to "normalize" and "operationalize" space within and outside the Air Force—in short, to institutionalize space. Unlike Air Force efforts in earlier years, however, the central priority now became making space essential to the warfighter rather than flying pilots into space.

Top, left: *In this Denver, Colorado, assembly plant, workers are refurbishing Titan IIs and building Titan IVs. (USAF)*

Top, right: *Following the* Challenger *tragedy, the Air Force developed a new launch vehicle, the Delta II, capable of launching 11,000 pounds into low Earth orbit. Here a Delta II launch vehicle lifts off from Cape Canaveral Air Force Station on 12 September 1996 carrying a Global Positioning System satellite into orbit. (USAF)*

Space Operations

The Persian Gulf war provided Air Force space leaders the opportunity to demonstrate the importance of space systems to combat operations. Space systems, traditionally strategic, proved sufficiently flexible to provide critical tactical support to the warfighters. For example, the integration of DSP warning and Patriot antimissile capability proved to be one of the great achievements of the Gulf conflict. Although the anti-Scud warning system exceeded every expectation, it took months to configure for tactical missile defense. Warning time for Patriot crews remained uncomfortably brief, underscoring the need for improved ballistic missile tactical warning.

Air Force weather satellites also made a significant contribution in the Persian Gulf war. DMSP provided cloud cover imagery, temperature, and moisture data on its twice-daily sweeps of the Gulf. Along with other military and civilian weather satellites, DMSP made possible the planning and execution of the most sophisticated air campaign in history. Imagery and data transmitted from the DMSP constellation helped planners develop real-time schedules, make immediate, accurate retargeting decisions for reconnaissance and tactical missions, and accomplish bomb damage assessments.

Deployed in the Gulf war, the Patriot air defense system relied on Defense Support Program satellites rather than their own radar system to provide warning of SCUD missile attacks. (U.S. Army photo)

243

U.S. Army personnel operate a hand-held GPS receiver that proved vital to operations during the Gulf war. The accuracy of hand-held GPS receivers has continued to improve and devices that permit ground forces to determine more accurate locations have changed the way ground units employ artillery and close air support. (USAF)

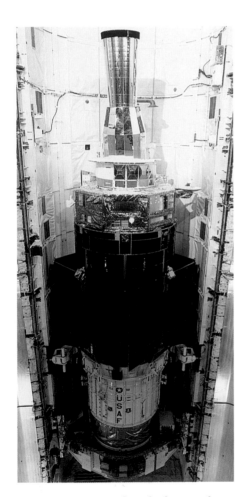

On Pad 39A awaiting launch, the cargo bay of the space shuttle Atlantis holds a Defense Support Program Satellite attached to an inertial upper stage booster. DSP satellites are large, multi-purpose satellites that can carry launch detection systems as well as other systems for communications, weather, or other purposes. (NASA)

DMSP also aided in the movement of troops during the ground war. Moreover, it helped predict and track rain and sand storms, track oil fires, spills, and clouds, and analyze the potential spread of chemical agents. General Norman Schwarzkopf, U.S. Commander-in-Chief of Central Command, thought so highly of DMSP that he always kept the most current DMSP products within arm's reach for quick reference. On balance, DMSP proved to be a crucial "force multiplier" during the conflict.

Despite DMSP's important service in the Gulf war, post–Cold War budget austerity convinced officials to combine military and civilian polar-orbiting satellite programs to save money. By the end of the 1990s, the National Oceanic and Atmospheric Administration (NOAA) became head of a unified system serving both civilian and military requirements.

GPS proved to be one of the great success stories of the Gulf war. During the buildup to Desert Storm, previously scheduled launches of GPS II-9 and II-10 increased the constellation to sixteen satellites. Planners also altered the orbit of GPS II-9 to optimize coverage over Baghdad, especially at night. At year's end, with the rephasing process completed and a replacement satellite launch scheduled for 30 January 1991, program managers expected the constellation to provide 24-hour two-dimensional and 19-hour three-dimensional coverage of Gulf operations.

During the conflict, the space-based navigation system supported every type of ground operation, from large-scale maneuvers to individual soldiers moving through the featureless desert. It also contributed to superb close air support coordination with GPS-equipped ground units and foreshadowed the advent of a new era in air-ground cooperation.

By 1995, the Air Force achieved full operational status with a constellation of twenty-four GPS satellites and began installing receivers in all operational aircraft, thus laying the foundation for future employment of GPS-guided munitions. Evolving GPS technology promised to continue revolutionizing the battlefield into the new century.

Communications satellites played a crucial role in the success of the Gulf war. During Desert Shield, the Coalition employed ten different communications satellite systems, which carried over 90 percent of U.S. communications into and out of the Gulf area. Commercial satellites augmented the military payloads and accounted for 24 percent of all satellite communications traffic.

The satellite communications network reflected system flexibility and cooperation between military, civil, and commercial space sectors. Air Force attention centered on DSCS, which for some time had provided long haul communications for all branches of the armed forces. DSCS satellites carried over 50 percent of communications traffic during the war and ensured effective command and control throughout the conflict.

At the same time, DSCS had not been designed to provide intra-theater communications between commanders in the field. Air Force operators found the system stretched to the limit, highly exposed to jamming, and far less mobile than ground forces desired. They looked ahead to upgrading DSCS, developing more mobile receiver terminals, and introducing a new system, Milstar (Military Strategic and Tactical Relay), to ensure reliable, global communications support—especially for tactical operations.

Milstar had emerged in 1981 as a system designed for both strategic and tactical operations. Desert Storm reinforced interest in promoting the system's tactical capabilities. In 1994, seven years after its projected launch, the first Milstar satellite went into orbit. In the new century, the Air Force anticipated a cheaper, lighter Milstar satellite with ten times the data rate of earlier satellites. At the same time, advancing commercial communications technology compelled the military to consider commercial augmentation of DSCS and Milstar systems.

The Gulf war experience confirmed that satellite launch capability remained the "Achilles heel" of the national space program. Since the early 1950s, launch systems and infrastructure had supported research and development rather than operational requirements. The advent of the Shuttle compounded the problem. Despite demand for expendable rockets after the *Challenger* tragedy, the space industry could not retool sufficiently fast to meet requirements. Aging boosters and range system components, and inefficient production lines and launch procedures resulted in an expensive, operationally limited system.

For years, space leaders had tried to solve the launch dilemma. No one wanted to link specific satellites to particular launch vehicles, thus requiring months of prelaunch preparation. The launch challenge for the 1990s found the Air Force cooperating with NASA and the NRO to develop an "assured launch strategy" based on lower costs and greater launch responsiveness.

The contribution of space systems to victory in the Gulf war served as the springboard for Air Force leaders to assert their vision for the nation's space program. Building on a generation of experience and leadership, they needed to institutionalize space within the traditional aviation-oriented service and ensure that space becomes a thoroughly integrated element of all Air Force operations. By establishing a solid space foundation within the service, the Air Force would demonstrate its commitment to support the warfighter, justify claims to space leadership, and continue to provide for the nation's security.

Top, left: An artist's rendering of a DSP satellite in orbit. Air Force Defense Support Program (DSP) satellites are a key part of North America's early warning systems. In their 22,300-mile geosynchronous orbits, DSP satellites help protect the United States and its allies by detecting missile launches, space launches and nuclear detonations. DSP satellites use an infrared sensor to detect heat from missile and booster plumes against the Earth's background. (USAF)

Top, right: Milstar is an advanced military communications satellite system. The operational Milstar satellite constellation consists of four satellites positioned around the Earth in geosynchronous orbits. Each mid-latitude satellite weighs approximately 10,000 pounds, and has a design life of 10 years. (TRW)

Milstar satellites represent the major Air Force and DoD communications system of the future. Launched atop a Titan IV/Centaur vehicle, the huge, 10,000-pound spacecraft serves as a "smart" switchboard in space, providing secure, jam-resistant worldwide communications. (Lockheed Martin Space System)

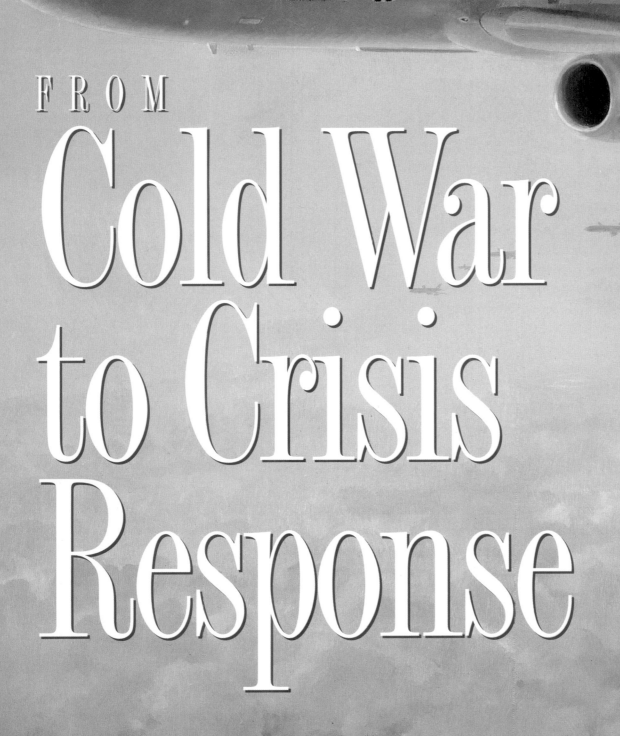

FROM
Cold War
to Crisis
Response

FROM
Cold War to Crisis Response

William T. Y'Blood, Ph.D.

Above: *Lockheed AC-130 Spectre gunships are potent weapons in almost any limited war environment. With sophisticated sensors and both 40-mm and 105-mm guns, the AC-130 provides effective support for friendly forces and delivers devastating fire on enemy targets. (USAF)*

Pages 246–247: *Completing the longest tactical bombing mission to date, 48th Tactical Fighter Wing F-111Fs from RAF Lakenheath fly around Spain in 1986 to bomb Libya. KC-10 tankers accompanied the F-111Fs, refueling them as needed, while other KC-10 and KC-135 tankers shuttled fuel to the accompanying tankers. In this print, flights of F-111Fs refuel from a KC-10 that is itself being refueled by another KC-10. ("The Lesson," Keith Ferris)*

The last two decades of the 20th century saw the supposed Soviet monolith crumble, leaving the United States as the dominant world power. That dominance led the United States to drastically rethink the size and role of its military forces. The possibility of nuclear confrontation between the United States and another nation eased considerably while the number of brush fire conflicts rose dramatically. Although reduced from a high of 608,000 personnel in 1986 at the height of the Reagan buildup to only 361,000 in 1999, the USAF frequently found itself called upon to douse those fires.

An aerial port team directs the unloading of cargo from a C-130 transport at Port Salines Airport in Grenada. During the Grenada crisis, and in other crises, the Military Airlift Command, since renamed the Air Mobility Command, delivered troops and high priority cargo and evacuated the wounded. (USAF)

Grenada: Operation Urgent Fury

The October 1983 operation, Urgent Fury, foreshadowed Air Force commitments for the next two decades. The overthrow of Grenada's Marxist-Leninist prime minister, Maurice Bishop, by members of his government seeking a closer alliance with Cuba and the Soviet Union threatened the safety of approximately 1,000 Americans living in that Caribbean nation. It also threatened to destabilize the region by spreading communism through the Eastern Caribbean. Following a presidential decision to intervene, the U.S. Joint Chiefs of Staff directed the Atlantic Command, a unified command headquartered in Norfolk, Virginia, to begin planning for an evacuation of American civilians from Grenada. It soon became apparent that much more than an evacuation operation would be required.

Eventually, approximately 20,000 U.S. personnel participated in Urgent Fury, including a battle group built around the carrier *Independence* and a Marine amphibious unit, Navy SEALS and Army Rangers, elements of the 82d Airborne Division, and Air Force gunship, transport, and reconnaissance aircraft. Among the first air units engaged were E–3A AWACS aircraft deployed from Tinker Air Force Base, Oklahoma, to Puerto Rico to monitor any movement of Cuban forces toward Grenada. Also

American medical students, endangered by the crisis in Grenada, board a Military Airlift Command C-141 at Port Salines for a flight back to the United States. A total of 622 American students and 87 foreign students were rescued. (USAF)

Right: *The Lockheed C-5 Galaxy, the heavy lifter for Air Mobility Command, is capable of airlifting heavy tanks, small submarines, and as many as six other aircraft in it cavernous cargo compartment. In this photograph, the aircraft is shown in a kneeled position with visor open, ready to load cargo. (USAF)*

These two General Dynamics F-16 Fighting Falcons are ready for action. The first prototype of the F-16 flew on 2 February 1974. Initially designed to accommodate equipment envisioned but not yet developed, this twenty-five-year-old fighter remains a current and effective first-line fighter in the first decade of the new century. More than 3,500 Falcons have been ordered for sixteen countries. (USAF)

A C-130 transport lifts off from a tropical air base. Note the jungle-covered hillside in the background and the swirl of condensation trailing behind the propeller blades. (USAF)

deploying to Puerto Rico, F–15Cs provided a distant combat air patrol for the invasion force in case Cuba made threatening moves southward.

The Army's First Ranger Battalion boarded six Air Force C-130 transports late on the evening of 24 October 1983. The first two planeloads of Rangers intended to parachute on the airport at Point Salines at dawn on 25 October and clear obstacles from the runway, permitting the remaining four C-130s to land. Halfway to the target, due to electrical problems on the lead C-130, plans changed. All of the First Ranger Battalion jumped onto Point Salines. Nineteen Air Force personnel—members of an Air Force Tactical Air Control Party and a Combat Control Team attached to the First Battalion—jumped with the Rangers. With the assistance of an AC-130H gunship from the 16th Special Operations Squadron, the Rangers forced the withdrawal of Cuban defenders and cleared the runway for the arrival of additional Army troops.

By early afternoon, C–141s landed with the first elements of the 82d Airborne Division. Tight parking caused by abandoned construction equipment forced diversion of succeeding C–141 flights to Barbados, where troops were transferred to smaller C–130s for the 45-minute flight to Grenada. By 2 November, Army troops had secured the island and

Air Force transports had evacuated American civilians. Successful despite numerous last minute ad hoc decisions, Urgent Fury demonstrated serious deficiencies in training, intelligence, and service coordination requiring immediate attention.

The weapons delivered by this F-111F streaking low across a Libyan airfield have closed all future flight plans for these Libyan-owned Russian-built Ilyushin Il-76 transports. The lights of Tripoli can be seen in the background. (Ronald Wong)

Libya: Operation El Dorado Canyon

Less than three years later, USAF aircrews saw action again, this time in response to state-sponsored terrorism. Libya, under the leadership of its anti-American dictator, Muammar al-Qadhafi, had become one of the world's leading promoters of terrorism. In the mid-1980s, terrorists became bolder, attacking targets, usually civilians, around the world. Although intelligence agencies had strong circumstantial evidence linking Libya to many of these attacks, they had no "smoking gun" to prove its involvement. Then, on 5 April 1986, a bomb blew up a Berlin discotheque, killing one American serviceman and his German girlfriend and wounding 79 Americans and 150 Germans. Prior to the bombing, electronic surveillance intercepted messages from Libyan officials in East Berlin stating that something had been planned. Additional intercepted messages conclusively proved Libya's involvement.

An A-10 of the 23rd Fighter Wing is loaded for combat. Its lethal cache of 30-mm armor-piercing cannon shells are visible in the foreground. The A-10's seven-barrel GAU-8 Gatling gun fires 6,000 rounds per minute. (USAF)

The United States mounted a joint USAF/USN operation, code-named El Dorado Canyon, directed against several targets in Libya. Hastily prepared plans called for F-111 Aardvarks from RAF Lakenheath to attack targets near Tripoli while U.S. carrier-launched aircraft attacked targets near Benghazi. Because neither France nor Spain granted overflight clearance, the F-111s flew a circuitous 3,000-mile route in complete

This Boeing KC-135 tanker from Mountain Home Air Force Base, Idaho, with boom extended is prepared to offload fuel over rugged country far from home. The tanker mission might take these aircraft to any location worldwide. (USAF)

A B-52 navigator works at his station during a combat mission. While the navigator does not have a window, he has an array of electronic equipment that enables him to know exactly where the aircraft is and where it is going without outside visual reference. (USAF)

Gunners in the cargo compartment of an AC-130 prepare to fire Spectre's 105-mm howitzer and 40-mm Bofors. These weapons are deadly against tanks, trucks, or troops. (USAF)

This AC-130 gun ship assigned to Air Force Special Operations units provides close air support for friendly forces while orbiting around the target. The awesome firepower of this aircraft can be seen in the smoke and tracers erupting from its guns. (USAF)

radio silence over the Atlantic, through the Strait of Gibraltar, and across the Mediterranean. Refueling support for the operation required twenty-eight KC-135s and KC-10s. Due to equipment malfunctions and navigational errors, not all of the F-111s dropped their weapons. Nonetheless, those that did wreaked havoc on their targets.

El Dorado Canyon was a bittersweet success: bitter because one F-111 and its crew was lost and because not all Aardvark bombing and navigation systems worked properly; sweet because the operation punished Qadhafi and his terrorist companions and diminished terrorist activities for some time afterwards.

Panama: Operation Just Cause

In 1989, the fall of the Berlin Wall symbolized the end of the Cold War. Politicians, seeking a "Peace Dividend," accelerated reductions in Air Force strength even while Air Force units deployed to meet a new crisis, this time in Panama.

The United States had maintained a presence in Panama since the Panama Canal was built in the early 1900s. Relations between the two countries were relatively stable until 1983 when Manuel Noriega assumed power. For some years, Noriega assisted U.S. intelligence agencies with information on Latin American drug trafficking and other sordid matters, while at the same time himself becoming heavily involved in such activities.

In 1989, President George H. W. Bush, determining that Noriega's actions represented a threat to the national interests of the United States, ordered an expansion of U.S. military forces in Panama, followed by an evacuation of U.S. civilians. When Noriega's police and members of his Panama Defense Force (PDF) continued harassing off-duty U.S. military personnel and ultimately killed several U.S. servicemen, President Bush responded. On 17 December, the U.S. undertook Operation Just Cause, a military operation to oust Noriega and establish a democratically elected government in Panama.

The presence of U.S. military forces in Panama conditioned military plans. In a way, Just Cause was an invasion from the "inside out," hardly the usual pattern. Even though U.S. forces were already present, the Air

Force gathered a sizeable fleet of C-130s, C-141s, and C-5s to bring in reinforcements and supplies. Combat aircraft, including AC-130s and tactical fighters, deployed to support the operation. Another aircraft, the recently unveiled F-117A, also played an important role.

Just Cause began on 19 December with C-141s dropping airborne troopers and Army Rangers on Panama's main airfields, the Torrijos International Airport and Tocumen Military Airfield, both near Panama City. A short time later, Rangers attacked an important PDF facility at Rio Hatos. AC-130 gunships provided devastating gunfire at both locations. By the following day, the battle was essentially over, although sporadic fighting continued for several days. Most defenders preferred to surrender after watching the awesome display of AC-130 firepower.

Just Cause again reflected the essential Air Force role in response to brush fire crises. Military Airlift Command transported more than 37,000 troops and 20,329 tons of cargo, while also supplying the gunships that proved so valuable to U.S. ground forces. Strategic Air Command tankers showed once more that no major operation in modern warfare could take place without tanker support. Tactical Air Command aircraft, though

Top: *This AC-130H gunship is poised for action. Note the 105-mm howitzer protruding horizontally from the rear of the aircraft while the 40-mm Bofors and 25-mm rotating canon are depressed approximately twenty degrees. AC-130U gunships with improved armament and improved avionics began entering active service in 1988. (USAF)*

Above, left: *Two General Dynamics F-16s escort a Lockheed F-117 Night Hawk stealth fighter. The F-117, first unveiled to the public following its employment during Operation Just Cause, is nearly invisible on radar. (USAF)*

Above: *The radical design of the F-117 Night Hawk makes this aircraft look unlikely to fly, but fly it does, and those unusual surfaces contribute to the stealth characteristics that make the F-117 very difficult to paint on radar. (USAF)*

Members of the Panamanian Defense Forces captured during Operation Just Cause receive water from a guard while awaiting transportation. U.S. forces detained approximately 5,800 prisoners during this operation, including Manuel Noriega, the Panamanian leader. (USAF)

Vietnam era McDonnell Douglas F-4s continued to serve well after the conclusion of that conflict. This F-4G Wild Weasel, armed with an electronics counter measures pod and two AGM-88 missiles is hunting for Iraqi SAMs during Operation Desert Storm. (USAF)

Opposite, top: *In the glow of an early moon, two F-117 Night Hawks fly across barren desert en route to Baghdad, Iraq, during Operation Desert Storm. ("Moon Shadows," Craig Kodera, U.S. Air Force Art Collection)*

less evident because their involvement was generally discrete, were always available.

A few months after the conclusion of Operation Just Cause, the Air Force established the Special Operations Command, separating fixed-wing gunships and special mission helicopters from the Airlift Command, and surprising those who still viewed the USAF as only a supporting player in military operations. The evolving role of the Air Force would be drastically revised just a little over a half year later when the service took the lead in dramatic fashion against another despot.

Iraq: Desert Shield and Desert Storm

When Saddam Hussein invaded Kuwait early on the morning of 2 August 1990, the Air Force had just two aircraft on the Arabian Peninsula, KC-135Rs, both operating with United Arab Emirate fighters in a refueling exercise. Only five months later, when Desert Storm began, 1,160 USAF aircraft were based in or near the Gulf region. More were present before the Gulf war ended.

The United Nations condemned the invasion and the Security Council approved the use of "all means necessary" to eject Iraq from Kuwait. The ensuing buildup of military forces between 7 August 1990 and 16 January 1991 became one of the most remarkable achievements in U.S. military annals. Fully 94 percent of MAC's C-5 fleet (118 of 126) and 74 percent of its C-141s (195 of 265) moved supplies and troops across an "aluminum bridge" from the U.S. to the Arabian Peninsula. This airlift, including SAC KC-135s and KC-10s in both airlift and refueling roles, hauled 99 percent of the troops into the theater. At its peak, 127 long haul transport aircraft

operated daily averaging one landing every 11 minutes. Additionally, more than 140 USAF C-130s operated in theater for tactical airlift. The tankers also maintained a hectic pace. During Desert Shield, KC-135s averaged 66 sorties flown and 175 aircraft refueled per day. When Desert Storm began, these numbers soared to 215 sorties flown and 839 aircraft refueled per day!

The Desert Storm air campaign began early on 17 January 1991 when Air Force combat aircraft, ranging from aging B-52Gs to stealthy F-117As, engaged Iraqi air defenses. From then until the ground offensive began on 24 February, Air Force and coalition aircraft battered Iraqi forces daily, paralyzing Saddam's command and control infrastructure. Particularly impressive, on day one, seven B-52Gs from Barksdale AFB, Louisiana, flew the longest combat mission in air warfare history to that date, striking targets north of Baghdad. Their mission accomplished, the bombers returned non-stop to Barksdale. This raid, which took more than 35 hours to fly, covered over 14,000 miles, encompassed four air refuelings, and powerfully demonstrated Air Force worldwide capabilities encapsulated in the phrase, "Global Reach—Global Power."

The Gulf war was remarkable for the speed, range, flexibility, lethality, and precision of modern airpower. Within a few days, the Iraqi air force was virtually exterminated. Forty-one Iraqi aircraft fell to coalition pilots, hundreds more were destroyed on the ground, and pilots scurried in the remaining aircraft for the safety of Iran. In contrast, only thirty-eight coalition aircraft, including fourteen USAF, were lost in combat during Desert Storm. This resulted in the remarkable loss rate of but 0.4 aircraft per 1,000 sorties.

The enemy's ground forces also suffered from attacks by USAF planes. A captured Iraqi officer commented that during the war with Iran, his tank was his friend because it sheltered him not only from enemy fire,

This F-117 emerges from a bunkered hanger somewhere in Saudi Arabia for another night's work during Operation Desert Storm. These hangers and other American facilities were constructed in Saudi Arabia years before the Iraqi invasion of Kuwait. (USAF)

This giant Lockheed C-5 Galaxy loads a cargo-handling vehicle that will be used at some remote destination. Specialized cargo-handling equipment allows the rapid loading and unloading of cargo aircraft, thus effectively increasing ever-scarce airlift capabilities. (USAF)

but also from the cold. Now the tank was his enemy because not even the blackness of night could protect his tank from air attack. Although still undergoing research and development, the new Joint Surveillance Target Attack Radar System (Joint STARS) demonstrated the promise of a new Air Force technology designed specifically to support the ground war. Well-armed with precision guided munitions (PGMs), and aided by Joint STARS, F-111Fs, A-10As, F-15Es, and F-16s became quite adept at "tank plinking." Even before the ground forces surged forward, air attacks had reduced Iraq's inventory of tanks and artillery pieces substantially.

More tanks and artillery pieces were destroyed when USAF planes supported the coalition ground forces in the land war. F-111s alone were credited with the destruction of more than 1,000 tanks and armored vehicles. The ground campaign was labeled the "100-Hour War," ignoring the air campaign preceding the allied ground attack. Under relentless pounding by USAF and coalition aircraft, Iraqi troops began streaming north out of Kuwait well before the ground offensive began.

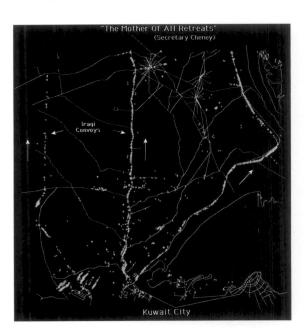

Synergy Over Kuwait

Brigadier General Ben Robinson, USAF (Ret)

On 29 January 1991, twelve days into Desert Storm, Air Force weapons controllers strain to see movement on green monitors that comprise the Joint Surveillance Target Attack Radar System (Joint STARS) installed in a Boeing 707 aircraft. Flying in darkness to monitor activity in Kuwait, crewmembers tune and retune monitors looking for any vehicle movement on the ground. Still in the test and development phase when Desert Storm began, two Joint STARS aircraft have been rushed to Southwest Asia in hopes that the new technology will be useful. Contractor personnel accompanied the Air Force crew to keep the black boxes working—to fix them if they broke—and to conduct test and development procedures under combat conditions.

In theory, weapons controllers on Joint STARS should be able to detect and track vehicles moving on the ground. The system had been tested successfully under controlled conditions. Would it work now?

As crewmembers watch, a green dot moves on the screen, then another. Excitement builds as the weapons controller, an Air Force captain, realizes that he is watching vehicles within Iraqi-occupied Kuwait move toward the Saudi border town of Khafji. The next task is to confirm the identity of the vehicles.

An E-3A Airborne Warning and Control System (AWACS), aircraft is flying nearby. A battle management aircraft, AWACS is primarily responsible for monitoring friendly and enemy aircraft locations and assigning friendly aircraft against enemy targets. Informed of the activity on the ground, a controller on AWACS diverts friendly aircraft to investigate. Enemy vehicles are sighted, engaged, and destroyed. Intelligence later determines that under cover of night, Iraqi forces had intended to provoke a major battle at Khafji, bleed coalition forces, and undermine American will to fight.

Thanks to equipment performance and crew cooperation, the Joint STARS and AWACS team not only foiled that plan, but also demonstrated a synergy between these two systems that has improved the effectiveness of both. From Desert Storm in Kuwait and Iraq to Operation Allied Force in the Balkans to Operation Enduring Freedom in Afghanistan, Air Force crews have integrated Joint STARS and AWACS to manage both the air battle and air attacks against ground targets. Together, these two systems have become a potent force multiplier.

Bottom, left: The E-8C has the range, speed, and endurance needed to rapidly project power over global distances. Its size, payload, electrical power, and cooling capability make it possible for Joint STARS to be equipped with a state-of-the-art 24-foot long, side-looking, phased array radar needed to perform persistent wide-area, surface surveillance and battle management. (USAF)

Bottom, right: Joint STARS Operations and Control subsystem consists of eighteen operator workstations, each with more than 500 MIPS of processing power. These workstations greatly enhance Joint STARS' ability to serve as a command and control node that can exploit real-time information on time critical targets with timely air attacks. (USAF)

During joint exercises with Egyptian military forces, two McDonnell Douglas F-15 Eagles from Mountain Home Air Force Base, Idaho, fly past the pyramids. (USAF)

A-10s of the 23rd Fighter Wing, with their ferocious paint jobs and more terrifying firepower, wait on the flightline of Ahmed Al-Jaber AB, Kuwait, in 1998. the 23rd Fighter Wing was in Kuwait in support of Operation Southern Watch. (USAF)

Balkan Wars

Meanwhile, aerospace power's increasing importance in modern warfare was dramatically underscored when ethnic hatreds exploded in the Balkans. When Soviet troops withdrew from Eastern Europe, the Yugoslav provinces of Slovenia and Croatia declared their independence. Bosnia-Herzegovina and Macedonia followed in 1992 and Kosovo in 1997. Yugoslavian President Slobodan Milosevic, a Serb, attempted to retain control of the independent-minded provinces by launching brutal attacks under the euphemism of "ethnic cleansing." From 1993 through 1995 in an attempt to end the fighting, NATO air units—preponderantly United States Air Force units—enforced a no-fly zone over Bosnia-Herzegovina.

Aviano Air Base in Italy was the primary base for these operations. Most aircraft encountered in violation of the no-fly zone were helicopters that could easily drop to low level and escape, but on 28 February 1994, F-16Cs intercepted six Bosnian Serb Super Galeb light attack aircraft and shot down four of them. Three of the Serbian planes fell to the missiles of one pilot.

When the Serbs continued ferocious attacks against their Muslim neighbors, particularly in a bloody mortar shelling on Sarajevo that killed a number of civilians, the UN directed air attacks against the assailants. An air campaign, dubbed Operation Deliberate Force, followed involving more than 200 aircraft. The Air Force flew more than 60 percent of the 3,515 sorties. The campaign, employing some 600 precision weapons in highly accurate strikes against air defense sites, command and control bunkers, and other military targets, shook Milosevic. He removed his weapons from around Sarajevo. Although the presidents of Bosnia, Croatia, and Serbia concluded a peace agreement, the Dayton Accord, in December 1995, Milosevic continued to create mischief. Refusing to abide by the Accord, Milosevic resorted to force to impose his will on Kosovo, Croatia, and Bosnia-Herzegovina.

NATO responded on 24 March 1999 with Operation Allied Force, an assault employing no NATO ground forces. The Air Force considered this air campaign equivalent to a major theater war. Designed to end Milosevic's brutality, Allied Force lasted 79 days, compelled Milosevic to withdraw his troops, led to his forcible removal from power, and his indictment for war crimes by an international tribunal.

Allied Force saw the largest gathering of USAF assets since the Gulf war, including over 100 F-16s, 184 KC-135s and KC-10s, 56 F-15C/Es, a number of B-1Bs and B-52Hs, and the combat debut of the B-2 bomber. Flying non-stop from Whiteman AFB, Missouri, six of the stealthy flying wings performed forty-nine missions delivering GPS-guided weapons that proved very accurate. Allied Force aircraft, flying about a quarter of the number of missions flown during Desert Storm, faced more than three times as many SAMs as encountered in that earlier conflict. The attackers lost two aircraft—an F-117 and an F-16, with both pilots recovered. Although Allied Force was somewhat limited in its effectiveness because of political considerations, it nonetheless demonstrated the tremendous potential of aerospace power in concluding this conflict.

Humanitarian Relief

During the last two decades of the century, in addition to combat operations, the Air Force became increasingly involved in humanitarian relief. These missions ranged from helping fight forest fires to supporting counter-narcotic operations to transporting huge amounts of supplies to hurricane or earthquake devastated areas both in the United States and overseas. Some of these missions lasted just a few days while others lasted several years.

Beginning in April 1991, Provide Comfort delivered life-sustaining support to the Kurdish people in northern Iraq after Saddam Hussein's Republican Guards forced the Kurds to flee their homes and take refuge in the mountains. At first, coalition forces intervened to drop relief supplies to the Kurds. Eventually the coalition established a security zone that allowed

Ground crew personnel of the 48th Tactical Fighter Wing at RAF Lakenheath, United Kingdom, inspect a GBU-28 laser guided bomb on an F-15 prior to takeoff. The GBU-28 is designed to penetrate hardened targets. (USAF)

An F-16 pilot removes his helmet and prepares to stretch after another combat mission. (USAF)

The team of airpower professionals who put the ordnance on the target includes an enthusiastic and dedicated crew on the ground. This maintenance crew no doubt inspired additional confidence in the pilot flying the aircraft they maintained. (USAF)

The crew chief completes a final weapons inspection on this F-16 Fighting Falcon prior to taxi at Aviano Air Base, Italy. (USAF)

Airlifting

Colonel Drue L. DeBerry, USAF (Ret)

Major Ray Baldridge, our operations officer, stuck his head in my office. "I need a navigator. You want to go fly?"

I looked up from the stack of paper on my desk. "Yes, sir."

Shadows crept across the parking lot outside my window on a cold February afternoon in 1966. I was completing a rare day working on my additional duty responsibility as administrative officer in the 40th Military Airlift Squadron at McGuire Air Force Base, New Jersey, after returning late Thursday from a "Thule turn-around"—a 24 hour round-trip mission from McGuire to Thule Air Base, Greenland. Our squadron, operating C-135s, was one of the few jet airlift squadrons in the Air Force. We kept one crew on hotel alert in base quarters at McGuire in case we were tasked for a short-notice mission.

"The command post just called. We have an emergency air evac from Rhein-Main. Army dependent. Twelve years old. Docs say he won't make it unless he gets to San Antonio by tomorrow. They need a jet. I'm sending the alert crew. I'll augment the pilots. I need a navigator."

"I'll go. When do we brief?"

"Two hours. Takeoff at 2100 or earlier."

As I drove home to pack, I ran the numbers in my head. With me and Major Baldridge augmenting, the crew would have three pilots and two navigators. We would become a "global" crew—able to work for 24 hours. The crew day would start at the 1900 briefing. Two hours to takeoff, nine hours from McGuire to Rhein-Main Air Base, Germany. Two hours on the ground to refuel. Twelve hours plus from Rhein-Main to Kelly AFB Texas, home of Wilford Hall Air Force Medical Center and its world-class burn trauma unit.

We launched 15 minutes early, cleared to Rhein-Main Air Base, Germany, by way of Gander, Newfoundland, and Shannon, Ireland. A medical crew met us at Rhein-Main. They loaded the patient with the help of our loadmaster while our flight engineer supervised refueling. Major Baldridge and I filed the flight plan from Rhein-Main to McGuire, where the aircraft would refuel and a fresh crew would complete the mission. "If the head winds are lighter than forecast, maybe we can re-file in the air for Kelly," I speculated.

We took off an hour and a half after landing in Rhein-Main and worked every trick we knew to conserve fuel and minimize flying time. Over Nantucket, with the fuel we had conserved so far, good weather ahead, and fingers crossed, we re-filed in the air for a direct flight to Kelly and landed there three hours later. Our patient, the 12-year-old son of a U.S. Army family, survived the flight. I said a quick prayer for his safety as I collapsed into bed at the Kelly bachelor officers quarters Saturday night. It felt good knowing that our crew had done everything possibly to get him to Wilford Hall quickly.

Left: A C-135 Stratolifter flies over the New Jersey coastline bound for Frankfurt, Germany, on a regular Military Air Transport Service flight. (USAF)

the Kurds to return to their homes. To protect the Kurds and humanitarian agencies delivering relief supplies, the coalition established a no-fly zone over northern Iraq prohibiting the operation of Iraqi aircraft, including helicopters. For more than a decade, to continue pressure on Hussein, that no-fly zone was maintained. The coalition eventually established a similar no-fly zone in southern Iraq to intensify the pressure.

Provide Promise, a similar operation running between July 1992 and January 1996, delivered nearly 56,000 metric tons of food, medicine, and other supplies, and airdropped another 18,000 metric tons of supplies to Bosnia-Herzegovina.

Many humanitarian relief operations were directed toward Africa during these same years. Air Force transports delivered famine relief supplies to the African nations of Chad, Niger, Mali, and Ethiopia. Brutal civil wars, coupled with droughts and other natural disasters, brought Air Force airlifters to Somalia's aid during Operation Provide Relief in 1992, and Continue Hope and Restore Hope in 1993 and 1994. In 1994, Air Force transports flew supplies into countries surrounding Rwanda for use by Rwandan refugees fleeing their country's bloody civil war.

The former Soviet Union also became a recipient of humanitarian aid in the early 1990s when sixty-five C-5s and C-141s flew 2,363 tons of food and medical supplies to twenty-four locations in the recently formed Commonwealth of Independent States.

From Urgent Fury in 1983 to Allied Force in 1999, the Air Force participated in major operations and countless smaller actions. Indeed, in Desert Storm and Allied Force, the USAF played a lead role. These operations disclosed requirements for new capabilities in unmanned vehicles, greater reliance on precision munitions, and innovations in operational concepts. Appreciation of those requirements would result in the creation of an Air Expeditionary Force to meet the challenges of the new century.

This Air Force pilot, flying an F-16 from Spangdahlem Air Base, Germany, displays an American flag from the cockpit before taxiing for another combat mission over the Balkans. (USAF)

An Air Force Reserve crew from the 439th Airlift Wing in Westover, Massachusetts, offloads equipment in Manas, Kyrgystan to support the humanitarian effort in Afghanistan. (USAF)

Sustaining
Air Power

Airmen

General John A. Shaud, USAF (Ret)

Training instructors confer before an inspection of the ranks during Basic Military Training at Lackland AFB, Texas. (USAF)

> *"The challenge for airmen from the beginning was discovering how best to man the equipment—and equip the man"*
>
> —ANONYMOUS

Above: *The graduation parade is the culmination of eight weeks of intense training for these airmen who are graduating from Basic Training at Lackland Air Force Base, Texas. (USAF)*

Regardless of rank or gender, the men and women, military and civilian who populate our service proudly answer to the title of airman for they are committed to operating, maintaining, and sustaining the United States Air Force. Without airmen, the Air Force would be nothing more than lifeless equipment, useless bases, and conjecture. People man the bases, employ the equipment, test the dreams, and transform the hardware into airpower. From early visionaries who exploited the military application of the airplane to today's airmen whose domain includes air and space, people have built a tradition of service, excellence, and integrity that distinguishes the Air Force.

Air Force people remain our most important resource. Through innovation and creativity, they apply technology to maintain the best Air Force in the world. The challenge to Air Force leaders has always been to recruit, train, and retain bright, intelligent people to serve.

Recruiting

In 2000, the aerospace team totaled 741,369 people, including 351,383 active duty personnel, 139,986 civilians, and 250,000 members of Guard and Reserve forces. In the normal course of events, about 10 percent of the active duty force annually retires or leaves the Air Force to pursue different career goals. The Air Force Recruiting Service, with more than 1,600 recruiters assigned to 1,100 offices in the United States and abroad, is charged with recruiting the more than 37,000 men and women annually needed to maintain the active duty strength of the Air Force.

Above: *Major Jay Aanrud (foreground), 39th Operations Support Squadron supervisor and Operation Northern Watch program manager, discusses flight safety procedures as Senior Airman Sarah Anderson (with binoculars) monitors incoming air traffic at Incirlik AB, Turkey, on 18 September 2001. (USAF)*

Page 262–263: *The California Air National Guardsman in this photo, a pilot from the 144th Tactical Fighter Wing, must feel like he is sitting on top of the world. The agile F-16 Fighting Falcon is a superb multi-role aircraft. (Ted Carlson)*

An Air Force recruiter speaks with a prospective airman about the many career opportunities the USAF offers. An Air Force recruiter discusses possible career fields with a future airman. Air Force recruiters are located in cities across the country, frequently in shopping centers and other easy access locations. (USAF)

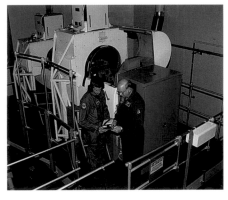

Undergraduate pilot training at Laughlin Air Force Base, Texas. A T-38 simulator student receives guidance from his civilian instructor. (USAF)

Above: *Senior Airman Elizabeth Hand works in radar approach control in base operations at Royal Air Force Lakenheath, United Kingdom. Her duties include providing expeditious air-flow for aircraft flying over RAF Lakenheath and RAF Mildenhall airspace. She is an air traffic controller with the 48th Operations Support Squadron, 48th Fighter Wing. (USAF)*

Right: *Staff Sergeant William LeSage, 31st Supply Squadron, Fuels Flight, Aviano Air Base, Italy, and deployed to Malacky Air Base, Republic of Slovakia, refuels an F-16 between sorties. He's one of 220 people deployed to support the 555th Fighter Squadron during a weapons training deployment. (USAF)*

Each recruit must be mentally, morally, and physically capable of meeting the challenges that come with working with high tech weapon systems in a dynamic operational environment. The recruiting talent pool consists of high school and college graduates, to include medical, legal, and religious professionals.

The excitement and promise of aviation are recruiting advantages for the Air Force, but with the explosion of information technologies and the hot economy of the 1990s, retention and recruiting became more difficult. In 1999 the Air Force missed its recruiting goal for the first time in twenty years. The value of retaining trained and experienced people became even more evident as recruiting goals increased in the first decade of the 21st century.

Recruiters conduct face-to-face interviews and advertise Air Force opportunities through radio, television, motion pictures, newspapers, and magazines. They also use new media such as computer games and the Internet as well as traditional methods such as mobile recruiting trailers that crisscross the country. Our most effective and entertaining advertising is the United States Air Force air demonstration squadron, the Thunderbirds.

The Thunderbirds and their red, white, and blue F-16 aircraft are known the world over for precision flying routines. Each year the Thunderbirds demonstrate teamwork and flying skills before millions of kids, teenagers, and adults. They are effective recruiters and Air Force ambassadors, but the Thunderbirds can be lethal too. In less than seventy-two hours, the squadron can be made combat-ready for worldwide deployment.

The Enlisted Corps

The Air Force enlisted force is arguably the most highly trained workforce in the world. From pararescue jumpers to flight line crew chiefs to members of the Air Force Band, the enlisted corps stands for excellence. From airman basic to the Chief Master Sergeant of the Air Force, they share a common bond of patriotism that unites them and sustains our Air Force.

Twenty-four hours a day, 365 days a year, airmen as young as eighteen patrol missile fields near Minot, North Dakota, in temperatures that vacillate between sweltering hot and subzero. In heavy monsoon rains, they service and launch aircraft from air bases at Yokota, Misawa, or Kadena in Japan; at Osan and Kunsan in Korea; and from Anderson Air Force Base on Guam. In scorching desert heat, airmen provide support for the pilots who fly missions over Iraq. They serve on airbases in Europe at Ramstein, Germany; Mildenhall, England; Aviano, Italy; and Incirlik, Turkey, often far from home and family and frequently in harm's way.

The air traffic controller that we count on to guide F-15s to land safely at Langley Air Force Base, Virginia, is highly sought after by control tower managers at New York's LaGuardia Airport, Atlanta's Hartsfield Airport, and Chicago's O'Hare Airport. Likewise, Air Force communications and computer systems operators are pursued by America's high-tech industries. The training, education, and experience our airmen gain in their Air Force responsibilities increases their value in a civilian market that can easily offer higher compensation. Still, many choose to serve in our Air Force.

Today's airmen are likely to be married and have families, and they are well educated, too. One hundred percent have high school or equivalent diplomas; 17 percent have associate degrees; and 5 percent have a bachelors degree or higher. Nearly two-thirds of all enlisted men and women in the Air Force are on their second or later enlistment.

Quality of service and quality of life have always been top priorities for our Air Force. This helped attract the best talent, particularly when there was a draft. Even at the start of the All Volunteer Force in the 1970s, recruiting continued to prosper due to the promise of aerospace careers. All of these careers begin at Lackland Air Force Base, Texas.

Above: *Wideband maintenance technicians review technical orders for satellite dishes used for voice and data communications at Schriever Air Force Base, Colorado. (USAF)*

Above: *Enlisted personnel monitor an exercise inside the range control center at Eielson Air Force Base, Alaska. (USAF)*

Above: *Senior Airman Rickett Edwards, fuels specialist from the 374th Supply Squadron, Yokota Air Base, Japan, ensures that JP-8 fuel samples are clean, dry, and serviceable at the Yokota AB laboratory. (USAF)*

Aerobics. Physical training during Basic Military Training at Lackland Air Force Base, Texas, is as rigorous as PT in any of the services. (USAF)

Enlisted Training

Lackland, known as the "Gateway to the Air Force," is the Basic Military Training center for all Air Force active duty, Guard, and Reserve enlisted personnel. During six weeks of intensive training, under the watchful eye of an experienced Military Training Instructor, some 45,000 new recruits annually learn how to salute, drill, and maintain physical fitness.

In addition to drill and physical training, new airmen study academic subjects at Lackland, including Air Force history, organization, military customs and courtesies, human relations, and financial management. Airmen learn basic military and warrior skills at Lackland, and they study the Air Force core values of *Integrity first, Service before self, and Excellence in all we do.*

Following completion of Basic Military Training, most new airmen enter one of several Air Force technical training schools to acquire the basic skills they will need at their first operational assignment. Many different specialized skills are required in today's Air Force. Jobs vary from flight engineer to medical technician—from aircraft maintenance to intelligence.

Primary technical training units are located at Goodfellow, Sheppard, and Lackland Air Force Bases in Texas; at Keesler Air Force Base, Mississippi; and at Vandenberg Air Force Base, California. Other technical training units are collocated with sister services. Professional instructors teach some 1,582 courses in 268 specialty skills at 121 affiliated schoolhouses worldwide. Subjects taught include aircraft maintenance, civil

Airmen examine an aircraft engine during technical training. With so much riding on the skills and training of the airmen, each of them understands that they must give their all on every task. (USAF)

Air Force Racial Integration

Colonel Alan Gropman, USAF (Ret)

The Air Force was the first American armed service to integrate racially. Integration began in May 1949, and was completed by mid-1951, essentially before any of the other services started their integration processes, and a generation before racial integration was accomplished in American society.

Reform came to the Air Force because several pragmatic leaders, undeterred by bigotry or racism, determined that mission effectiveness would be improved by racial integration. The central Air Force racial integration hero was Deputy Chief of Staff for Personnel, Lieutenant General Idwal Edwards. Edwards concluded that segregation was wasteful—maintaining two sets of barracks, mess halls, recreation facilities, transportation, etc.—and, worse, segregation deprived the Air Force of skilled African Americans who could fly and fight, and who could maintain and arm aircraft. The 332nd Fighter Group proved his point.

An organization in which all of the aircraft maintainers, armorers, cooks, clerks, and pilots were black and were supervised and commanded by blacks, the 332nd established a brilliant record in North Africa, Sicily, and Italy. Manned by Tuskegee Airmen—graduates of the segregated pilot training program at the Tuskegee Institute—the 332nd flew 200 missions escorting American bombers and never lost one to enemy fighters. Profoundly influenced by the record of the Tuskegee Airmen, Edwards knew blacks could do anything whites could do if given the opportunity.

The Air Force announced it would integrate racially before President Harry S Truman issued Executive Order 9981 in late July 1948, calling for equal opportunity in the Armed Forces. The Air Force did so to make itself more effective, and to make better use of all its personnel, to enlist people with talent—people who could perform the military mission. The wisdom of that decision is evident in today's Air Force, where black NCOs and officers fill important leadership and management positions—and where four black officers have earned promotion to four-star rank.

Top: Colonel Benjamin O. Davis, Jr., in a cockpit of a P-51, commanding the 332nd Fighter Group, Ramatelli Air Base, Italy, in 1944. (USAF)

Below, left: The integrated Air Force was apparent during the Reforger exercise in 1980. (USAF)

Below, right: (Left to Right) Lieutenant General Ira C. Eaker, Truman K. Gibson, Brigadier General Benjamin O. Davis, Colonel Benjamin O. Davis, Jr., at Godman Army Air Field, Kentucky, in 1945 for the activation of the 477th Composite Group with Colonel Davis commanding. (USAF)

Above: *Up and over. Trainees scale a wall during Warrior Week, an integral part of Basic Military Training at Lackland AFB, Texas. (USAF)*

engineering, medical services, computer systems, security forces, air traffic control, personnel, intelligence, fire fighting, and space and missile operations. Each year, over 175,000 students graduate from one of these technical training courses.

Specialized training continues on-the-job after the airmen arrive at their operational duty stations. In addition, mobile training teams travel to operational locations to provide instruction in new techniques and new technologies. Airmen also enroll in Air Force correspondence courses that continue to expand their specialty skills. Training continues long after airmen graduate from entry-level training courses.

Above: *An MH-53J Pave Low III crew chief from the 16th Special Operations Wing inspects the exterior of a helicopter during Operation Enduring Freedom. (USAF)*

Right: *An Air Force B-1B Lancer crew chief from the 405th Air Expeditionary Wing documents her maintenance log during Operation Enduring Freedom. (USAF)*

The Community College of the Air Force

As the Air Force matured, a system was needed for continuing the academic education of the enlisted force. The Community College of the Air Force (CCAF) established by General John D. Ryan in 1972 and now located at Maxwell Air Force Base, Alabama, fulfills that requirement.

At CCAF, the emphasis is on the individual who receives credit toward a basic associate degree through the completion of formal Air Force training classes. The desire among today's youth for continuing education results in CCAF having a direct and positive impact on recruitment, readiness, and retention.

CCAF mailed its first official transcript in November 1972 and awarded its first associate degrees in applied science in 1977. Since then, CCAF has awarded more than 220,000 associate degrees. It has more than 6,800 faculty members and 373,000 registered students attending affiliated schools located in thirty-five states, the District of Columbia, Guam, and seven foreign countries.

Members of the newly created 18th Logistics Readiness Squadron (Provisional) salute during an assumption of command ceremony at Kadena Air Base, Japan. The readiness squadron—a merger of the former 18th Transportation Squadron and the 18th Supply Squadron—is the first such squadron formed under initiatives developed to improve logistics handling. Similar mergers are expected elsewhere throughout the force. (USAF)

The Noncommissioned Officer

The preparation of the enlisted force for leadership starts on day one at Lackland. New airmen learn how to follow, and by example, experience, and instruction, they learn how to lead. As leadership skills mature, airmen are promoted into the ranks of Air Force noncommissioned officers (NCOs). Airmen attain NCO status upon promotion to staff sergeant. Promotion is based upon performance reports, promotion fitness exams, specialty knowledge tests, time in grade, time in service, and earned military decorations. NCOs hone their leadership, communications, and management skills through a series of professional military education experiences: Airman Leadership School for airmen first class; NCO Academy for technical sergeants; and Senior NCO Academy for select master and senior master sergeants.

Noncommissioned officers—the men and women who earn the right to wear four or more chevrons with a distinctive star—are the day-to-day hands-on managers in the Air Force. While aircrews composed mainly of officers fly combat missions, NCOs sustain the fight through first-line management of aircraft maintenance, weapons loading, and countless other duties that keep the combat forces in the air.

The performance of these duties is measured regularly, and is a major factor in further promotion to technical sergeant, master sergeant, senior master sergeant, and chief master sergeant. NCOs who attain the grade of chief master sergeant have attended the Senior NCO Academy for an additional six weeks of professional military education and are experienced leaders and highly skilled managers of people, processes, budgets, and resources.

From his perch in the range safety tower, Technical Sgt. Frank Lubas, 2nd Security Forces Squadron, Barksdale Air Force Base, Louisiana, observes the skill of an Air Force Special Operations Command security forces shooter. (USAF)

In honor of the Air Force's 54th anniversary, Chief of Staff of the Air Force General John P. Jumper administers the oath of appointment to fifty-four airmen, ranging in ranks from senior airman to chief master sergeant, gathered in the Pentagon auditorium for a special reenlistment ceremony on 17 September 2001. (USAF)

271

General Motors to General Officer

Major General Jeanne Holm, USAF (Ret)

Like many others, I began my Air Force career in the Army. On December 7 1941, Pearl Harbor Day, America had slightly more than a million men in arms and only a few thousand female military nurses. Twenty years old and patriotic like many of my friends, I wanted to enlist. Being a woman, and not a nurse, I couldn't. Even while nurses along with defeated American troops endured the Bataan death march, women were barred from military service. That began to change—slowly—in May 1942 when the Army authorized the Woman's Army Auxiliary Corps, the WAAC, a sort of limited service for women. I enlisted in July as a driver. The Army put me behind the wheel of a GM truck.

By spring 1943, WAAC strength grew to 60,000, but questions lingered. Were we "persons in the military service?" The answer was "yes" for some things and "no" for others. We were not entitled to the franking privilege on mail, any medals, or military honors at burial. We were not subject to military law except when overseas, and we could not be confined in the guardhouse. Instead of qualifying for normal commissions, we could only be commissioned as a "Third Officer," a position I earned in January 1943.

We were neither fish nor fowl. The Army fixed that in September 1943, disestablishing the WAAC and creating instead the Women's Army Corps as part of the Army. With more than 40,000 WACs, the Army needed female lieutenants and captains. WAACs who did not want to join the WACs were sent home. I stayed as a WAC and was promoted to captain by the end of the war.

Like so many others, I left active duty in 1946 and went to college. During the 1948 Berlin crisis, I was recalled to active duty, and in 1949, I transferred to the Air Force. I was ordered to Erding Air Depot, Germany, as assistant director of plans and operations—the beginning of a challenging and rewarding career. I never drove another truck.

Now, a half-century later, women are fully integrated into every facet of Air Force operations. I'm proud to have been part of that transition.

Bottom, left: Photograph showing the uniform spectrum for members of the Evacuation Group from the Army Nurse Corps in 1945. (U.S. Army)

Bottom, right: Women now have many opportunities. Here a female mechanic works on the flightline. ("The Mechanics," Ronald Weiss, U.S. Air Force Art Collection)

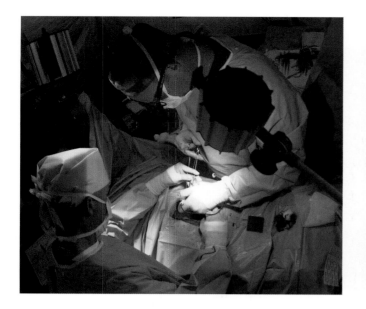

The Officer Corps

Commissioned officers enter the Air Force through the Air Force Academy, the Reserve Officer Training Corps (ROTC), or Officer Training School (OTS). While each commissioning source offers unique features of flexibility to Air Force personnel managers, officers from all three sources share equal opportunities within the Air Force.

OTS, located at Maxwell Air Force Base, Alabama, has been the most rapidly responsive source of new officers when the Air Force requires expansion—and in 2002 was operating at full capacity. Originally established to train new officers during wartime, today OTS provides a selective commissioning program for college graduates with particular academic skills. Enlisted Air Force members with the requisite qualifications are eligible to compete for OTS appointments.

In the first decade of the new century, the Air Force was annually commissioning 1,700 officers through the twelve-week OTS program. In addition to the officer candidate program, the Air Force also conducts a four-week Commissioned Officer Training program for 1,750 newly commissioned judge advocates, chaplains, and medical officers who enter the Air Force each year.

While the need for lawyers and medical officers is apparent, from time to time the question arises, "Why commission chaplains?" The answer is that the spirit of the airman requires nourishment, too. The Pledge of Allegiance states that we are "one nation under God, indivisible, with liberty and justice for all." It speaks volumes for the health of our republic that the nation has seen fit to commission chaplains of various faiths to provide for the spiritual needs of airmen.

The Reserve Officer Training Corps is the second most flexible officer source for the Air Force and offers programs for college freshmen through graduate students. Although ROTC produces officers for all career fields, it is a particularly important source of technical majors.

The ROTC four-year program is attractive to America's top high school seniors, allowing them to compete for generous scholarships to attend schools such as Duke, Georgia Tech, Georgetown, MIT, and others.

Top, left: Joint operations in the the operating room. An Air Force surgeon from the 28th Air Expeditionary Wing and a Navy physician from Naval Support Facility remove scar tissue from a patient during Operating Enduring Freedom. (USAF)

Top, right: Captain Luis Debonopaula, navigator (left) and Captain Ken Mershow, electronic warfare officer (center) from the 15th Special Operations Squadron describe the navigational system unique to the MC-130H Talon to First Lieutenant Daniel Maspero. Maspero is an Argentine air force C-130 pilot with the 1st Squadron. The American unit, from Hurlburt Field, Florida, was in Argentina to support Cabañas 2001, a multinational peacekeeping exercise that took place in Salta. (USAF)

Air Force Test Pilot school instructor Major Phil Edwards, left, prepares Lieutenant David Ramsey, a U.S. Naval Test Pilot School student, for an exchange program training sortie. (USAF)

Officer Training School fitness test. The emphasis on physical readiness does not only apply at the enlisted level. Officer trainees at Maxwell AFB, Alabama, must run a mile and a half in a specified time in order to graduate. (USAF)

Enrolled students who have begun a college curriculum are eligible to compete for admission into a one-year or two-year ROTC scholarship program. In either the one-year, two-year, or the four-year program, students enroll in Air Force ROTC classes as electives and normally receive academic credit. The aerospace studies curriculum includes courses on the organization of the Air Force, the evolution of airpower, national security strategy, management and leadership, and other subjects. Experienced Air Force officers, most with advanced degrees, teach ROTC classes.

More than 140 college campuses host Air Force ROTC detachments. The Air Force ROTC program commissions officers from the full spectrum of academic disciplines, liberal arts to engineering and computer science, and currently awards about 60 percent of scholarships to technical disciplines. When cadets complete Air Force ROTC and graduate from college, they are ready to matriculate into the officer ranks of our Air Force. These new officers provide a wealth of leadership talent.

ROTC scholarships generally cover the majority of tuition and most lab fees and book costs. ROTC contract cadets also receive a monthly stipend, which varies from $250 per month for freshmen up to $400 per month for seniors. The two-year and new one-year programs provide ROTC with better responsiveness to changing Air Force requirements. ROTC is the largest source of commissioned officers for the Air Force, commissioning more than 2,000 new officers annually.

The Air Force Academy is the third source of commissioned officers for the Air Force. From the beginning, Air Force leadership included graduates from the U.S. Military Academy at West Point, New York, or the Naval Academy in Annapolis, Maryland. Drawing heavily on the experience of these service academies, in 1954, the Air Force established its own academy in Colorado. The primary mission of the Air Force Academy is to inspire and develop outstanding young men and women to become Air Force officers with the knowledge, character, discipline, and motivation to lead the world's greatest aerospace force.

Since the first class entered in 1955, the Academy has done just that—provided motivation and inspiration, military training, and a

university-level education to graduates. The Academy requires that each cadet complete a rigorous four-year college curriculum leading to a Bachelor of Science degree in any one of twenty-nine academic majors. The core curriculum, required of all cadets, includes forty-eight semester hours in engineering and basic sciences as well as forty-one hours in humanities and social sciences. Cadets also receive instruction in aero-space studies, leadership development, and airmanship, including soaring and powered flight. Athletics are an important part of the Academy experience. Every cadet must compete at the intercollegiate or intramural level in one of approximately twenty-seven sports.

Graduates of the Academy are obligated to serve on active duty in the Air Force for a minimum of five years. In the opening decade of the 21st century, Air Force Academy alumni number more than 33,000. More than half still serve on active duty. Two Academy graduates, General Ronald Fogleman and General Mike Ryan became Air Force Chiefs of Staff. Thirty-one Air Force Academy graduates have been selected as Rhodes Scholars.

Most newly commissioned Air Force officers from OTS, ROTC, or the Air Force Academy immediately enter a technical training program such as aircraft maintenance officer school, or space and missile operations training. Approximately 1,600 new lieutenants enter flight training each year. A few new officers with appropriate college degrees go directly to one of the less technical operational assignments in the Air Force like administration or public affairs.

The breath-taking architecture of the Air Force Academy Chapel remains an inspiration for Academy graduates long after their days as cadets. (USAF)

Well-deserved smiles abound at the Air Force Academy graduation ceremony. The sight of women graduating has been a welcome part of this special day for over 25 years. (USAF)

275

United States Air Force Academy

Colonel Mark K. Wells, USAF

From the moment a young man or woman first arrives, the Air Force Academy challenges them with an extraordinarily demanding program of academics, athletics, character development, and military training. Most are not prepared for the intense stress, relentless physical challenge, and broad-ranging academic curriculum they face over the next four years. That so many succeed, and do so with such astonishing levels of performance, is a remarkable tribute to the nation's young people.

A period called Basic Cadet Training, or "Beast," largely defines a new cadet's first six weeks at the Academy. Starting at dawn and extending into the hours of darkness each day, these new cadets are transformed from civilians to members of the armed forces. This task is largely the responsibility of cadet upperclassmen, advised and supervised by commissioned officers and Air Force NCOs. Focusing on discipline, followership, Air Force organization, heritage, customs, and culture, training takes place both in the cadet area and outdoors in a military training area called "Jack's Valley." Cadets face and overcome daunting mental, physical, and emotional challenges throughout this inaugural period.

Military training—a structured program requiring cadets to practice leadership skills in a controlled leadership laboratory—continues from the moment new cadets arrive until they throw their hats into the air at graduation. Over four years, cadets progress through responsibilities roughly analogous to those of airman, noncommissioned officer, junior officer, and commander. Military training also encompasses airmanship programs, including soaring, parachuting, and power-flight. Nothing so much distinguishes a cadet and makes him or her proud as winning and wearing badges of airmanship qualification.

Not long after acceptance into the Cadet Wing, new cadets collectively acknowledge their acceptance of the tenets of the Cadet Honor Code. By promising that

"We will not lie, steal, or cheat, nor tolerate among us anyone who does," cadets underscore their firm commitment to the bedrock of the Academy's character development program and spiritually join thousands of their predecessors, accepting their own individual obligation to personal integrity. This is no easy thing for young people, especially in an era of morale relativism and libertarianism. Yet, most cadets measure up. Not surprisingly, years later, graduates cite the Cadet Honor Code as the most important core value they take from their Academy experience.

Cadets are proud of the Academy's academic reputation and repeatedly identify it as the number one reason they came to the institution. Classes are small, numbering about twenty cadets. Each cadet is expected to engage intellectually with the instructor and fellow students in courses ranging from military history to quantum physics—from civil engineering to military law. With a core curriculum of eighty-nine semester hours in basic and engineering sciences along with humanities and social sciences, plus additional courses for an academic major, the overall program demands much from those who hope to succeed.

A typical academic day starts with a 5:30 wake-up, 6:30 breakfast, and classroom instruction that begins at 7:30 and extends well into the late afternoon. The cadet schedule also includes a noon-meal formation, military training periods, physical education classes, and intramural or intercollegiate athletic practice. Dinner, administrative duties, and class preparation typically occupy cadet evenings past 11:00 p.m.

The final pillar of the Academy experience is athletics. The overall goal of athletics is to encourage graduates to make a life-long commitment to physical fitness. Year-round, cadets engage in seemingly endless intramural sports, physical education, recreational

activities, or intercollegiate sports. The roads and trails that wind around the imposing granite, steel, and aluminum edifices of the Academy cadet area are dotted with runners. Varsity teams compete at the NCAA Division I level against some of the top schools in the nation in football, ice hockey, basketball, baseball, soccer, track, lacrosse, wrestling, golf, gymnastics, and swimming.

In peace and war, graduates of the Air Force Academy serve the nation with distinction. Their record measures the success of the institution. One graduate, Captain Lance P. Sijan, earned the Medal of Honor posthumously for extraordinary heroism while a captive of the North Vietnamese. When his biographer asked about the people and institutions that had forged Captain Sijan's character, he was told, "Go to the Academy. You'll see where Lance learned his sense of duty." That sense of duty demands that each individual cadet meet very high character, military, athletic, and academic standards—standards the nation requires of an officer corps entrusted to lead the United States Air Force.

Above: Celebration and tradition. Academy cadets toss their hats into the air at the conclusion of the Air Force Academy graduation ceremony. (USAF)

Middle: A cadet crawls under a barbed wire entanglement on the assault course at the Academy. All first-year cadets go through two weeks of field training in nearby Jack's Valley as part of their summer basic cadet training program. (USAF)

Left: Capt. Allan W. Howey, an instructor at the Air Force Academy, teaches the finer points of history. (USAF)

Air Force Chaplains

Major Steven A. Schaick, USAF

As a little boy growing up in Oshkosh, Wisconsin, all I ever wanted to do was fly. All my hopes and dreams were packaged in the majesty of flight. As a young man, flying taught me that life is about seeing and believing— a union of fact and mystery. Flying invited me to trust, to obey, to believe. Flying led me to the chaplaincy.

Having been ordained and commissioned, I discovered that Air Force chaplains wear many hats. Job number one is to ensure the free exercise of religion. Additionally, we preach, teach, counsel, and contribute as we can to the spiritual and moral health of Air Force members and their families. While stationed in Blytheville, Arkansas, my congregation consisted of B-52 and KC-135 crewmembers and maintainers. I laughed with many and cried with some. I married a few—I buried a few. And when the 97th got an invitation to participate in the Gulf war, their chaplain went too. On the morning of February 3, 1991, one of our B-52s crashed in the Indian Ocean. My next three days were in solitary confinement with the survivors. We prayed together, we cried together. We told stories—some funny, some tragic. And God showed up, put his arms around us, and convinced us that we were not alone.

I don't know a chaplain who really believes he or she is qualified to do their job. Each of us represents a distinct religious expression while serving a highly diverse population. We wrestle with providing meaningful ministry to those in deployed locations and to the service members, civilians and family members who stay home. At our best, we encourage the weary, caution the conceited, and provide a compass heading for all who seek what is right. At our best, we help commanders take care of people. And for this chaplain, there is no greater honor.

Top, left: Final march. A funeral detail carrying a flag-draped coffin slowly marches through Arlington National Cemetery. (USAF)

Above: High honor. An Air Force chaplain presents the American Flag to the family of a deceased airman. (USAF)

Left: Prayerful moment. An Air Force chaplain prays with a pilot on the flight line. (USAF)

Flying Training

The Air Force sets very high standards for entry into flight training and for graduation with an aeronautical rating of pilot or navigator. Candidates are screened using aptitude tests, physical exams, and flight simulators. Initial screening assures that the young officer selected for flight training has a reasonable chance to complete the program and receive Air Force wings.

For pilot training, the screening process includes a physical fitness test and initial in-flight instruction at civilian flying training programs around the country, where prospective USAF pilots are required to earn their private pilot's license. Then the fledgling pilot enters formal Air Force flight training. After completing undergraduate pilot training, the new pilot receives specialty training in fighters, bombers, transport aircraft, or helicopters. To be successful, the Air Force pilot must exhibit three attributes. These could be called the gifts for flying. The first is hand-eye coordination, the second is the ability to prioritize multiple tasks, and the third and most telling is a stomach for combat. You can have the best hand-eye coordination in the world and keen situational awareness but without courage, you cannot perform in high threat environments.

While Air Force navigators are less dependent on hand-eye coordination, they must possess courage, the ability to prioritize multiple tasks, and sound mathematical skills. To survive and be effective in combat, both pilots and navigators must have a warrior spirit. In the opening years of the 21st century, of the 1,600 officers entering flight training annually, approximately 1,100 pilots, and 360 navigators graduated.

The Air Force conducts primary pilot training in T-37 aircraft at Sheppard AFB and Laughlin Air Force Base, Texas; Vance Air Force Base, Oklahoma; and Columbus Air Force Base, Mississippi. Student pilots who successfully complete primary training go on to one of four advanced training

Four Northrop T-38 Talon trainers in formation as part of the basic undergraduate pilot training for those selected for assignments in bombers and fighters. Student pilots learn precision formation flying, including aerobatics, before they receive their wings. (USAF)

T-37B trainers lined up for the next "class" at Laughlin AFB, Texas. (USAF)

The Raytheon T-6A Texan II will replace the T-37Bs as the primary Air Force pilot training aircraft. A single engine turboprop aircraft, the Texan is fitted with a zero altitude, zero airspeed ejection seat and has a maximum speed of 368 miles per hour. The U.S. Navy is also adopting the Texan as a primary flight trainer. (USAF)

Crewmen from a Lockheed C-130 Airborne Command, Control, and Communications (ABCCC) aircraft discuss the next mission. Effective communication in the air and on the ground is essential for all personnel. (USAF)

Prior to arrival over the drop zone, the cockpit of this C-130 is all business as the pilot briefs his intentions to the copilot and navigator. Each member of this team has unique responsibilities that can spell the difference between success and failure—and sometimes, between life and death. (USAF)

Above: *The Raytheon T-1 Jayhawk trainer is a medium range twin engine jet transport version of the Beechcraft 400A used to train students to fly airlift, tanker, and bomber aircraft. It has a maximum speed of 538 miles per hour and a range of 2,400 miles. (USAF)*

Right: *A T-37 instructor pilot and his student discuss the day's sortie. The trust between flight instructor and student is a two-way relationship. (USAF)*

tracks leading to an operational assignment flying transports or tankers, bombers or fighters, multi-engine turboprops, or helicopters. During the yearlong flying program, student pilots fly about 200 hours. At the completion of advanced training, students graduate with the aeronautical rating of pilot and go on to specialized qualification training in specific aircraft.

The Air Force conducts undergraduate navigator training jointly with the Navy at Randolph Air Force Base, Texas, and at Naval Air Station Pensacola in Florida. After navigators receive their wings, they go to specialized training in specific aircraft such as C-130s, F-15Es, or B-1s.

Officer Training and Education

In the first twenty years of an Air Force career, most officers will spend more than four years attending specialized technical training or flight training, as well as professional military education. After acquiring operational experience, many officers will spend another two or three years teaching in one of the Air Force schools. Education and training is a continuous process because technology and employment strategies continue to evolve. More than half of all newly commissioned officers immediately enter a specialized technical training program designed to prepare them for a career in space or missile command and control, aircraft or missile maintenance, communications, intelligence, civil engineering, or some other non-flying specialty. Training time to achieve initial qualification in these technical specialties may last only a few months, followed by operational experience and additional training for advanced qualification.

Technical training and flight training are intended to teach skills required to perform specific tasks and missions. Professional military education, on the other hand, is intended to educate officers in service and joint doctrine, and to develop the critical judgment required to direct or support combat operations.

Professional Military Education

We train managers and educate leaders. Basic officer skills of leadership and management are developed through resident, seminar, and correspondence programs sponsored by Air University at Maxwell Air Force Base, Alabama. Air University programs emphasize leadership, communication skills, military doctrine, and the development and application of air and space power. The Air and Space Basic Course (ASBC) is a four-week program for second lieutenants and selected civilians to introduce fundamental concepts of air and space employment. ASBC's mission is to inspire new USAF officers to comprehend their roles as airmen, live by our core values, articulate and demonstrate our core competencies, and dedicate themselves as warriors. Squadron Officer School is a five-week program for captains that instructs young officers at the tactical level of war and develops dynamic leaders committed to the profession of arms.

Air Command and Staff College (ACSC) is the intermediate professional military education school that teaches officers to be successful at the operational level of war. ACSC educates officers to lead in developing, employing, commanding, and supporting air and space power across the spectrum of service, joint, and combined operations. Along with Air Force officers, ACSC classes include officers from the other services, government employees, and foreign military officers.

Advanced learning: future instructor pilots take notes and listen intently at Randolph AFB, Texas. The role of a flight instructor is intense and demanding, requiring the skills of both an expert pilot and a gifted teacher. (USAF)

Air War College is the senior service school that teaches joint operations and employment of air and space power in support of national security. Its mission is to educate senior officers to lead at the strategic level of war. Students from all four services attend the war college, as do Air Force

281

Officers in the classroom. Academic instruction does not stop at the undergraduate level. Post-graduate studies are encouraged, and reflected in the nearly 60 percent rate of officers holding either a master's or professional degree. (USAF)

civilians and personnel from various government agencies. The student body also includes foreign students from allied and friendly nations.

At the intermediate and senior service levels, to foster increased understanding and cooperation between the Air Force, Army, Navy, Marines, and armed forces of allied nations, selected officers attend professional military training schools operated by a sister service or the Joint Chiefs of Staff. Unlike the service-related schools, joint schools such as the Joint Forces Staff College, the Industrial College of the Armed Forces, and the National War College feature a balanced faculty and curriculum that emphasize the integrated employment of all services rather than the particular strengths of any one service.

Postgraduate Education

In addition to technical training and professional military education, the Air Force officer is challenged to pursue graduate studies. The Air Force Institute of Technology (AFIT) at Wright-Patterson Air Force Base, Ohio, stands out as the beacon for aerospace research and study. AFIT opened in 1919. Since then, it has educated more than 300,000 military and civilian personnel, awarding undergraduate and graduate academic degrees in disciplines such as aeronautical engineering, applied mathematics, and engineering physics.

The School of Engineering is but one of the academic settings, and disciplines, offered at the Air Force institute of Technology (AFIT) at Wright-Patterson AFB, Ohio. The program sponsors degrees at the top universities in the country. Officers desiring advanced degrees can also apply to attend civilian universities. (USAF)

The Air Force also sends officers to graduate-level programs at civilian colleges and universities nationwide. The results are that our officer corps is one of the most educated in the world. Nearly 60 percent have either a master's degree or a professional degree. Some 1,400 hold earned doctoral degrees. As technology advances, the requirement for education increases. The officer corps is constantly developing and adapting to changing national security needs and rapidly changing technology.

Special Operations in Afghanistan

Technical Sergeant Calvin, USAF

Military planners estimated that it would take until spring 2002 to defeat the Taliban forces in Afghanistan. They underestimated the effectiveness of airpower. As part of a small U.S. Special Forces team, I entered Afghanistan in late October 2001 near the Panjshir Valley where stagnant battle lines had divided Taliban and Northern Alliance forces for nearly three years. Our mission was simple: help the Northern Alliance break through Taliban lines and liberate Kabul.

I was the only Air Force combat air controller on the ground in Afghanistan. On the third night, from a 10,000 foot mountain ridge, we spotted a Taliban camp. After I visually identified, selected, and confirmed the target, I called for an air strike—the first ground-directed air strike of Operation Enduring Freedom. It would be the first of many.

During the next twenty-five days, I made hundreds of air strike calls and Northern Alliance troops gained ground. For sixteen years, I had trained for a mission like this—one that tested all my skills as a combat controller. We made textbook progress until the twenty-fifth day. Then the enemy struck back.

Our team was on top of a building when we came under intense gunfire—including antiaircraft artillery fire. I grabbed the radio, called for any available aircraft, and slid off the roof. As I did so, a Northern Alliance officer pounced on top of me, shielding me from enemy fire. Later, through an interpreter, I found out why. He said that if something happened to him, someone else would step in to take his place. If something happened to me, the planes could not come.

Navy and Air Force fighters and bombers did come, and the offensive continued. Our team moved into Bagram. After Northern Alliance forces cleared the Bagram Airfield, I surveyed and opened the airfield for military operations and for aircraft delivering humanitarian aid from international non-government agencies. Then we moved on to Kabul.

After ensuring the city was secure, our team headed directly to the American Embassy, which had been closed since 1989. Inside, the first thing I noticed was the American flag, crumpled on top of a pile of straw where someone had tried to burn it. I walked over, picked it up, and saw that the flag was soiled but intact. We carefully folded our flag and felt proud of what we had accomplished for America.

In Afghanistan Air Force combat controllers combine the ancient with the modern. This combat controller rides horseback to an observation point where he will employ the latest satellite communications technology to direct air strikes in support of Operation Enduring Freedom. (USAF)

The Total Force

Today, it would be impossible for the active-duty Air Force to meet all of its assigned responsibilities without the participation of the Air National Guard, the Air Force Reserve, and the Air Force civilian workforce. Air National Guard and Air Force Reserve forces account for 100 percent of the air defense mission, 64 percent of our total tactical airlift capability, 55 percent of our aerial refueling capability, 38 percent of our tactical fighter strength, and 27 percent of our strategic airlift. The Guard and Reserve are trained and equipped as equals to the active duty force and routinely deploy side by side with active duty personnel.

Two Lockheed HC-130P pilots from the 129th Rescue Wing practice low altitude terrain following at dusk. Flying HC-130s or helicopters, rescue crewmembers often risk their lives to rescue downed crews in wartime and to aid victims of peacetime disasters. (USAF)

The men and women of the Air National Guard number approximately 108,000 and are part of the militia tradition that dates back to before the American Revolution. They augment the active duty Air Force by participating in operations and exercises worldwide. They are unique in that Air National Guard forces are commanded by the governors of the fifty states, Puerto Rico, Guam, the Virgin Islands, and the commanding general of the District of Columbia National Guard. Primary responsibilities of the Air National Guard include combat and airlift missions, air rescue, refueling, and special operations.

The people of the Air Force Reserve Command (AFRC) are known as Citizen Airmen. Their mission is to provide trained units and individual personnel to accomplish assigned tasking in the support of national objectives. Major mission categories include fighter, bomber, air refueling, airlift, and space operations. Today's Air Force Reserve numbers approximately 140,000 people.

A crew member from the 28th Air Expeditionary Wing prepares a 2,000-pound bomb for loading into a B1-B bomber during Operation Enduring Freedom. (USAF)

Air Force Reserve Command, with headquarters at Robins Air Force Base, Georgia, is organized into three numbered Air Forces; the Fourth located at March Air Reserve Base, California; the Tenth located at Naval Air Station Fort Worth Texas; and the Twenty-Second located at Dobbins Air Reserve Base Georgia.

In the wake of the terrorist attack against the United States in September 2001, Guard and Reserve forces assumed major new air defense responsibilities. Unlike active duty forces, most Guard and Reserve units are located near large population centers for the convenience of these part-time warriors. Consequently, many Guard and Reserve fighter squadrons were ideally located to provide combat air patrols over New York, Washington, Denver, and other American cities. Air National Guard F-15s and F-16s, along with Air Force Reserve F-16s began patrolling American skies around the clock in September 2001. As conditions stabilized and fewer airborne patrols were required, Guard and Reserve pilots sat ground alert, prepared to scramble, intercept, and escort or destroy any aircraft that showed hostile intent. The successful undertaking of this new mission further reflects the total integration of Guard and Reserve units into the Air Force.

These Air Force airmen, reenlisting in a ceremony conducted in the Pentagon less than a week after terrorists attempted to destroy the building, represent the diversity, the commitment, and the intensity that marks service in the United States Air Force as a very special career and a very special way of life. (USAF)

The Air Force employs more than 140,000 civilian workers. With an average length of service in excess of sixteen years, many fill key positions, providing the long-term stability needed to complement the more dynamic mobility of active duty Air Force personnel. You will find these dedicated public servants in jobs at base level, at major command

headquarters, and in the Pentagon. They are particularly concentrated in Air Force Materiel Command, where more than 58,000 play a vital role in acquisition and logistics.

Air Force civilians perform day-to-day and long-range activities to manage the integrated research, development, test, acquisition, and sustainment of our weapons systems. In many cases, they represent a depth of specialized knowledge and corporate memory that is an essential stabilizing force. Like the active duty force, the civilian work force is organized hierarchically with some 164 designated as Senior Executive Service (SES). Members of the SES typically fill senior staff and policy positions at headquarters locations.

Industry at work: A C-130J production line in Marietta, Georgia. The military-industry partnership has played a key part in enabling American forces to lead the way around the world. (USAF)

The Public-Private Partnership

No examination of the human factor would be complete without acknowledging the public-private partnership between our Air Force and the men and women employed by the nation's defense contractors. These dedicated citizens have been there from the beginning, on the assembly lines of Douglas, Curtiss, Fairchild, and other contractors that have faded from the defense landscape. Today they work for Boeing, Lockheed Martin, Northrop Grumman, Raytheon, and others. They are professionals in what they do—designing and building the systems that equip and protect our airmen when they are called upon to go in harm's way.

The responsibilities and dedicated service of the men and women employed by defense contractors does not end when the aircraft or the radar rolls off the production line at Boeing or Raytheon or elsewhere. Contractor teams frequently accompany weapons systems into operational deployment, and occasionally into combat, to assure that systems work properly. It is not uncommon for a flight crew returning from a mission

Diane Perasso demonstrates new capabilities of the Theater Battle Management Core Systems software package for General Lester Lyles, commander of Air Force Materiel Command, and others after the ribbon-cutting ceremony for the experimental combined aerospace operations center at Langley Air Force Base, Virginia. (USAF)

Air Force in Film

Lieutenant Colonel Jeffrey C. Prater, USAF (Ret)

The Air Force story encompasses far more than official studies, combat footage, or oral testimony. In reality, it has enjoyed a symbiotic relationship with American popular culture—particularly in motion pictures. Historical fidelity has prospered when filmmakers and actors shared meaningful associations with the military, and when screenwriters and novelists could call upon their own martial experiences.

The motion picture industry and military aviation, historic contemporaries, quickly established a close relationship. In 1927, former Lafayette Escadrille pilot William Wellman directed Wings, the first Hollywood film to receive an Academy Award for Best Picture. By 1938, many studios were receiving support from the Army Air Corps (AAC); Victor Fleming used March Field, California, to film YB-17 sequences for Test Pilot. In 1941, Randolph Field, Texas, hosted Paramount's filming of I Wanted Wings (based on Beirne Lay's best-selling novel).

The year 1943 gave us Air Force, a film suggested by Army Air Forces (AAF) commanding general "Hap" Arnold, and directed by World War I aviator Howard Hawks. That same year, Walt Disney shot the animated version of Major Alexander P. de Seversky's book, Victory Through Air Power. In 1944, Spencer Tracey portrayed Lieutenant Colonel James Doolittle in Thirty Seconds Over Tokyo.

In 1948, Air Force and Air National Guard assistance allowed Fighter Squadron to relate the exploits of European P-47s, and Clark Gable starred in Command Decision, a film based on the Broadway play by former Eighth Air Force officer William Wister Haines. Based on the novel by former AAF officers Major Sy Bartlett and Colonel Beirne Lay, Twelve O'Clock High (1949), captured the drama of B-17 operations over Europe.

As the Cold War intensified, Hollywood and the Air Force emphasized strategic nuclear themes. Footage shot at March Air Force Base, California, helped illustrate the development and employment of the B-29 Superfortress in Wild Blue Yonder (1952). The exploits of the "Enola Gay" and her crew were featured in Above and Beyond (1953), based on the original screenplay by Beirne Lay. Strategic Air Command (1955) depicted SAC in the 1950s, and starred James Stewart, former B-24 pilot and future Air Force Reserve brigadier general. Perhaps the best representation of SAC in the 1960s was A Gathering of Eagles (1963), shot with Air Force assistance at Beale Air Force Base, California.

If the Air Force story is indeed an amalgam of facts and cultural fictions, the better fictions have been those afforded official support and informed by personal experience. Air Force personnel continue to support Hollywood today, armed with the knowledge of our past and a vision of the future of aerospace power.

Top: Future Air Force Reserve brigadier general Jimmy Stewart portrays a professional baseball player and B-36 aircraft commander in Warner Bros. 1955 film, *Strategic Air Command.*

Left: Warner Bros. skillfully captured the early days of the Pacific war in *Air Force* (1943). The cast included (l to r) Charles Drake, John Garfield, Gig Young, Harry Carey, Moroni Olsen, George Tobias, and Stanley Ridges.

employing a new weapons system to be met by an Air Force maintenance team as well as a contractor support team—both teams equally concerned about mission accomplishment and the correction of any problems the crew encountered.

Quality of Life and Service

The United States Air Force was born of technology. Today, as always, the key to a strong Air Force is the retention of skilled airmen and civilians who understand that technology. Our retention of these experienced professionals now and in the future depends on providing them adequate compensation and an employment environment that includes fair treatment, equal promotion opportunities, first-rate training, equipment, and work facilities. For them and their families, we must provide adequate housing, medical care, educational opportunities, and recreational facilities. We call this basket of requirements quality-of-life issues, and they are a high priority for Air Force leaders at every level because we know that retention of trained and experienced men and women is critical to the defense of this nation. It takes many years to replace the technical sergeant, the major, or the mid-level civilian manager who leaves the Air Force for career opportunities outside the service.

We ask for their total loyalty to the Air Force mission. In return, we can offer a quality of life that assures a reasonable level of comfort and security for them and their families. In the end, it is patriotism, a personally felt sense of mission, camaraderie, and quality of service that motivates airmen in the United States Air Force.

Let me conclude this chapter with a personal note. I was inspired every day of my thirty-five years in the Air Force to be among so many people working for high purpose. I felt privileged to serve along side each of them in the profession of arms. It is an honor to be an airman.

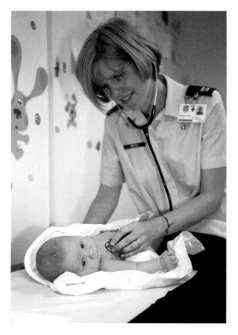

Capt (Dr.) Christine Nefey, a primary care physician, checks-up on five-week-old Nicholas Raiken at Lakenheath Air Base, United Kingdom. The level of care and quality of life for airmen and their families is paramount to the Air Force. (USAF)

Bottom, left: *A member of the 128th Air Refueling Wing, Wisconsin Air National Guard, arrives home to greet his family upon return from Operation Enduring Freedom. (USAF)*

Bottom, right: *A collective hug. An airman from the 305th Air Mobility Wing returns from Operation Enduring Freedom to his waiting family. (USAF)*

Research, Development, Acquisition & Logistics

General Ronald W. Yates, USAF (Ret)

The talented and committed people who serve in the United States Air Force are our most precious resource. They stand ready, every day, to risk their lives in defense of this nation. The nation owes them the very best equipment that American industry can produce so they can perform their job effectively and with minimum risk. This chapter describes how the men and women of the Air Force Material Command (AFMC) deliver and sustain the weapons systems and the technology needed by our fighting forces. The command—and every individual in it—takes this responsibility very seriously.

The Air Force Material Command is responsible for integrated research, development, test, and acquisition of weapons systems and equipment required by the Air Force. After weapons systems are fielded, AFMC provides operational support during the useful life of the system, then disposition of systems after they are withdrawn from service. Thus, AFMC has cradle-to-grave responsibility for the equipment used by today's modern aerospace forces. These responsibilities start with the basic science that is only a gleam in a scientist's eye. Then the command turns these ideas into engineering realities and helps industry produce the equipment needed to arm our fighting forces in the field. AFMC supplies airmen with everything from communion wafers to satellites, from ICBMs to stealthy aircraft.

More than 90,000 people are employed in these varied missions, including 26,000 active duty personnel and nearly 6,000 members of the Air National Guard (ANG) and the Air Force Reserve (AFR). The command is the home of over 7,000 Air Force scientific and engineering experts. Nearly

Top: *The McKinley Climatic Laboratory at Eglin AFB, Florida, produces environmental extremes under controlled conditions to test military weapon systems like this early model B-52. (USAF)*

Above: *Master Sergeant Todd Green, Joint Close Air Support team member, loads firing schedules into a database recorder during a live-fire exercise. The Electronic Systems Center at Hanscom AFB, Massachusetts, provides communications infrastructure to frontline units for use on the battlefield. Hanscom's Theater Deployable Communications program office provides communications equipment such as computers, telephone switches, satellite terminals, and radios. (USAF)*

Opposite: *An F-15E Strike Eagle of the 46th Test Wing, Eglin AFB, Florida, launches a GBU-15 precision-guided munition on Eglin's weapons test range. The 46th Test Wing is responsible for developmental flight-testing of all air-to-air and air-to-ground weapons in the Air Force inventory. (USAF)*

Airman 1st Class Ronnie Brickey, an Explosive Ordnance Disposal apprentice with the 48th Civil Engineering Squadron at Royal Air Force Lakenheath, United Kingdom, operates the MK III RONS Robotics system. The RONS Robotics system is an all-terrain, tracked vehicle with manipulator arm and TV cameras for remote investigation, handling, and disposal of explosive materials. (USAF)

60,000 civilians—more than 40 percent of all civilians in the Air Force—work for AFMC.

To accomplish its broad and diverse responsibilities, the command is organized into functional centers for oversight of specialized tasks. The activities of these centers are concentrated at thirteen bases in ten states. From headquarters at Wright-Patterson AFB, Ohio, the commander of AFMC directs the activities of four major product centers, two test centers, three air logistics centers, two specialized centers, and one laboratory.

Basic Research in Science and Technology

The Air Force invests in science and technology because experience has taught us that it is necessary if we are to keep our fighting forces dominant in combat. General Hap Arnold said, "The first essential of airpower is pre-eminence in research," and Air Force history has proven him correct. The Air Force funds science and technology in coordination with the other Services and the Defense Advanced Research Projects Agency. Air Force funding is applied to research with potential application to military needs of our warfighting commands. AFMC keeps the Air Force on the cutting edge of technology by sponsoring research in colleges and universities, in many U.S. industries, and in the Air Force Research Laboratory (AFRL).

Air Force research is recognized throughout the world as first-rate. Through the years, the Air Force has sponsored the work of thirty-eight Nobel Prize winners. The AFRL sponsored the work of Nobel Laureates in medicine, chemistry, and physics. Jack Kilby, of Texas Instruments, won the 2000 Nobel Prize in physics for inventing the integrated circuit. Mr. Kilby gave credit to the Air Force for supporting his initial work on integrated circuit concepts. His research not only transformed the Air Force, but our society as well.

There are numerous instances where Air Force technologies have transferred to the civil sector and directly benefited industry. For example,

Above: *This Convair NC-131H operated by Air Force Research Laboratory's Air Vehicles Directorate provided a total in-flight simulator for early work on a fault-tolerant digital airborne data system. (USAF)*

Right: *Air Force engineers use computational fluid dynamics prediction modeling to analyze airflow entering an F-15 engine inlet. The model is flying at mach 0.6 with a 30-degree angle of attack and a 10-degree angle of sideslip. (USAF)*

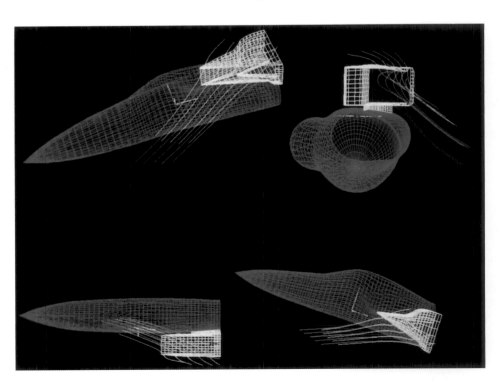

290

the Air Force funded much of the pioneering work on the computer mouse developed at Xerox's Palo Alto Research Center. Almost all commercial aircraft engines trace their heritage to military research, and close cooperation between AFRL and the propulsion industry continues today. AFRL research into composite materials for aircraft and spacecraft led to a more general use of composites across our economy in auto parts and sports equipment such as golf clubs, tennis racquets, and fishing rods.

In general, technologies requiring large up-front investments and many years to mature and pay back that investment are difficult for industry to fund. A clear example is the materials research that has been so critical to both airframe and spacecraft development and propulsion advances. In this field, as in others, Air Force research benefited domestic industry. In turn, our nation is benefited and maintains a more competitive posture with foreign industries that often are directly subsidized by their governments.

The Air Force Materiel Command attracts unique individuals whose special talents and interests set them above their peers. We send them to

Arnold Engineering Development Center at Arnold AFB, Tennessee, provides government and industry with the world's largest array of aerospace ground test and evaluation facilities and capabilities. The center maintains a $7.3 billion infrastructure consisting of fifty-eight aerospace test and flight simulation facilities. This photograph shows a compressor and supersonic wind tunnel circuit at the Center. (USAF)

America's best universities for advanced degrees in science, technology, and management. We familiarize them with problems our fighting forces face and expose them, first-hand, to those problems in the field. In turn, they apply science and engineering to find solutions to make our warfighting forces more effective and safer. We motivate them to stay with our Air Force and to serve their country in a unique capacity critical to our national survival. These Air Force scientists and engineers create the leading-edge technology that keeps our warfighting forces ahead of the rest of the world. They are the "secret sauce" in our recipe for future air dominance wherever the Air Force may be called on to protect our national interests.

The Air Force Research Laboratory

The Air Force Research Laboratory (AFRL) manages all science and technology research for the Air Force whether or not that research is conducted within AFRL. In addition, AFRL is responsible for evaluating and buying commercial and university technologies that may benefit the Air Force. To accomplish these tasks, AFRL employs approximately 8,400 government and non-government personnel—many with PhDs and advanced degrees in science and technology. The Air Force Laboratory is funded at approximately $2.75 billon per year.

The AFRL mission is to lead the discovery, development, and integration of affordable war-fighting technologies for aerospace forces. AFRL, with

Above: Inside Arnold Engineering Development Center's sixteen-foot supersonic wind tunnel, vertical turning vanes guide airflow around corners in the tunnel's closed-circuit tunnels. Panels on the walls of the supersonic circuit contain insulation. Air in the circuit sometimes reaches 650 degrees Fahrenheit during tests. (USAF)

Opposite, center right: The NAVSTAR Global Positioning System (GPS) is a constellation of orbiting satellites providing twenty-four-hour navigation services, including accurate three-dimensional location information (latitude, longitude, and altitude) to an unlimited number of users. GPS satellites emit continuous signals accurate to within a millionth of a second. NAVSTAR is currently undergoing dramatic modernization changes to its architecture to create a new military-only signal that will provide increased security, higher accuracy, and improved targeting capability. (USAF)

Opposite, bottom left: Wind tunnel tests at Arnold Engineering Development Center provide information helpful in eliminating or controlling vehicle instability. Here engineers test a wind tunnel model for a long-range strike aircraft. (USAF)

Opposite, bottom right: Arnold Engineering Development Center engineers first tested the Patriot missile in the 1960s. At that time, the Patriot had only a generic name—SAM D—and was not yet part of the U.S. Army inventory. (USAF)

headquarters at Wright-Patterson AFB, Ohio, accomplishes its mission through nine Technology Directorates and the Air Force Office of Scientific Research (AFOSR). These Technology Directorates are generally collocated with significant AFMC laboratory facilities, although additional research sites and laboratory facilities are located at other installations around the United States and overseas.

The Air Force Office of Scientific Research is located in Arlington, Virginia. Responsible for managing basic science research for the Air Force Research Laboratory, AFOSR invests in long-term research related to aerospace science and engineering. Nearly 80 percent of this research is conducted in academia and industry, with the remaining 20 percent conducted in AFRL. AFOSR maintains a worldwide exchange program for scientists and engineers and is sponsoring basic research in plasma aerodynamics, shape memory alloys, all-nitrogen rocket fuel, agile laser protection, micro satellites, quantum computers, and many other revolutionary scientific concepts.

The Air Vehicles Directorate, located at Wright-Patterson AFB, Ohio, concentrates on technologies that support cost-effective, survivable, aerospace vehicles. The core technology areas of engineers in this directorate include aeronautical sciences, control sciences, structures, and integration. They developed fly-by-wire technologies that control most modern military and commercial airplanes in the sky today. The directorate is focused on developing vehicle technologies that increase capabilities in aircraft sustainment, unmanned air vehicles, space access, and strike missions.

The advent of Unmanned Air Vehicles (UAV's) and the mission capabilities these new aircraft possess pose new challenges for aircraft control, reliability, and affordability. While the directorate introduces new technologies for these air vehicles, it also develops more affordable lifting vehicles for space.

Working in concert with the Air Vehicles Directorate, the Materials and Manufacturing Directorate develops new materials and manufacturing technologies for use in aircraft, spacecraft, missiles, rockets, and ground-based systems. This Wright-Patterson AFB directorate also has responsibility for structural, electronic, and optical components and provides quick-reaction

Above: *This aerial view of Arnold Engineering Development Center shows some of the world-class test and evaluation facilities used by Air Force and industry engineers in the design of aircraft and spacecraft for the future. (USAF)*

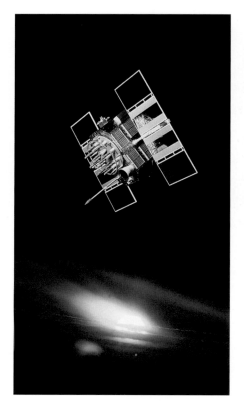

This photograph shows wind tunnel tests of a Boeing ABL-1 Airborne Laser aircraft model. In addition to military aircraft and spacecraft, many commercial aircraft are also tested in the several one-of-a-kind wind tunnels at the Arnold Engineering Development Center. (Boeing)

Technical Sergeant Robert Huffnagel from the 35th Maintenance Squadron, Misawa Air Base, Japan, closely monitors an F-16 aircraft engine on afterburner during operations in an engine test cell. (USAF)

support to solve materials related problems. The Materials and Manufacturing Directorate develops manufacturing process technologies as well as computer-integrated manufacturing and design for military needs. In addition to the creative work in composites and stealth technologies, the directorate has developed many of the materials that define military and commercial airframes, spacecraft, and jet engines today. Engineers and scientists engaged in this work are among the foremost experts in the nation on metals, composites, ceramics, sensor materials, laser hardened materials, polymers, and coatings.

The Propulsion Directorate is responsible for nearly all aspects of power technology, including air and space vehicle propulsion. The directorate has developed propulsion systems for aircraft, space launch vehicles, orbit transfer engines, in-orbit spacecraft, air launched missiles, and ICBM's. Assigned engineers have also played an important role in the Air Force's directed energy program as well as advances in fuels and lubricants, batteries and thermal power management, and megawatt-class power systems.

The Human Effectiveness Directorate concentrates on technologies for training personnel, the interface between people and weapons systems, and protection of Air Force people in hostile environments. The directorate has focused on night vision training, information systems training, and distributed mission training—allowing people in simulators from around the world to train together as if they were side-by-side. Engineers working on crew system interfaces have produced new visual displays, aural displays, and bioacoustics that integrate data from a wide variety of sensors and present it to the war fighter for timely and accurate decision. This directorate is also responsible for chemical and biological defense and for determining how crews can sustain operations for extremely long durations.

Engineers in the Space Vehicles Directorate are responsible for spacecraft structures and control, launch vehicle structures, and micro-satellite concepts and technologies. In order to protect U.S. space systems, they focus on space hazard warning and mitigation, ionospheric specification and forecasting, background clutter prediction, detection and decision aids, and threat warning and attack reporting. In the area of spacecraft payloads, they focus on radiation-hardened microelectronics, space based sensing, including space infrared technologies, and space antenna technologies. They also work on autonomous spacecraft maneuvering and balloon and satellite flight experiments.

The Directed Energy Directorate is the center of expertise for laser development within the Department of Defense. Work in this directorate includes the development of high-power microwaves, lasers, adaptive optics, imaging, and effects. The people in this directorate are responsible for keeping the Air Force in the lead in laser-guided weapons and in the use of the laser itself as a weapon. The Air Force has transitioned laser technology from this directorate into the Airborne Laser project—the installation on a Boeing 747 of a powerful laser capable of destroying an Intercontinental Ballistic Missile (ICBM) shortly after launch. In addition to creating the laser, the directorate pioneered work to precisely steer and point the laser and to compensate for atmospheric disturbances that it will encounter when it is fired. The directorate is responsible for high power microwave research for both electronic attack and active non-lethal denial.

The Munitions Directorate, located at Eglin AFB Florida, is responsible for developing, demonstrating, and transitioning science and technology into air-launched munitions to defeat fixed ground targets, mobile ground targets, and airborne targets. Efforts focus on all-weather precision guidance, directional warheads, high-resolution laser radar, and smart bomb dispensers. This Directorate developed the technology for the smart

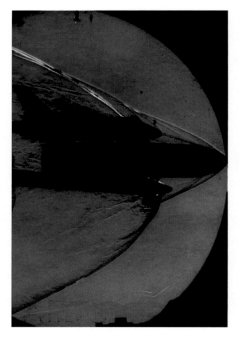

Space Shuttle separation tests performed at the Arnold Engineering Development Center examined dual solid booster separation from the shuttle and external tank. This Schlieren photo shows a test in wind tunnel A in the von Kármán Gas Dynamic Facility in the center in 1974. (USAF)

Above: *This computer-aided design and manufacturing system is being used to evaluate potential airframe designs at the Arnold Engineering and Development Center at Arnold AFB, Tennessee. (Lockheed)*

Left: *General John Jumper, middle, Air Force Chief of Staff, discusses the capabilities of small diameter bombs. The small diameter bomb with diamond-back range extenders was displayed recently at the third Air Armament Summit at Eglin AFB, Florida. Boeing and Lockheed Martin small diameter bomb prototypes will be flight tested at Eglin. (USAF)*

P.J.Weisgerber

This illustration depicts an artist's conception of the Airborne Laser aircraft disabling an outbound ballistic missile during the boost phase. In addition to developing the capability to defend the United States from ballistic missile attack, the United States is also developing the capability to defend forward deployed forces. (USAF)

weapons used by the Air Force with such devastating accuracy during the Gulf war and in the recent conflicts in the Balkans.

The Information Directorate is focused on global awareness, dynamic planning and execution, and global information exchange. To provide global awareness, the directorate is working to fuse information into a single consistent operating picture for the war fighter, providing both situational awareness and strike assessment. The goal is to remove the fog of war and give commanders and combatants alike an integrated picture of what they

This is an artist's conception of logistics operations. A CH-47 Chinook helicopter is departing with supplies for a forward operating base as a Lockheed C-5A Galaxy lands. New logistics concepts are being employed to reduce stockpiling large quantities of supplies forward. (USAF)

are facing without requiring them to interpret conflicting information from individual sensors. In the pursuit of dynamic planning and execution, engineers are looking for ways to enable commanders to shape and control the pace and phasing of engagements by exploiting global awareness.

Global information exchange initiatives seek to increase global communications capabilities to our aircraft by a thousand-fold. This requires assured and survivable networking, ability to detect information warfare attacks on our information systems, protection of our systems from such attacks, and the ability to react to any such attacks. To meet the demands of warfighting in the information age, the directorate has partnered with other elements of the federal government, national intelligence agencies, numerous allied nations, state and local governments, and more than fifty universities.

The science and technology frontiers probed by AFRL activities touch every aspect of the Air Force today and will characterize the Air Force of the future. Through investments in science and technology, the Air Force has learned that the true measure of success is not patents or even Nobel Prizes. Success depends on developing a problem solution that is attractive and affordable, then demonstrating that the risk of the technology is low enough for industry to bid it back to us in a product that we want.

Staff Sergeant Anthony Parker gathers the proper tools to connect members of the 555th Fighter Squadron to the multi-router system. Parker, of the 31st Communications Squadron, Aviano Air Base, Italy is a computer systems operator journeyman with the 31st Air Expeditionary Force Package. The 31st is deployed to Sidi Slimane Air Base, Morocco, to provide communication support during an exercise with the Royal Moroccan Air Force. (USAF)

The Airborne Laser program office located at Kirtland AFB, New Mexico, is currently developing systems to destroy scud-like missiles such as those used during Desert Storm. This is an artist's conception of two Airborne Laser aircraft engaging multiple outbound ballistic missiles during boost phase. (USAF)

United States Air Force Museum

Colonel Richard Uppstrom, USAF (Ret)

The Air Force has accumulated a wealth of history, heritage, and tradition that is ably presented in this book. Histories tend toward the written word and the two-dimensional image. The story of the Air Force has also been comprehensively collected, compiled, and presented in three-dimensional form by the United States Air Force Museum at Wright-Patterson Air Force Base Ohio, and at various base-level museums at other Air Force bases. These Air Force museums present a textured history that visitors can see, feel, and sometimes even smell.

Have you ever touched the corrugated siding of a Nissen hut on a cold day or noticed the peculiar odor of hydraulic fluid that clings to the AC-130A on display in the Museum Airpark? Have you imagined what stories these artifacts witnessed? Have you stood in awe before the B-47 Stratojet housed in the museum and marveled at the graceful sweep and sheer beauty of those wings? Visitors at the USAF Museum can trace the birth and growth of the Air Force from the acquisition of its first airplane in 1908 to today's global operations. Displays integrate the hardware items with stories of people who maintained, managed, supported, and operated our increasingly complex Air Force.

The USAF Museum's display scheme includes over 300 aircraft and missiles, representing every era of Air Force history. The spruce and linen combat fighter of World War I stands not far from the most modern aircraft of the 1930s. World War II and the Korean War combat aircraft represent an era of staggering production numbers and strike force size that will probably never again be equaled. Aircraft once cloaked in deepest secrecy, like the SR-71 Blackbird and F-117 Nighthawk, represent another look at technical innovation.

Dominating major galleries are the looming presence of the B-36 Peacemaker, B-52G Stratofortress, and the ever-modern XB-70 Valkyrie, each contributing to the story of the Cold War. From the smallest escape and evasion compass to some of the largest and most complex flying machines ever built, from the familiar to the obscure, the interrelationship between people and machine is highlighted with bold exhibit design and innovative visual concepts. These exhibits depict the personal dedication and technical accomplishments of the men and women of the United States Air Force.

Since its almost accidental inception in 1923, the museum collection has grown to over 75,000 artifacts. Many of these are on display at the United States Air Force Museum located on Wright-Patterson Air Force Base in Dayton, Ohio. The museum is open daily except Thanksgiving, Christmas, and New Year's Day. Admission is free. The oldest and largest military aviation museum in the world grows and operates through generous funding support provided by the Air Force Museum Foundation, a private non-profit organization.

Visitors to the Air Force Museum can see exhibits of the most modern Air Force aircraft such as this F-117 stealth fighter as well as historic aircraft from World War I, World War II, the Korean War, and the war in Southeast Asia. (USAF)

Engineering, Manufacturing Development, and Production

The Product Centers develop, acquire, and modernize weapons systems for the Air Force. Each Center has a highly competent engineering workforce that is up-to-date on every facet of modern weapons technologies. Air Force industrial design expertise is recognized worldwide as the finest of any government agency anywhere. The people assigned to AFMC Product Centers and the contractor teams with whom they work are well educated, highly motivated, responsive to the needs of the warfighting commands. They take enormous pride in their reputation and in the weapons systems they produce.

The Aeronautical Systems Center (ASC) is the largest of the AFMC Product Centers. In 2001, ASC's annual budget was almost $11 billion and the center employed more than 19,000 military and civil service personnel. ASC's portfolio of forty-seven major acquisition programs included fighter, bomber, transport, reconnaissance, and trainer aircraft. This center has a magnificent legacy. Established near the Wright brothers' home in Dayton, Ohio, it has been home to many pioneers of aviation, including Hap Arnold and Jimmy Doolittle. The Aeronautical Systems Center and its predecessor organizations have played a major role in every aircraft flown by the Air Force. In spirit if not in fact, ASC is the Wright brothers' "bicycle shop."

ASC responsibilities extend to engines that power the machines, avionics that enable the pilots to fly and fight the aircraft, support and training systems, electronic counter measures (ECM) that defend the aircraft, and all the cockpit and life-support systems that keep the crew alive in all conditions including ejection. In short, ASC is responsible for everything necessary to make the aircraft an efficient and combat effective system. That is why aircraft programs are managed by organizations called *System* Program Offices (SPOs). This concept is also captured in the center name—

This F-16 is launching an early version of the AIM-120 AMRAAM missile, an air-to-air weapon with beyond-visual-range capability. (USAF).

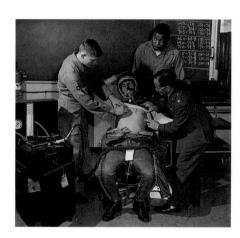

Captain Henry P. Nielsen, project officer and one of four volunteers for bailout at 90,000 feet, has electrodes attached to record heart readings during his simulated assent and descent in an altitude chamber at Wright Air Development Center. (USAF)

This Martin X-24B Lifting Body Research Vehicle has just been released from a Boeing NB-52 test aircraft stationed at Edwards AFB, California. (USAF)

Air Force aeromedical researcher Major John Paul Stapp is shown on a decelerator test vehicle at Edwards AFB, California. The machine came to a stop from 120 miles per hour within nineteen feet in .228 seconds. Stapp also tested the effects on the human body of ejecting from a high-speed aircraft. (USAF)

Above: Major Christian Ledet, a flight surgeon in the Iowa National Guard's 132nd Fighter Wing, prepares to test a liquid-filled full-body anti-G suit at Edwards AFB, California, while flying an F-16 Falcon. The anti-G suit is designed to protect fighter pilots as they make rapid turns or changes in flight path. (USAF)

Right: Technicians at Ogden Air Material Center, Utah, complete work on a Boeing Minuteman III missile that has been returned to Air Material Command for routine periodic maintenance. (USAF)

Aeronautical *Systems* Center—intended to convey that the responsibilities of the center are far larger than the aircraft alone. Those responsibilities include everything on the ground to make the aircraft effective in the air. It is the *system* that determines effectiveness, not merely the aircraft.

ASC is ably augmented in its mission by a subordinate organization, the 311th Human Systems Wing, located at Brooks AFB, Texas. Personnel assigned to the 311th Wing are responsible for integrating and maintaining the human in Air Force systems. The wing produces equipment that assesses and manages health, safety, and environmental risks for the USAF. They not only manage more than 140 technical acquisition and sustainment programs, they also train more than 6,000 aeromedical personnel annually including Air Force flight nurses and Air Force flight surgeons.

The Space and Missile Systems Center (SMC), located in Los Angeles, California, is the acquisition arm for Air Force space systems. Personnel assigned to the Space and Missiles System Center research, develop, and acquire all ballistic missiles, space launch boosters, satellites, and supporting ground systems for the Air Force. Their primary customer is Air Force Space Command located at Peterson AFB, Colorado. The center also supports Space Command with satellite tracking, space data acquisition, and command and control of space vehicles. SMC employs over 5,500 people and has an annual budget of almost $6 billion.

The primary technical arm of SMC is the Aerospace Corporation, a Federally Funded Research and Development Center (FFRDC). FFRDCs were founded to enable the military to compete with industry for scarce technical talent in rapidly expanding fields, and where a military acquisition agency was geographically located near its industrial partners. The Los Angeles area and the space industry are prime examples of this situation.

SMC developed the first American ICBMs— Atlas, Titan, and Minuteman. The Peacekeeper missile, one of the most successful acquisition programs of all time, was also developed by SMC. These ballistic missiles were developed and acquired as *systems*—meaning they included all command and control elements, silos, supporting equipment, and training for the Air Force personnel who operated and maintained these staples of the Cold War.

The Joint Strike Fighter

Charles T. Burbage

At 5:20 on the morning of 23 June 2001, test pilot Simon Hargreaves began his walk to the X-35 concept demonstration vehicle for the Short Takeoff and Vertical Landing variant of the Joint Strike Fighter. It was a picture perfect Sunday morning in the high desert of California—a day that would forever change the course of aviation history.

Since the days of Leonardo da Vinci, the inventive imagination of man has been teased by the challenge of high performance flight without the requirement of a runway. Adding the dimensions of sustained supersonic flight in a platform shaped to evade radar detection stretched this challenge against the laws of physics and aerodynamics. If successful, the test today would ensure the winning edge for what many thought would be the largest contract in the history of the Department of Defense.

Augmenting the thrust of a basic engine had been an elusive goal. Years before Simon's flight, a handful of visionary engineers within Lockheed Martin conceived an idea whereby the energy of a twin-spool jet engine turbine could be harnessed at both ends. Raw thrust from the tail pipe could be augmented with mass flow from a fan driven by a traditional turbo shaft. If it worked, the dilemma of inadequate thrust margin for vertical launch and recovery of a tactical fighter would be solved. If not, the role of STOVL fighters in future conflict and the flexibility they provide to expeditionary forces and small-ship operations would forever be questioned.

For two months, the test team had conducted a detailed series of ground tests with the X-35 vehicle bolted to a test rig to measure forces and moments. The vehicle control system must control vertical flight with a series of engine thruster controls and smoothly transition to wing-borne flight, with the same pilot controls now managing conventional flight control surfaces.

At 5:38, Simon strapped into the cockpit. Shortly after 6:13 the X-35B accomplished the first vertical takeoff and landing with an augmented thrust system. On 20 July, Major Art Tomasetti, the X-35B test pilot, completed a short takeoff, level supersonic dash, hover, and vertical landing—a flight profile referred to by Lockheed Martin as Mission X.

Bottom, left and right: The Lockheed Martin Corporation began the system development and demonstration phase of testing the JSF in October 2001. This phase will evolve the aircraft, now known as the F-35, from a concept demonstrator to a combat-capable fighter. Flight test is scheduled in late 2005. The Air Force will be the largest JSF customer, purchasing 1,763 of the conventional takeoff and landing versions of the aircraft, shown left in prototype. The Air Force version of the JSF is designed primarily for air-to-ground combat to replace the F-16 Fighting Falcon and A-10 Thunderbolt II and to complement the F-22 Raptor. The X-35 flight tests and hover tests were so successful that the Department of Defense selected Lockheed Martin as the prime contractor for the Joint Strike Fighter. The Marine Corps plans to procure the vertical takeoff version shown below. (USAF)

Boeing continues the development of the Evolved Expendable Launch Vehicle (EELV) with this test of a new solid booster rocket. The driving force behind the EELV is the need to make space launch more affordable by evolving a family of unmanned, expendable space launch vehicles from existing systems. (Boeing)

SMC also develops space boosters that power our military and commercial satellites into orbit. System Program Offices at SMC evolved Atlas and Titan missiles into modern space boosters and have added Centaur, Delta, and inertial upper stage rockets to our nation's launch repertoire. Other program offices developed military satellites critical to worldwide military operations in the 21st century, including the Defense Satellite Communications System (DSCS) that enables worldwide military communications under all circumstances and Global Positioning Satellites (GPS) that play a crucial role in navigation, precise positioning, and guidance for smart weapons.

SMC is developing a new generation of space boosters, the Evolved Expendable Launch Vehicle, EELV, which promises cheaper and more reliable access to space. The center is also developing the Space-Based Infrared System (SBIRS) that will eventually replace older satellites that now provide launch indications for the Ballistic Missile Defense system. SMC is continuing to evolve and improve the GPS constellation to provide more accuracy and more reliability for military users and greater access to a rapidly growing community of commercial users on land, sea, and air. SMC people are the "Buck Rogers" team of today's Air Force, and they have made our country a space-faring power

The Electronic Systems Center (ESC), located at Hanscom AFB Massachusetts, employs approximately 6,500 people and manages an annual budget of more than $3.5 billion. The MITRE Corporation, a FFRDC, is the primary technical arm of ESC. The center is responsible for more than 200 programs—both ground and airborne—associated with military command and control. ESC manages aircraft programs where the aircraft is already developed and the focus of the program is the command and control equipment inside the aircraft. Examples include the Airborne Warning And Control System (AWACS) that is crucial to the control of the air battle, the Airborne Battlefield Command and Control Center (ABCCC) for controlling air support of ground troops, and the Joint Surveillance Target Attack Radar System (Joint STARS) used to track moving targets on the ground. All of these aircraft played key roles during the Gulf war and the Balkans conflicts.

ESC provides command and control equipment used in the Cheyenne Mountain complex near Colorado Springs, Colorado, as well as the massive radars and the space sensors that feed information to Cheyenne Mountain. Additionally, ESC is responsible for developing and equipping an Air Operations Center for the use of air component commanders in joint operations.

The Air Armament Center (AAC), located on Eglin AFB near Ft Walton Beach, Florida, employs approximately 6,800 people, manages an annual budget of approximately $3 billion, and is the focal point for all Air Force armaments. AAC conducts research, development, and acquisition for more that forty weapons systems, including the Advanced Medium Range Air-to-Air Missile (AMRAAM) used by the Air Force, the Navy, and allied nations. This radar guided missile was responsible for a number of aircraft kills in the Gulf war and in the Balkans. AAC also manages the Joint Direct Attack Munition (JDAM), a GPS guided 2,000-pound bomb effective at night and in inclement weather, as well as the Joint Air-to-

A "Clean Room" technician at the Westinghouse Advanced Technology Division laboratory examines silicon wafers bearing large-scale integrated circuit chips. (Westinghouse)

Surface Standoff Missile (JASSM), a long-range weapon under development for use by all U.S. services.

AAC is also a major test center. It has a test wing and test ranges that enable its systems program office to be geographically located near the testing of their products. This is a unique advantage and is a key reason why AAC is able to react quickly to emerging combat requirements. During the Gulf war, for example, when the joint forces air commander urgently needed to strike a very deeply buried and hardened bunker, AAC designed, built, tested, and produced unique bombs in weeks to do the job. The urgency was such that while the bombs were still warm from the explosive mixture poured into them, they were loaded on aircraft and shipped to a Gulf airbase. They were dropped on the target within four hours after arriving in the combat zone.

The Role of American Industry

AMC product centers contract with American industry to design, develop, and produce equipment the Air Force uses to train and to wage war. Industrial contractors create weapons systems designed to Air Force stated requirements. They devise efficient manufacturing and assembly techniques and plumb the whole range and depth of American industry to assemble the thousands of subcontractors required to efficiently produce a major weapons system. Further, contractors manage the complex flow of new engineering designs, parts, people, and facilities to keep the production lines operating efficiently. They adjust this vast enterprise to accommodate technical surprises, government funding variances, labor disputes, and in some cases, wartime accelerations. They maintain a diverse workforce expert in technical management, systems engineering, production design, training systems design, product and logistical support, contracting, financial management, subcontractor management, and other important disciplines.

This photo, taken from the interior of a Boeing KC-135, shows another KC-135 awaiting depot-level maintenance in a hanger at the Sacramento Air Logistics Center, McClellan AFB, California. The KC-135 Stratotanker's principal mission is air refueling. This unique asset greatly enhances the USAF's capability to accomplish its primary missions of Global Reach and Global Power. Air Force tankers also provide aerial refueling support to Navy and Marine Corps aircraft as well as aircraft of allied nations. (USAF)

Above: *A Boeing technician checks data during a structural mode interaction test on the X-32B Joint Strike Fighter concept demonstrator. (USAF)*

Left: *Technicians prepare a satellite for testing in an electromagnetic quiet room. This anechoic chamber removes all electronic noise and simulates the environment that satellites experience in space. (USAF)*

303

Air Force Captains Virgil Grissom (left) and Leroy G. Cooper float in a C-131 aircraft during a zero gravity flight in the early days of the space program. The aircraft coasted over a parabolic arc to achieve weightlessness for up to thirteen seconds. The two astronauts are wearing full pressure suits similar to the type they will wear in space. (USAF)

National Air and Space Administration test pilot Neil Armstrong stands beside the X-15 research aircraft following a mission in December 1961. In his first flight in the X-15, Armstrong reached a speed of 2,454 miles per hour and an altitude of 80,000 feet. (NASA)

American industry is unequalled in managing complex production and support enterprises. Efficiently applying new technologies to military needs, American companies produce combat systems that dominate the battlefield whether operated by the Air Force or our allies. Aerospace production constitutes the largest favorable balance of trade of any export category for the United States. Clearly, the world market recognizes the military and economic value of U.S. aerospace products.

The contractors and the AFMC product centers enjoy a healthy tension and circumspection that helps avoid surprises and provides a broad array of options for every program dilemma that arises. The orientation of the product center is to cover the program at all levels of the government—Air Force, DOD, and Congress. The orientation of the contractors is to cover the program at all levels of the industrial base. These complimentary orientations, while not exclusive, form the team that is necessary to manage the entire program. This team is bound by mutual respect, complementary skills, experiences, and a shared desire to provide the Air Force with cost effective weapons systems that will defeat any threat. The combined development prowess and technical management capabilities of the product centers and American industry are unequalled anywhere in the world. That strength keeps the Air Force out in front in aerospace power.

Test and Evaluation

The only way to know if the product centers and the contractors "got it right" is to actually test the product to see if it meets design goals. Further, the product needs to be evaluated to confirm that it meets military requirements and can deliver the desired combat capabilities. This test and evaluation is conducted at three test centers in AFMC for all aircraft and air munitions. Test and evaluation of space systems is conducted at Air Force Space Command launch facilities at Cape Canaveral, Florida, on the east coast and Vandenberg AFB, California, on the west coast. The space and missile test data flows to SMC for analysis and evaluation. For command and control systems, test locations vary widely, but are mainly with the warfighting commands.

Air Force Material Command operates three test centers: the Air Force Flight Test Center (AFFTC) at Edwards AFB, California; the Air Armament Center at Eglin AFB, Florida; and Arnold Engineering Development Center located at Arnold AFB, Tennessee.

The Air Force selected Edwards Air Force Base in the Mojave Desert north of Los Angeles, California, as the location for the Air Force Flight Test Center because geographical and weather phenomena of the area make it an ideal flying location. The base is located adjacent to Rogers and Rosamond dry lakebeds. These lakebeds provide over sixty-five linear miles of useable landing area and can accommodate landings by any aircraft designed to date. AFFTC operates the Edwards Flight Test Range comprising over 300,000 acres as well as the airspace above 20,000 square miles of the desert southwest. Dry lakebeds exist throughout the vast Edwards testing complex and most make excellent emergency landing fields—an important consideration when flight-testing a new aircraft. Many test pilots and many one-of-a-kind aircraft have survived emergency landings on these dry lakebeds.

Edwards AFB is a place rich in aeronautical history. It has been home to most of the legends of Air Force flight-testing. Chuck Yeager first broke the sound barrier above the Edwards test range, and he made most of his historic test flights from Edwards. Many great test pilots followed Yeager through the early morning calm above the California high desert, including Scott Crossfield, Neil Armstrong, Frank Borman, Tom Stafford, Jim McDivitt, Dave Scott; Bob Rushworth, Pete Knight, and Joe Engle. Most of the original astronauts were experimental test pilots and most

Air Force Captain Joe Engle, a test pilot assigned to the Air Force Flight Test Center (AFFTC) at Edwards AFB, California, prepares for another mission. The AFFTC is the AFMC center for research, development and test and evaluation of aerospace systems for the United States and its allies. (USAF)

Above: *Another test pilot carrying the pressure suit air conditioning unit escorts Major Bob White to debriefing after another successful test flight in the X-15. The young man in the photo may also have plans to become an Air Force test pilot. (USAF)*

Left: *The North American X-15A-2 experimental aircraft streaks away immediately after being launched from a B-52. The A-2 version of the X-15, equipped with external auxiliary fuel tanks, achieved a maximum altitude of 354,200 feet and a maximum speed of 4,534 miles per hour. ("Launch of the A-2,", Mike Machat)*

came from Edwards. Today, AFFTC continues to supply outstanding men and women for our astronaut corps. AFFTC is also the home of the Air Force Test Pilot School, which trains flight test pilots, flight test engineers, and flight test navigators.

The Air Armament Center (AAC) testing complex is located on Eglin AFB, Florida, the largest military installation in the Department of Defense. Eglin consists of more than 700 square miles of land area and more than 93,000 square miles of water ranges for testing and training. The 46th Test Wing is responsible for developmental flight-testing of all air-to-air and air-to-ground weapons in the Air Force inventory. The wing tests weapons to ensure that they meet design parameters, and to confirm weapons systems compatibility with specific aircraft. Wing test pilots check for safe separation characteristics of the weapon from the aircraft throughout the envelope of aircraft performance, and they determine the accuracy of the weapon-

Top: *This F-15E Strike Eagle assigned to the 46th Test Wing, armed with a GBU-27 bomb, circles above one of the many test ranges at Eglin AFB, Florida. (USAF)*

Above: *Technical Sergeant Dan Stevens, 411th Flight Test Squadron at Edwards AFB, California, uses a non-contact infrared thermometer while curing the coating on an F-22 Raptor. (USAF)*

Right: *This Northrop T-38 aircraft is part of a fleet of specialized aircraft maintained by the Aeronautical Systems Center at Wright Patterson AFB, Ohio, to test equipment for existing and future Air Force aircraft. (USAF)*

aircraft combination. The objective of this comprehensive evaluation is to give combat commanders maximum flexibility to tailor aircraft employment in a combat situation.

Arnold Engineering Development Center (AEDC) near Tullahoma, Tennessee, named in memory of General Hap Arnold, commemorates his strong convictions regarding the importance of technology to the future of the Air Force. AEDC is the largest aerospace ground test and evaluation complex within the Department of Defense. This $7 billion infrastructure consists of fifty-eight aerospace test and simulation facilities including wind tunnels, altitude jet and rocket test cells, ballistic ranges, arc heaters, and space chambers. Twenty-seven of these facilities are unique in the United States and fourteen are unique in the world. The scientists and engineers of AEDC perform tests, engineering analysis, and technical evaluations for all U.S. armed services, other governmental agencies including NASA, and the commercial aerospace industry. The center employs 3,000 military and civilian personnel. Every high-performance aircraft and missile in the Department of Defense inventory has been tested in the ground test facilities here.

Above: The Global Hawk is a long-endurance, high-altitude unmanned aerial vehicle (UAV) intended for multiple battlefield applications. It is capable of surveying an area the size of the state of Illinois, or 40,000 square miles, in just twenty-four hours. It has a range of 13,500 nautical miles at altitudes approaching 65,000 feet. (USAF)

Page 308–309: B-52 aircraft received depot-level maintenance and modification at Kelly AFB, Texas, in the world's largest maintenance hangar before that base was closed. The hangar could accommodate fourteen B-52s. The Oklahoma City Air Logistics Center is now responsible for maintenance and modification of the B-52—a fifty-year-old airplane that is expected to remain in active service for another quarter century. (USAF)

Below: F-16B assigned to the 412th Test Wing, Edwards AFB, California, observes a Beech C-12 Huron on a test flight. (USAF)

Sustaining Combat Forces: The Air Logistics Centers

After Air Force equipment is deployed to the field, it is necessary to sustain that equipment so it is ready for use. Equipment is maintained at operational locations by trained Air Force technicians with the assistance of contractors. However, Air Force maintenance technicians accomplish the vast majority of the work. After initial training in the basics of their specialty, these technicians normally receive advanced training in skills necessary to become proficient on a specific weapons system. Normally, training materials and instructional courses pertinent to a specific weapons system are developed under a contract administered by the systems program office.

At operational locations, to keep the equipment in service, maintenance is conducted on weapons system at the squadron level. For example, after flying, an aircraft must be inspected, refueled, and rearmed to prepare it for the next sortie. This routine maintenance may require changing tires, servicing hydraulic and pneumatic systems, and servicing oxygen systems. Squadron assigned crew chiefs perform all of this maintenance. When aircraft repair is necessary, technicians skilled in specialties pertinent to the specific component of the weapons system perform that maintenance. For example, if the aircraft radar has failed, repair usually requires troubleshooting the radar system to identify and remove the failed component and replace it with one that is serviceable. Serviceable components are kept in base supply to meet this requirement.

In some cases, the failed equipment is repaired in shops on the base. In other cases, the base maintenance technician only removes and replaces equipment and defective items are shipped elsewhere for repair. The decision concerning what and how much to repair at the operating location is based on economic, technical, and training factors and varies from weapons system to weapons system.

When it is necessary for equipment to be sent from the base for repair, it is normally sent to an Air Logistics Center (ALC). The ALC is responsible for managing the flow of supplies worldwide to all of the weapons systems in the Air Force. Centers determine how many parts of each type must be kept in base supply so that systems at that base are ready for use. When parts are returned to centers for repair, the ALC either repairs the part in-house or sends it out on contract to commercial sources of repair. In either case, after the part is repaired, it is returned to inventory at the depot until supply levels at operating locations fall below minimum levels.

In most cases, ALCs conduct major inspections, depot level maintenance, and repair on aircraft, missiles, and other complete systems. This work may be performed at the operational location by a depot repair team, but it is usually performed at an Air Logistics Center. With responsibility for supply chain management, parts repair, and major maintenance overhaul, ALCs require a large, ready, trained work force and massive, well-equipped facilities ready to sustain the Air Force in peace or war—and obviously there is a monumental difference between these two conditions.

C-17 Globemaster III Production

Howard Chambers

After the Vietnam War, the Air Force established requirements for a new jet transport combining the mobility of the C-141, the cargo carrying capabilities of the C-5, and the maneuverability of the C-130. The Boeing C-17 Globemaster III was designed to meet those requirements. The Air Force and Boeing, working as an integrated team encouraging employee involvement and lean aircraft manufacturing techniques, began delivering C-17s to operational squadrons in 1993. In 1998, the C-17 production program received the Malcolm Baldridge National Quality Award in recognition of Boeing's world-class management, engineering, and supplier relationships.

Building a C-17 begins three years before delivery. Pratt & Whitney fabricates C-17 engines in Connecticut and ships them to Texas so Vought Aerospace can complete engine-nacelle assembly. Vought, like other suppliers, ships components and subassemblies to Long Beach, California, where Boeing kits all materials required to complete final assembly of a C-17.

Boeing builds the aircraft as four major subassemblies—wing, forward, center, and aft fuselage. The aircraft structure is primarily aluminum with some steel, titanium, and composites. The wing is built in two halves and then structurally joined by a centerline splice. Assembly starts with pre-formed skins to which stringers and spars are attached using automated tools to reduce labor and increase quality. Concurrently with centerline splice activity, leading and trailing edge components and systems are installed, followed by the fuel systems.

While the wing is being assembled, work proceeds on the fuselage. Fuselage components consist of longerons, frames, skin panels, blankets, wiring, tubing, and many other detailed items. Fuselage panel sections are joined together using some of the world's largest automated equipment. The forward fuselage assembly comprises the cockpit. The center fuselage begins with assembly of the cargo floor. Fittings for the main landing gear are added. The aft fuselage includes the composite vertical stabilizer and the C-17 cargo door, the largest opening ever designed for a pressurized aircraft.

Completed major sections are moved to a computer-controlled laser-targeting alignment tool that assures all aircraft sections are joined quickly and accurately. After installation of 120 miles of wiring, Boeing conducts an all-up aircraft check of hydraulic, environmental, electrical, and mechanical systems. Once systems checkout, the aircraft is painted, moved to the ramp for engine runs, final systems verification, and production flight test by the Air Force-Boeing team—and another C-17 enters service.

Left: Each C-17 requires 24,000 drawings, 9.1 million parts including over 1.3 million fasteners, 113 assembly fixtures, 2,100 mechanics, and 326 days. (Boeing)

Below: The first C-17 was delivered to Charleston AFB, South Carolina in June 1993. Today, fifteen C-17s are delivered each year. (Boeing)

The Air Force has three ALCs—Ogden Air Logistics Center located at Hill AFB, Utah, Oklahoma City Air Logistics Center located at Tinker AFB, Oklahoma, and Warner Robins Air Logistics Center located at Warner Robbins AFB, Georgia. Support requirements for all Air Force equipment is divided between these three ALCs.

Ogden ALC is responsible for supporting the F-16, the A-10, and the Minuteman and Peacekeeper ICBM's. Ogden is also the leading provider of rocket motors, small missiles, air munitions and guided bombs, and is the ammunition control point for the USAF. In addition, this center annually overhauls more than 19,000 aircraft landing gear, brakes, struts, and wheels—which constitutes 100 percent of the Air Force inventory and 70 percent of the DOD inventory. Ogden ALC is the repair center for composite structures on the B-2, C-17, F-117, and V-22 aircraft. This center is also responsible for providing imaging and reconnaissance equipment, simulators and training devices, avionics, hydraulics, pneudraulic and radar components, instruments, gas turbine engines, shelters, and many other critical parts and components to keep the Air Force operationally ready.

The Oklahoma City ALC, the largest Air Force industrial complex, provides worldwide logistics support for the E-3 AWACS, C-135 and KC-135, B-52, B-1, B-2, and Navy E-6 aircraft. The ALC manages and maintains an inventory exceeding $33 billion with nearly 23,000 engines, 3,000 missile systems, and 24,000 components supporting 2,261 aircraft. This center

Technicians in this electrical accessories unit at the Oklahoma City Air Materiel Area are responsible for more than 300 different electrical items used on jet engines and Air Force aircraft. They face an ever-changing workload as different items flow through this shop. (USAF)

Under the Strategic Arms Reduction Treaty that became effective in December 1994, the Aerospace Maintenance and Regeneration Center at Davis-Monthan AFB near Tucson, Arizona, assumed responsibility for reclaiming components from 365 B-52 aircraft scheduled for disposal. (USAF)

Over the years, many planes in storage at the Aerospace Maintenance and Regeneration Center (AMARC) were regenerated to become Full Scale Aerial Targets (FSAT) or drones. The FSAT program was started in 1972 with the conversion of F-102 aircraft and continues today with the conversion of F-4s. Since the beginning of this program, AMARC has delivered approximately 784 drone aircraft, including F-102s, F-100s, F-106s, and F-4s. (USAF)

Shauna Sullins installs a wire harness in an A-10 Thunderbolt II. She works in "Hog Heaven," the A-10 production section of the aircraft directorate at the Ogden Air Logistics Center at Hill AFB, Utah. (USAF)

Bottom, left: *This photograph, taken in 1970, shows an armada of grounded aircraft stored at the Aerospace Maintenance and Regeneration Center near Tucson, Arizona. Fifty-one 52G-model aircraft remain intact at AMARC. Under the provisions of the Strategic Arms Reduction Treaty (START), AMARC has successfully planned, managed, and supervised the destruction of 314 B-52 heavy bombers. (USAF)*

Bottom, right: *Approximately 700 F-4 Phantoms remain in storage at AMARC. These aircraft will be used to provide spare parts to friendly nations who still operate F-4s or for conversion to unmanned drones for use as aerial targets. (USAF)*

also provides logistic support for 417 commercial derivative aircraft, executive support aircraft including the U.S. presidential fleet, and advanced cruise missiles.

Warner Robins ALC is responsible for the F-15, C-141, C-130, C-5, U-2, Joint STARS, the worldwide military command and control system, the LANTIRN navigation and targeting system, and helicopters. It is the repair center for life support equipment, propellers, and most electronic warfare equipment.

The ALCs are now partnering with the commercial aerospace industry in the management and maintenance of major weapons systems. This partnership is a tailored blending of the best talents of industry and government personnel, and the best use of expensive facilities and equipment, to create a "best value" method of providing logistics support to the Air Force.

The Aerospace Maintenance and Regeneration Center

The Aerospace Maintenance and Regeneration Center (AMARC), located at Davis-Monthan AFB near Tucson, Arizona is affectionately known as the "bone yard" because it is the final resting place of Air Force aircraft. Here, in the dry desert, decommissioned aircraft are carefully mothballed for possible future use or for reclaimed parts. Some aircraft are temporarily stored until the Air Force or an American ally needs them. Some are eventually brought back to flight status as aerial targets, or "drones," to be used in testing and operational training. In fiscal year 2000, AMARC returned

eighty-one aircraft and 18,657 parts to the operational Air Force. This center also stores and manages more than 318,000 line items of production tooling and special test equipment for many late model Air Force aircraft in case production lines for those aircraft should be reopened.

Above: *The Aerospace Maintenance and Regeneration Center at Davis-Monthan AFB, Arizona, consists of 2,600 acres where more than 4,500 aircraft are stored. Some of the aircraft will return to active service, others yield parts and assemblies to keep the active inventory flying, and still others end up in museums or as static displays. (USAF)*

Summary

The system used to create and refine the weapons of our Air Force was derived over more than five decades and is the result of hard lessons—some learned in combat and many learned at the cost of American lives. It is not a perfect system and it continues to evolve and improve. Nevertheless, for all its imperfections, our system produces the premier fighting air force in the world today.

Aerospace dominance is not just the result of our equipment, because our leadership, combat tactics, and training play critical roles in forging this shield of national power. However, our dominance would not be possible without the equipment with which we fight. Moreover, it is clear that our nation has a blend of talent from Air Force and industry that is unique. This blend of efforts generates major advances in equipment concepts and assures that we field combat capabilities decades before our adversaries.

All of these strengths come from our people. They are our treasure and our secret ingredient. They keep us ahead and they keep us safe. We owe them our freedom and our heartfelt thanks . . . everyday.

Above: *Airman Rhea Lora, 1st Supply Squadron receiving clerk, uses a hand-held scanner to quickly process arriving items. The Air Force Materiel Command is responsible for supplying the warfighter with the right product, in the right place, at the right time while also sustaining systems and spare parts that ensure readiness. (USAF)*

313

Today's Expeditionary Air Force

General Michael E. Ryan, USAF (Ret)

An orbiting satellite has a machine-level conversation with an Air Force downlink site somewhere on our globe. The conversation produces a picture for the air commander of a surface-to-air missile radar site in the battle area. Minutes later, an unmanned aerial vehicle (UAV) flies near the missile radar site. The UAV sends a stream of data portraying the precise location of the radar site. The data is uplinked to a stealthy strike aircraft and passed to its satellite-guided weapons. The commander authorizes a strike and the strike aircraft obliterates the missile site in a cloud of dust and flame. This is but one example of the intertwined, near real-time, system-of-systems architecture conceptualized in the phrase Air Force Global Vigilance, Reach, and Power.

The Air Force continues to evolve from the rich aerospace heritage detailed in previous chapters of this book. Change is a prominent feature in that heritage. Never content to rest on our success, we always look forward—to the next challenge, the next technological breakthrough, or the next operational innovation. The Expeditionary Aerospace Force, a product of this drive to transform and improve, blends lessons learned during the Cold War, Desert Storm, and Balkan campaigns with proven new technologies to meet changing mission requirements.

As we formed our Air Force from the Army following World War II, we created organizations that reflected missions and aircraft types. Bombers were strategic, fighters were tactical, interceptors were defenders, and cargo and troop carriers were transport. While that model served us well as airpower came of age during the 20th century, those organizational structures tended to segregate capabilities rather than integrate

Above: The Global Hawk unmanned aerial vehicle, developed by the Air Force as a long-endurance, high-altitude UAV, has multiple battlefield applications. It gives military commanders the ability to "see" movements of enemy assets from great distances with startling clarity and near-real-time accuracy. The Global Hawk made aerospace history as the first UAV to fly unrefueled 7,500 miles across the Pacific Ocean from America to Australia in April 2001. (USAF)

Opposite: On 6 September 1995, an F-16C fired the first AGM-88 High-Speed Anti-Radiation Missile (HARM) in combat, successfully suppressing the enemy air defenses over Bosnia-Herzegovina. The F-16 has evolved into an excellent multi-role fighter and hunter/killer. ("Six Shooter," K. Price Randel)

This illustration shows one member of the Defense Support Program satellite constellation. This system has been operational since the early 1970s, providing the United States global vigilance from the highest ground, space. (USAF)

Above: *The C-17 Globemaster III is the newest, most flexible cargo aircraft to enter the Air Force inventory. It is capable of rapid strategic delivery of troops and all types of cargo to main operating bases or directly to forward bases in the deployment area. The C-17 can take off and land on runways as short as 3,000 feet and only 90 feet wide. The C-17 made its maiden flight on 15 September 1991, and the first production model was delivered to Charleston Air Force Base, South Carolina, on 14 June 1993. (USAF)*

Opposite, bottom: *A tent city is a familiar scene whenever a component of the Expeditionary Force is deployed. Here, in Qatar, the tents border an airfield. (USAF)*

Below: *Most USAF combat and mobility aircraft can refuel in-flight. This is an American capability essential to our expeditionary mission. The KC-135 aircraft, pictured here with a B-1 and a complement of F-15C/Es and F-16s, was the primary refueling platform in the 1999 Kosovo conflict. (USAF)*

them. In an unpredictable world following the end of the bipolar standoff between the United States and the Soviet Union, we needed new ways to organize and fight. We needed an Air Force designed for frequent expeditionary employment.

Steps Toward the Expeditionary Aerospace Force

In our first step toward the Expeditionary Aerospace Force construct, the Air Force underwent major organizational changes in the last decade of the 20th century. Forces were realigned and integrated into functional organizations such as combat, mobility, and support. At the same time, the Air Force reconfirmed the air component structure characteristic of theater operations. In the air component structure, one air commander manages and delivers the totality of a region's air resources as directed by a theater Commander in Chief (CINC). This enables the Air Force to retain integrated operational capabilities and it facilitates unified command.

In the post–Cold War era, the Air Force was reduced to 60 percent of its former size, with overseas organizations most affected. With Cold War strategic stability waning, long contained regional conflicts flared. When the Air Force was called to respond, we did so with expeditionary forces. In Southwest Asia, in the Pacific, and in the Balkans we deployed

into unprepared locations—often standing up new bases or reopening old ones—to execute the missions. Throughout the decade of the 1990s, the Air Force deployed at a pace 300 to 400 percent busier than during the Cold War. We manned these newly established expeditionary bases primarily with individuals rotating from our 40 percent smaller force. This requirement taxed the deployed force and left home bases undermanned. We were organized for a cold war but living in a very hot peace.

Despite expectations that such an active tempo would die down, our day-to-day commitments remained high, placing increased pressure on our people and resources and threatening both readiness and retention. When we realized that the demands upon the Air Force would not abate, we implemented an Expeditionary Aerospace Force (EAF) concept to accommodate mission requirements.

The Expeditionary Aerospace Force

The EAF concept is both organizational and operational. Organizationally, the Air Force shift to the EAF provides an inclusive, unifying theme that ties all our people together in shared challenges, shared goals, and shared successes whether on deployment or at home. The success of an expeditionary mission depends on organizations that train, transport, sustain,

Above: Deep Submergence Rescue Vehicle Mystic (DSRV 1) inches aboard an Air Force Reserve C-5A "Galaxy" aircraft for transport. The C-5 includes a forward cargo door visor and ramp, and an aft cargo door system and ramp. These features allow drive-on/drive-off loading and unloading of the cargo compartment. (US Navy)

EXPEDITIONARY AEROSPACE FORCE (EAF):

The EAF is the total Air Force including active duty, Air Force Reserve, Air National Guard, Air Force civilians, and Air Force contractors. The EAF concept provides an inclusive, unifying, organizational theme that shares the challenges, goals, sacrifices, and successes of deployed forces across the Air Force family. This requires an expeditionary mindset in every airman and every Air Force activity from acquisition to training—from tactical forces to strategic forces.

AEROSPACE EXPEDITIONARY FORCES (AEF):

AEFs are composite combat organizations drawn from across the entire Expeditionary Aerospace Force (EAF) to create a tailored force designed to meet any contingency requiring deployment. Composed of wings, squadrons, and specialized units, an AEF is a powerful force that delivers the full capability of airpower.

An AC-130 gunship dispenses defensive flares. The defensive flares are dropped to defeat heat-seeking surface-to-air missiles by drawing them away from the aircraft. Gunships like these provide impressive ground attack capabilities. (USAF)

Above: A B-1 along with its fighter support, a pair of F-16s, runs through a training exercise over the western deserts of the United States. The teamwork of the AEF is apparent wherever one of its component wings is at work. (USAF)

Right: A Rockwell B-1 bomber moves into position to refuel from a Boeing KC-135R Stratotanker. ("Team Mates," Keith Ferris)

and augment that expeditionary force no less than the deployed forces. Airmen from all across the Air Force contribute to our expeditionary capabilities—from those who provide the deterrent umbrella under which we operate, to those who deploy, to those who operate the fixed facilities on which we depend for support. Everyone contributes to the mission of forward deployed forces. The Expeditionary Aerospace Force embodies these organizational concepts.

Operationally, the Expeditionary Aerospace Force consists of deployable assets like combat aircraft and combat support personnel as well as non-deployable assets like space control links or nuclear forces and associated personnel. The majority of our operational capabilities are organized into deployable teams at squadron or wing level. Other specialized and limited capabilities support deployed operational forces from fixed bases in the United States. This is the case for many of our high demand intelligence, surveillance, and reconnaissance (ISR) assets and personnel.

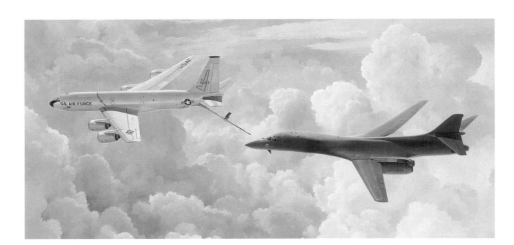

Left: *Captain Jim Smith and his crew chief hold a last minute discussion at the cockpit of his F-16, before flying another mission out of Aviano Air Force Base, Italy, in support of operations in the Balkans. (USAF)*

Above: *A 910th Airlift Wing C-130H, equipped with a Mobile Aerial Spray System (MASS), sprays larvacide to kill mosquitos on a weapons range at Cherry Point Marine Corps Air Station, North Carolina, on 22 August 2000. The Youngstown, Ohio, reserve wing has the only aerial delivery capability in the Defense Department. (USAF)*

An F-117 bomber is prepped for a nighttime mission. Its stealthy design enables it to attack enemy air defenses and lead the strike force in the initial attack. (USAF)

The EAF includes deployable and non-deployable warfighting capabilities. Every Air Force organization is assigned to one of four interdependent EAF categories: Prime Forces, Expeditionary Forces, Mobility Forces, and Foundation Forces.

Prime Forces include command and control capabilities, as well as nuclear, space, and special operations forces. These Prime elements help protect and focus the expeditionary force.

Deployable operational assets are organized into ten Aerospace Expeditionary Forces (AEFs). Each AEF consists of all the combat and support elements—fighters, bombers, tankers, intra-theater airlift, combat search and rescue, plus intelligence, surveillance, and reconnaissance (ISR) aircraft—needed to carry out expeditionary operations.

Mobility Forces provide transportation and logistics support for deployed AEFs and other U.S. military forces including the most urgent military cargo, from troops and equipment to humanitarian aid.

Foundation Forces provide the acquisition, medical, depot, training, and infrastructure resources needed to keep the entire Expeditionary Air Force operating.

To more effectively utilize our resources and provide some predictability for all of our people—including commanders, Guard members, reservists, their families, and their employers—we schedule actual and on-call deployments according to a 15-month cycle. This cycle allows us to manage the deployment and the effects of the operations tempo on our people. The Expeditionary Aerospace Force concept commits everyone in the Air Force to a common mission, a common vision, and a common goal for excellence. Our transformation into an EAF is far from a one-time event. On the contrary, two years into this effort we continue to innovate and improve, to fill shortfalls, and balance capabilities.

We've defined the four components of the Expeditionary Aerospace Force and the reasons that led to this new organization. How do the parts fit together?

Armament technician Senior Airman Hector Huguet of the 23rd Expeditionary Fighter Squadron checks over an air-to-air missile on an F-16CJ Fighting Falcon before takeoff from Incirlik Air Base, Turkey, as part of Operation Northern Watch. The operation involves patrolling the northern no-fly zones of Iraq. (USAF)

The MH-53J's mission is to perform low-level, long-range, undetected penetration into denied areas, day or night, in adverse weather, for infiltration, exfiltration and resupply of special operations forces. The MH-53J Pave Low III heavy-lift helicopter is the largest and most powerful helicopter in the Air Force inventory, and the most technologically advanced helicopter in the world. It can transport 38 troops or 14 litters and has an external cargo hook with a 20,000-pound capacity. Refueled at very low altitudes by the MC-130, the MH-53J operates over long ranges with great endurance. (USAF)

The Minuteman III missile has been the backbone of the U.S. land-based nuclear missile deterrent force for decades. This photo displays an effective test launch of a missile randomly selected from the operational field. After removing the warhead, test missiles are launched from Air Force facilities in California. (USAF)

Prime Forces

Capabilities grouped in our Prime Forces share two distinguishing factors—limited availability and specialized application. Air Force Special Operations Command (AFSOC) and Air Force Space Command (AFSPC) are the primary contributors to Prime Forces. Air Force Space Command's ICBM force is an example of Prime non-deployable operational capability. The deterrent force of ICBMs has been a keystone of U.S. national security for over 40 years. In addition to strategic deterrence, Space Command systems support all our deployable forces with the warning, communication, weather, global navigation, timing, and intelligence capabilities that assure we control the ultimate "high ground." These systems remain constantly vigilant, deployed, and active.

In contrast, Air Force Special Operations Command forces only deploy when regional commanders require their specialized capabilities. Because AFSOC assets are unique and limited, we group these forces in AEF Prime rather than assigning special operations elements to each of the 10 AEFs.

Finally, certain regional command and control elements within Pacific Air Forces, United States Air Forces in Europe, and other regional command structures are also assigned to AEF Prime. These command elements provide operational direction of deployed AEFs.

Aerospace Expeditionary Forces

Aerospace Expeditionary Forces are the core of our deployable combat power and forward presence. Two-thirds of the Air Force is allocated among 10 organized AEFs, each with roughly equivalent capabilities. Two AEFs are on-call or deployed at all times, providing the air compo-

Left: *AEF personnel exit a KC-10 transport to assume their responsibilities during a forward deployment. Large transports and cargo aircraft such as the the KC-10 enable U.S. forces to quickly establish self-sufficiency anywhere in the world. (USAF)*

Above: *Airmen unload cargo, here personnel baggage, from a transport plane upon arrival at their new deployment. (USAF)*

Above: *Major Sue Majzun, commander, and Technical Sergeant Vincent Maynard, radio maintenance technician, in the 910th Communications Flight, Youngstown Air Reserve Base, Ohio, review procedures while climbing a High Frequency radio antenna tower. (USAF)*

nent commanders with ready and complete aerospace force packages that can be tailored to conduct concurrent contingencies. Each AEF deploys with an integrated mix of strike aircraft and precision munitions. Airlift and rescue also deploy with an AEF when these capabilities are required to accomplish the mission. Rapid response to acts of aggression requires a significantly different force package than rapid response to earthquakes or famine. We deploy an AEF designed to meet the theater requirements.

Pacific Air Forces, United States Air Forces in Europe, Air Combat Command, Air Force Reserve Command, and the Air National Guard are the primary contributors of forces for our 10 AEFs. A notional strike

An F-16 of the 78th Expeditionary Fighter Squadron fired on and downed a hostile Yugoslavian MiG-29 on 4 May 1999 during Operation Allied Force. ("Snakebite Over Serbia," by K. Price Randel)

A "New Mexico triad" (AEF-deployed members of the new Mexico Air National Guard) flies over Kuwait in support of operation Southern Watch in May 1998. (USAF)

Airman 1st Class Heather Schaefer (right) and Airman 1st Class Angel L. Daly, both members of the 86th Services Squadron, Ramstein Air Base, Germany, serve the first hot breakfast to U.S. troops deployed to Tirana, Albania, on 20 April 1999. The airmen are deployed to Tirana in support of Operation Sustain Hope. (USAF)

package AEF consists of approximately 100 multi-role fighter and bomber aircraft to provide air-to-air superiority, suppression of enemy air defense (SEAD), precision guided munitions capability, standoff capability, close air support (CAS), and long-range strike. Command and control elements, ISR platforms, intra-theater airlift, and air refueling tankers deploy in support of AEF strike assets.

Most important to our people, the AEF structure provides predictability for their lives, stability for their training, and structured time for their reconstitution after deployment. By scheduling actual and on-call deployments according to a fifteen-month cycle, the EAF construct allows us to manage the effects of the operations tempo on our people. Predictability is key to optimizing peacetime participation of guardsmen and reservists who must balance military duties with full-time civilian employment.

Our unpredictable world demands employment flexibility and our AEFs are our primary means to fulfill these demands. During a fifteen-month full rotation period, each AEF is either deployed or on alert for deployment for three months. Two AEFs are always on-call or deployed. Typically, two AEFs are sufficient to satisfy our global deployment obliga-

tions. One AEF can surge to provide air superiority while striking some 200 targets per day, around the clock. In a small-scale contingency, one AEF can provide intelligence, surveillance, reconnaissance, and command and control of aerospace forces over an area roughly half the size of Texas.

In case of a pop-up contingency, we also have a smaller Aerospace Expeditionary Wing (AEW) on-call 365 days a year. Two AEWs alternate this on-call duty every 120 days. The AEWs supplement the AEFs by serving as a "911" force.

AEFs have become the measure of our day-to-day commitments worldwide. They also form the force packages for theater conflict planning. Two AEFs and one AEW represent about 20 percent of our combat forces—the maximum sustained commitment the Air Force can maintain without adversely impacting training or readiness.

Mobility Force

Mobility Forces provide rapid global reach not just for the Air Force, but also for all U.S. military forces. Whether projecting power in the form of pallets of aid or pallets of weapons, we need strategic agility and mobility to rapidly position and reposition forces worldwide. AEFs are deployed and sustained by a fleet of inter-theater transports and refueling aircraft that provide that global mobility to our Expeditionary Aerospace Force.

A B-1B Lancer crew and its crew chief, all from the 28th Air Expeditionary Wing, discuss the maintenance log before leaving on a combat mission in support of Operation Enduring Freedom in Afghanistan. (USAF)

An F-16 is led out of its weather-protective shelter. Such cover and planning enables the 24/7 operational capacity of the AEF. The F-16 is the primary Air Force strike aircraft and is expected to remain so for another two decades. (USAF)

The Joint Surveillance Target Attack Radar System (Joint STARS) is an airborne platform equipped with a long-range, air-to-ground surveillance system designed to locate, classify and track ground targets in all weather conditions. Its capabilities make Joint STARS effective for dealing with any contingency, whether actual or impending military aggression, international treaty verification or border violation. The E-8C, a modified Boeing 707, carries a phased-array radar antenna in a 26-foot canoe-shaped radome under the forward part of the fuselage. (USAF)

Relief supplies are unloaded from a USAF C-141 transport. Humanitarian missions to Africa and elsewhere around the world have become as prevalent an AEF focus as military operations. (USAF)

Consisting of an air transportation network, Mobility Forces move the most urgent cargo, from troops and equipment to humanitarian aid. As we have cut U.S. forward based-forces and bases, this air transportation network has become increasingly important.

Mobility Forces are organized into Lead Mobility Wings (LMW). Each of the five LMWs is aligned with one AEF pair to provide rapid initial expeditionary response. Like all others, Air Mobility Command units require support. As a deployment engages and long-term support is required, mobility assets build an air bridge for persistence and sustainment. The Lead Mobility Wing can provide the air mobility expertise and leadership for humanitarian relief crisis and noncombatant evacuation. LMWs also provide the skill necessary to assess expeditionary base airfields and determine follow-on airlift requirements.

Greater predictability has helped stabilize the operations tempo of our mobility units. Using the AEF rotation schedule as a planning tool, we've reduced the inter-theater airlift required during the deployment and redeployment phase occurring every 90 days as AEFs rotate responsibilities. Increased reserve force participation and greater leveraging of commercial airlift are producing efficiencies, and are just the first fruits of our transition to an EAF construct. As our AEF experience grows and our people continue to innovate, we'll use mobility assets even more effectively.

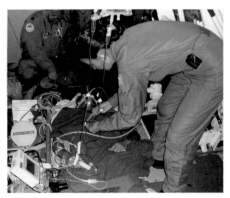

Foundation Force

Underlying Prime, AEF, and Mobility Forces are our Foundation Forces. Foundation Forces include everything from basic and technical training provided by Air Education and Training Command (AETC) to Air Force Materiel Command's (AFMC) system development, acquisition, and sustainment. Additionally, medical care for service members, their families, and retirees is a part of this critical support foundation.

With 65 percent of the total force in deployable billets, Air Force personnel must accept the "expeditionary" mindset of our service from day one. Through basic military training, officer induction programs, and the Aerospace Basic Course, Air Education and Training Command reinforces the expectation that everyone supports the expeditionary operation—overseas or at home. The vast majority of functions required at home bases are also required at deployment locations. To function fully and effectively, deploying AEFs take with them a complement of combat and support specialties: chaplain, public affairs, personnel, contracting, services, medical, and more.

Just as Air Education and Training Command instills an "expeditionary" mindset in all our training, so the Air Force Materiel Command (AFMC) ensures this attitude is common across acquisition functions, logistical support, and even in our science and technology development. In addition to providing logistical support for deployed weapons systems as well as the munitions expended by those systems, AFMC delivers maintenance information to the AEFs. AFMC is rapidly replacing legacy information systems—printed documents—with web-based information systems that are easily accessed by deployed war fighters.

Yet, another major component of our EAF foundation is the Air Force medical community. From the moment enlistees enter initial training, the Air Force provides medical care for them and their families. Operationally, our medical community is very active. In addition to flight medicine specialties, they conduct emergency medical evacuations and maintain capabilities to treat mass casualties. Day-to-day, their emphasis on preventive medicine helps keep our service members healthy while meeting the medical needs of families and retirees.

Global Vigilance, Reach, and Power

Airman Shaun Partridge and Technical Sergeant Maria Kamrowski, of the 363d Communications Squadron, prepare to lower a quick reaction satellite antenna in order to repair a broken pedal in March 2002. They are deployed to Saudi Arabia in support of Operation Southern Watch. (USAF)

Above: The Space Based Infrared Radar System (SBIRS) High is slated for a first launch in 2005. This constellation will initially augment, then replace, the Defense Satellite Program constellation, first launched in the 1970s. The new constellation will be able to detect a broader range of infrared signals greatly enhancing coverage and providing better situational awareness to the warfighter. (USAF)

Right: The Navstar Global Positioning System (GPS) is a space-based constellation of orbiting satellites that provides navigation data to worldwide military and civilian users. The GPS constellation is designed and operated as a 24-satellite system, consisting of six planes, with a minimum of four satellites per plane. The satellites orbit the earth every 12 hours, emitting continuous navigation signals. With the proper equipment, users can receive these signals to calculate time, location, and velocity so accurately that time can be figured to within a millionth of a second, velocity within a fraction of a mile per hour, and location to within 100 feet. The USAF launches, maintains, and upgrades this constellation for the nation. (USAF)

The EAF is our organizational and operational construct for delivering Global Vigilance, Reach, and Power for the defense of the United States. These three components of air and space power are intertwined and interdependent. Together they enable effective engagement of adversaries with such speed and precision that we're able to deny those adversaries the traditional sanctuaries of night, weather, terrain, and even time.

Information is power. The integration of manned, unmanned, and space platforms shortens the time required to make battlefield decisions and act on them, enabling the U.S. to outmaneuver adversaries in both space and time. By transparently linking manned, unmanned, and space surveillance assets, we will continue to tighten our decision cycle. This is the essence of gaining and maintaining decision dominance over an adversary. Global vigilance gives us this edge, whether we are gathering information for the battle area, working to foil the plans of terrorists, or keeping watch on nature's threats.

Historically, knowledge for waging battle came from the best vantage point—the highest ground. Today, our global vigilance starts with a system of systems in the highest locale—space. Air Force–launched satellites provide communication (Defense Satellite Communications System, Military Strategic and Tactical Relay), navigation (Global Positioning System), and weather (Defense Meteorological Satellite Program) capabilities, crucial to the operational commander. We will continue to improve our capabilities in the space medium with systems such as the Space-Based Radar and Space-Based Infrared Satellite. These systems will

Predator in Combat

Captain Joseph M. Rizzuto, USAF

The radio crackled with activity as aircraft arrived. We had been holding over the mountains of Afghanistan for hours. The war against the Taliban and Al Qaeda had progressed into a cave-by-cave search. Our cameras pinpointed enemy positions—even darkness could not hide their locations. An AC-130 Spectre gunship checked-in, ready to shoot. We talked the gunship onto an enemy position and watched as the 105-mm rounds ripped the mountainside apart. Debris, dirt, and destruction flew. For an intense three hours, we directed gunship fire onto enemy strongholds. Other gunships stacked miles away waited their turn. As one ran out of ammunition or fuel, another moved into position. Finally, the target list was exhausted. We searched all the locations again where the enemy had been spotted, but there was no sign of activity there now. Flames flickered on the mountain. Nothing else moved.

Intently concentrating on the mission, I jumped when my replacement pilot tapped me on the shoulder. I stood and she settled into the seat to continue the search. As I opened the back door of the Ground Control Station, the early morning air hit me. I walked to break-fast, amazed at the technology behind remotely piloted aircraft that allowed me to fight on the front lines thousands of miles away one minute and safely walk to breakfast the next.

From Predator surveillance during the past two months, I had watched bombers, fighters, and gunships pour on the firepower. I was thankful to be part of an Air Force that could rain destruction wherever it was needed, and not one of the enemy soldiers hiding on that mountain.

During Operation Enduring Freedom, the Predator Unmanned Combat Air Vehicle revolutionized air warfare by blending intelligence gathering with operational strike missions. With loiter times of more than twenty-four hours, Predator gave us persistent surveillance. Talking directly with fighter, bomber, and gunship crews, Predator pilots in our Ground Control Station relayed real-time battlefield intelligence to the strikers. No longer dedicated only to intelligence, surveillance, and reconnaissance, Predator now engages in armed reconnaissance Killer Scout missions, close air support for ground troops, base security, and combat search and rescue. This range of missions will certainly continue to expand in the future. Not the most glamorous assignment in the Air Force for a pilot, flying unmanned aerial vehicles from a ground station is nevertheless an exciting responsibility at the cutting edge of Air Force combat capability.

This Predator vehicle is only one part of a system that includes other air vehicles, a ground control station, associated satellite communications suite, and over fifty people. The Predator was effectively used in combat over Bosnia and Kosovo while still undergoing its initial operational test and evaluation. (USAF)

Air Force Reserve Bombers

Lieutenant Colonel Steve Kirkpatrick, USAFR

Tiger 02, our forward air controller (FAC), was cold, tired, and on the move. Every time he keyed the radio, I heard small arms fire and mortar explosions in the background. My navigation team, two weapons experts, furiously uploaded target position data into twelve 2000-pound satellite-guided Joint Direct Attack Munitions. My electronic warfare officer kept the rest of the crew abreast of changes in our dynamic combat environment. I checked my watch again and realized that we had received the satellite e-mail informing us of Tiger 02's dire situation only twenty minutes earlier. He was our local ground controller, responsible for targeting Taliban and Al Qaeda positions in the area of Kabul. Taliban fighters had detected him and were closing on his position. Now, we were pushing our single B-52 toward the enemy carrying the equivalent firepower of six F-15E fighter-bombers.

We coordinated with Tiger 02 to strike four different targets hoping to halt the Taliban attack against his position. After weapons impact, Tiger 02 informed us that each of our precision guided bombs had found the target, foiling the enemy attack. He also reported that Taliban fighters were now ripe for an attack with our internal load of twenty-seven 500-pound "dumb bombs."

Satellite data constantly updated our targeting computers as we prepared to attack Taliban bunkers along a ridgeline adjacent to our FAC's position. We had absolutely no room for error. The navigator began the countdown to weapons release as open bomb-bay doors caused airflow to buffet the aircraft. A low frequency rumble and a sudden increase in altitude signaled "bombs away." Less than a minute later, radio static gave way to excited shouts from our ground controller. Muffled sounds of heavy weapons detonations provided background noise. Our twenty-seven Mark 82 bombs cut right down the center of the Taliban lines. Over the radio, we heard the FAC team and friendly Afghan fighters break into a spontaneous celebration. We nosed our aircraft south and headed home with the knowledge that B-52 tactics were changing.

As the commander of the 93rd Bomb Squadron, a reserve B-52 bomber unit, I know that the doctrine of "Total Force" calls for Air National Guard and Air Force Reserve units to serve side-by-side with the regular Air Force in times of conflict or national emergency. After the terrorist attack against America on 11 September 2001, I knew that our young men and women would be busy. In the first days of Operation Enduring Freedom, hundreds of reserve personnel, both officer and enlisted, said goodbye to their families and jobs and deployed for war. I am proud of each one of them.

This B-52 will soon launch against targets in Afghanistan. The weapons load team loads a Multiple Ejector Rack with Mk-84 2000lb general purpose bombs equipped with Joint Direct Attack Munition kits. The fins or strakes attached to the bomb double the range of a normal Mk-84. When dropped from 40,000 ft it will fly about fifteen miles. The tail kit contains a GPS receiver and three steerable fins to guide the bomb to the target. The cost of the kit is approximately $22,000. (USAF)

provide integrated detection and tracking of theater threats and targets, and early detection and warning of missile launches.

Unmanned aerial vehicle (UAV) programs like Predator and Global Hawk augment space assets. The penetration and loiter capabilities of UAVs enhance their usefulness for surveillance and reconnaissance missions. By removing the human from the platform, we increase the amount of time a platform can "look and listen" and we avoid human losses.

Manned systems like AWACS, the RC-135J Rivet Joint, U-2 reconnaissance aircraft, and E-8B JSTARS will remain critical components to help commanders see through the fog of war. Combined with unmanned aerial vehicles and space capabilities, manned platforms provide redundancy for us while simultaneously complicating enemy efforts to foil our systems.

Above: Two Air Force Reserve Command B-52s are shown here in flight practicing conventional ordnance delivery. At the end of the Cold War, a number of B-52s were transferred to Reserve units to further develop conventional weapons capabilities. In addition to delivering conventional bombs, these B-52s are also capable of delivering cruise missiles and precision guided munitions. (USAF)

Below: An RQ-4A Global Hawk unmanned aerial vehicle touches down at Edwards AFB. The Global Hawk is designed to provide battlefield commanders with near real-time, high-resolution, reconnaissance imagery. Flying at extremely high altitudes, Global Hawk can survey large geographic areas giving military decision-makers the most current information. (USAF)

Above: *The U-2 is a single-seat, single-engine, high-altitude, reconnaissance aircraft. It carries a variety of sensors capable of simultaneously collecting signals and imagery intelligence. It can use both line-of-sight and beyond-line-of-sight data links. Current models are derived from the original version that made its first flight in August 1955. The U-2 provided critical intelligence data during Operations Desert Storm and Allied Force. (Guy Aceto)*

The first C-5 was delivered in June l970 and the last in March of 1989. The C-5 Avionics Modernization Program began in 1998 and includes upgrading avionics for international Global Air Traffic Management compliance. A second part of the modernization plan is a re-engining and reliability improvement program including new engines, pylons and auxiliary power units, with upgrades to aircraft skin and frame, landing gear and pressurization system. (USAF)

Lockheed Martin and Boeing have joined forces to produce proposals for the Evolved Expendable Launch Vehicle (EELV). The EELV program is poised to provide more affordable and reliable access to space for the United States. (Boeing)

Our ability to rapidly project and sustain combat forces depends on the availability of tanker and airlift resources. As threats to U.S. interests have changed in recent years, the size and weight of U.S. mechanized firepower and equipment has significantly increased air mobility requirements. Newer and more flexible airlift aircraft, in sufficient quantity, are needed for rapid response to contingency requirements, including combat, peacekeeping, and humanitarian missions.

The C-17—newest member of the airlift family—is capable of both inter-theater and intra-theater delivery of troops and cargo to main operating bases or directly to forward bases in the deployment area, including small and austere airfields. The flexibility and performance of the C-17 force significantly improves the ability of the total airlift system to fulfill worldwide air mobility requirements of the United States.

Our other out-size capable carrier, the C-5, is beginning a critically important test. To improve mission capability and availability, a C-5 modernization test will evaluate the feasibility of a comprehensive approach to enhancing the aircraft while simultaneously reducing the cost of ownership. Four C-5Bs will participate in the initial evaluation. The results of these tests will help the Air Force decide whether a fleet-wide C-5 modernization effort is cost effective.

Our global reach into space will be improved by procurement of the Evolved Expendable Launch Vehicle (EELV). With the EELV launch system, the Air Force will be better able to tailor launches for light, medium, and heavy lift. The EELV is also more responsive than legacy systems—a necessity as our nation, and particularly the military, becomes increasingly dependent upon space assets.

Our global reach also incorporates our ability to react quickly and decisively with nuclear deterrent forces, these forces are forecast for further enhancements. ICBMs continue to stand alert every hour of every day. The Strategic Triad is no less important today than during the Cold War. With the continued spread of nuclear weapons, deterrence will be an essential mission well into the future.

Noble Eagle

Major Dan Caine, District of Columbia Air National Guard

I was the Supervisor of Flying for the 121st Fighter Squadron, "The Capital Guardians," on the morning of 11 September 2001 when the United States was attacked. Our F-16C+ aircraft—just back from a successful Red Flag deployment—sat on the ramp at Andrews Air Force Base, Maryland, still configured with external fuel tanks and targeting pods. Like Americans across the country, squadron personnel clustered around television sets watching in amazement as the World Trade Center towers collapsed. From Andrews, we saw smoke billowing from the Pentagon.

The ringing telephone jerked me back to reality. The U.S. Secret Service, calling from the White House, told us that another airliner was inbound. They wanted defensive fighter cover over Washington. I handed the telephone to my wing commander then ordered our munitions loaders to start loading wartime missiles. In the meantime, we launched two aircraft armed only with 20-mm guns. Squadron pilots, Guardsmen living across the metropolitan area, began arriving in the squadron ready to fly. My wingman and I went to our jets and waited as missiles were loaded. Our maintenance personnel were amazing—they worked like the best NASCAR pit crew and got us airborne in record time.

Airborne, communications were chaotic. I contacted FAA air traffic controllers at Reagan Airport and began training them to run active air defense intercepts. In the next few hours, we ran more than twenty-five intercepts. When I could not raise an intercepted aircraft on the radio, I fired self-protection flares to scare them away from potential targets. Several times, I found myself over the mall at very low altitude in pursuit of unknown aircraft. Flying over the Capitol building, I realized it had been evacuated.

More F-16s took off from Andrews. F-15s and F-16s arrived from Langley Air Force Base, Virginia. A Reserve KC-10 and an Air National Guard KC-135 arrived. At one point, I had eight fighters stacked in combat air patrols at various altitudes over Washington and two tankers working over Andrews. Later, as I landed my F-16, I knew we had set a pattern for operations that would protect the nation's capital. The Air Force maintained that defensive combat air patrol over Washington for the next six months. During that same period, deployed to Afghanistan, I met some of the same Air Reserve and Air National Guard pilots that I had encountered over the capital on 11 September

On September 11 2001, F-16s from the District of Columbia Air National Guard began flying combat air patrols over the nation's capital. (USAF)

People—Our Power

America's Air Force is the finest in the world and is incredibly busy across all the far reaches of this globe. America's airmen are engaged in the full spectrum of missions in defense of America. In Southwest Asia, our professionals have been engaged in combat operations for the past decade. Almost daily, our aircrews are fired upon and respond with force to police the no-fly zones in northern and southern Iraq. It is a perilous mission for peace and stability in the region. Many of our people live in austere conditions—some on their fourth or fifth rotation—but on every visit I've seen pride in their purpose and professionalism in their performance.

That professionalism is just as obvious when natural or humanitarian disasters strike. When floodwaters devastated the people of Mozambique and South Africa, our airmen were there to respond. Air Force people and aircraft distributed relief supplies, conducted aerial assessment of damage and water levels, and flew critical search and rescue missions. In a 21-day international effort, our airmen moved hundreds of displaced people and distributed two million pounds of relief supplies. Americans did not do it alone. We were part of a team of nations and organizations concerned for the welfare of those suffering.

We're a part of the peacekeeping team providing stability in the Balkans. Over 2,000 of America's airmen are supporting Balkan air operations. In just two years, we flew over 31,000 sorties providing the top cover for NATO peace efforts in this fragile region of the world.

On this side of the Atlantic, in Central America, Air Force airfield experts, traffic controllers, and security forces are supporting JTF-Bravo at Soto Cano Air Base in Honduras. Here, airmen support drug interdiction efforts, search and rescue activities, and humanitarian operations. Air Force medical teams travel to Honduras every year, as volunteers, to perform life-changing surgeries. Such work is win-win for the Air Force. The medical teams get valuable training in field conditions, patients benefit from medical care not otherwise available, and we build goodwill in the region.

Back home, the missions are just as diverse and demanding. For instance, at Vandenberg AFB, our west coast facility for both ICBM tests and the space shuttle, we recently conducted our 1,800th launch. We've continued to train allied personnel from around the world, building international bonds, and the foundations for service interoperability. In the western United States, year after year, active, reserve and Air National Guard aircraft, including specialized C-130s, dispense millions of gallons of fire retardant over treacherous terrain to fight forest fires.

In the Far East, our forces sit on constant alert—vigilant and prepared to respond to threats to our alliances.

The people of the Air Force do these missions with truly remarkable professionalism. Year after year, despite these intense demands, we've achieved unprecedented records in flying safety. While one accident and loss is one too many, we've managed to keep our trends in safety going in the right direction even as our fleet of aircraft continues

Above: *Weapons loaders from Virginia Air National Guard's 192nd Fighter Wing perform End of Runway (EOR) procedures before an F16C takes off in support of Operation Noble Eagle on 30 October 2001. (USAF)*

Above: *An airman runs through an operational checklist. The tent city set up as part of Operation Bright Star, is visible in the background. (USAF)*

Right: *The flight crew prepare for the long haul—a flight to Korea—on the flight deck of their C-130. (USAF)*

to age. This is a real testimony to our maintainers and our crewmembers. These records are all the more impressive when you consider the conditions under which they are performed and the scope of our worldwide operations.

In 1999, we won a tremendous victory over aggression and inhumanity in the Balkans. In the television coverage of the air war over Serbia, you didn't see how much time our people spent loading pallets or building tent cities. You didn't see the shortfalls endured by units back home to ensure the front-line forces had everything they needed. You seldom saw the pain of separation from loved ones or the sacrifices of our families. And you didn't hear complaints. What you did hear was how proud our people were of what they do and who they do it with. "People first" is not just a slogan—it's a priority. Over the past several years, we've worked hard to improve the quality of life for our people. Quality of life is indeed part of our readiness equation. The one issue that has concerned us the most in the past several years has been people. It is possible to have the best equipment in the world, but without world-class people, it's only machinery.

In June of 2000, we published our vision for America's Air Force—Global Vigilance, Reach, and Power. We declared up-front that our people are the foundation of our force. That report pledged "We will never forget the trust the American people place in us. They count on us to protect their ideals, their security, and their prosperity—and they give us their finest young men and women to sustain that effort. We will keep faith with those young men and women—America's airmen—and they will keep faith with the nation. Together we are America's Air Force."

The virtues of the AEF are many, but one of the great benefits is the positive effect for our people. We want to retain our people because we need experienced personnel prepared to deploy with no notice and to fight and win. The AEF schedule is a retention booster because it puts

Above: *Armed and ready at Ramstein Air Force Base, Germany. In today's unstable world, Air Force personnel must keep constant vigil. (USAF)*

Left: *Airmen push a cart of ordnance into position to reload aircraft for their next mission. The entire AEF team must function as one to keep any mission operational. (USAF)*

Staff Sergeant Tim Phillips, a crew chief assigned to the 75th Airlift Squadron, Ramstein Air Base, Germany, performs post-flight aircraft checks on a C-9 Nightingale. The C-9 crews fly medical airlift missions throughout Europe to transport patients to the Landstuhl Regional Medical Center in Germany for major medical care. (USAF)

predictability into people's lives and into their deployments, and it distributes the burden more equitably. Time away on deployment—away from family, away from educational facilities, away from jobs in the case of our guard and reserve members—is tough but necessary. The AEF makes that burden easier to bear while also increasing our effectiveness.

THE
Air Force of
Tomorrow

Future Systems

John Correll

The Air Force enters the 21st century with an expanding mission. Even more so than in the past, it will be the force the nation relies on for long-range power projection and rapid response to distant trouble. Building on capabilities demonstrated in the air campaigns of the 1990s, the Air Force will act as a powerful striking force in its own right and as an enabler of land and sea forces missions.

Airpower tasks will range from theater conflict and humanitarian relief to defense of the American homeland. In addition, the force will take on new responsibilities in space. In May 2001, Secretary of Defense Donald H. Rumsfeld designated the Air Force as the Department of Defense executive agent for space. If the move into space works out as planned, the Air Force will eventually conduct operations in a seamless domain of air and space that reaches from tree-top level to high Earth orbit and beyond.

Let us imagine the Air Force—the aerospace force—as it might look twenty years into the future. It will have come a long way from the World War II days of piston engines and iron bombs, but the heritage and traditions of the force will still be there. Casting ahead to 2020, USAF "Vision Force" planners in the Pentagon see three broad trends developing: the number of unmanned aircraft will increase; the number of manned aircraft will decrease; and numerous missions, especially Intelligence, Surveillance, and Reconnaissance, will migrate to space.

This force of the future will have fewer aircraft and fewer people, but the capabilities will dramatically exceed those of today. Even so, not

Above: *The most spectacular unmanned vehicle in operation so far is Northrop Grumman's Global Hawk. In 2001, it flew nonstop and unmanned from California to a precision landing in Australia. It can fly without assistance to a point 4,000 miles from its base and conduct surveillance over an area the size of Illinois for twenty-four hours before returning home. It is the probable successor to the fabled U-2 spy plane, shown at lower right of this illustration. (Erik Simonsen)*

Opposite: *The Air Force Special Operations Command plans to use the CV-22 vertical take-off and landing aircraft to transport troops and equipment deep into enemy territory. The CV-22, planned to replace some Air Force helicopters, is a variant of the Marine Corps MV-22. (USAF)*

Pages 336–337: *The concept demonstrator for the F-35 Joint Strike Fighter (JSF) is shown here in flight over Edwards AFB, California. The JSF is a multinational cooperative development program that will field a family of next-generation strike fighters to replace the F-16 and the A-10. The United States Navy, the United States Marine Corps, the Royal Air Force, and the Royal Navy also plan to deploy the JSF. (USAF)*

Above: *The F-22 Raptor achieves its capability from a combination of features: advanced stealth, supersonic cruise, and operation at high altitudes. These characteristics will enable the F-22 to fly through defenses that would be deadly for other fighters. (USAF)*

Above: *The Boeing B-52 will remain in the Air Force inventory as a conventional cruise missile carrier for the next several decades. Its standoff precision strike capability will augment bomber and fighter attack until the elimination of enemy defenses permit conventional attack with large quantities of precision bombs. An Air Launch Cruise Missile (ALCM) is prepared for loading. (USAF)*

Right: *The Northrop Grumman B-2 will provide long range stealthy penetration in the initial phases of combat operations and then convert range to endurance to support ground forces. (USAF)*

everything will be different. A number of holdover aircraft will still be in operation. Incredibly enough, that force will include the B-52 bomber, which joined the Air Force inventory in the early 1950s. It is expected to be in the operational lineup to observe its 75th anniversary of active service in 2027.

These "legacy systems" from the past will operate alongside such leap-ahead systems as the Unmanned Combat Air Vehicle. The UCAV will be one of the stealthy "front four"—along with the F-22 fighter, the Joint Strike Fighter, and the B-2 bomber—around which the Air Force plans to build its global strike capability.

Manned Fighter Aircraft

Of these, the one arguably closest to the Air Force's heart is the F-22 Raptor. It will rule the sky well into the 21st century. In appearance and basic mission, it is a fighter, but it will perform in missions ranging from air superiority to strikes against heavily defended targets deep in enemy territory.

The F-22 derives its capability from several features. It has all-aspect stealth, presenting a low profile to radar from any direction. It will also be considerably stealthier than any other aircraft in the air. It will have super-cruise—it will be the first fighter able to sustain supersonic speeds for extended periods, and to do so without use of fuel-guzzling afterburners—and an operating ceiling above 40,000 feet. It will slip undetected through advanced air defenses that would be a barrier for F-15s and F-16s. Thrust-vectoring nozzles will give the F-22 great agility, but the intention is not to get into a turning fight at close range. The pilot is supposed to see the enemy aircraft and attack before he is detected himself.

Air supremacy is the primary mission of the F-22, establishing control of the air space, clearing the way for the B-2s and the other strikers, and providing cover for less-stealthy electronic aircraft. However, it will also carry eight small-diameter smart bombs, tucked away internally, so it can take part in the strike mission as well. About the only shortcoming of the twin-engine F-22 is that the Air Force will have only a few hundred of them.

That's where the Joint Strike Fighter (JSF) comes in. It is a lower-cost, single-engine fighter. It will not have the speed, the range, or the same

Elimination of an aircraft's tail reduces weight, drag, and radar signature. The B-2 bomber, already in service, manages quite well without a tail. However, the conceptual Lockheed Martin X-44 fighter (illustrated here) goes further. It has no flaps, ailerons, rudder, or other control surfaces. It uses thrust-vectoring exhaust nozzles instead to change pitch and yaw. (Erik Simonsen)

The F-35 Joint Strike Fighter will not have as much range, speed, or stealth as the F-22. However, it will be available in greater numbers, and its role will be to grind out sorties, day after day, as the battle persists. (Erik Simonsen)

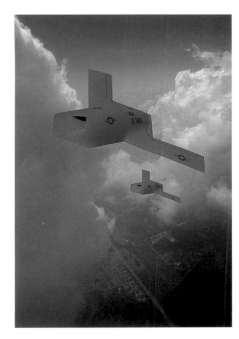

The Unmanned Combat Air Vehicle is one of the aircraft that will define the stealthy Air Force of 2020. It will be used extensively for the most dangerous missions, reducing the number of airmen who must put their lives at risk. (Erik Simonsen)

The technology demonstrator for the UCAV, the Boeing X-45A, rolled out in 2000. The airplane will generally fly preprogrammed missions, but a human operator at a distant terminal will release weapons. It will be employed initially to suppress enemy air defenses, but other missions will follow. (Boeing)

degree of stealthiness the F-22 has, but it will join the force in great numbers. The Joint Strike Fighter program is huge, providing thousands of airplanes to the U.S., British, and allied armed forces. Once the F-22 and the B-2 thin out the most lethal threats, the Joint Strike Fighter will be the airplane that grinds out the attack sorties, day after day, if a conflict persists. It will fill roughly the same niche in 2020 that the F-16 does today.

The JSF will have some air-to-air capability, but its main role will be ground attack. In its stealthy configuration, it will carry two 1,000-pound bombs internally. When stealth is not required, it can mount additional weapons externally.

Meanwhile, unmanned aircraft are already coming on strong.

Unmanned Aerial Vehicles

Unmanned aerial vehicles (UAVs) have three big advantages: They don't get tired, they don't get bored, and they are fearless. These characteristics make them ideal for long-endurance missions, less interesting work—such as flying great circles in the sky to maintain surveillance—and missions that go into extremely dangerous air space.

The most spectacular unmanned aerial vehicle thus far has been Global Hawk, a long-endurance reconnaissance aircraft roughly the size of a business jet but with a wingspan of 116 feet, considerably longer than that of the fabled U-2 spy plane. The flowing lines of the Global Hawk fuselage are graceful, even with a hump in front that covers a large satellite dish. Inside, it is packed with radar, electro-optical and infrared sensors. Its images of China Lake Naval Air Station California, taken from 61,000 feet and a slant range of twenty-four kilometers, are clear and detailed.

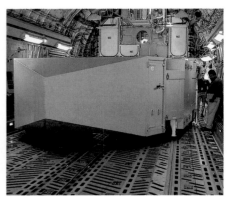

Top, left: *The Predator, built by General Atomics Aeronautical Systems, was a star of operations in Afghanistan. Among other things, it provided a live video transmission that gave commanders an immediate picture of the battle area and provided them with targeting information. (USAF)*

Above: *The Unmanned Combat Air Vehicle is designed to be stored unassembled in a container until it is needed. Workers can then unpack it and reconstitute it in an hour. (USAF)*

Left: *The Northrop Grumman entry was another prototype considered for the Unmanned Combat Air Vehicle. It bears a distinct family resemblance to the B-2. (Northrop Grumman)*

Global Hawk's rated endurance is thirty-six hours, but in a typical mission profile, it would fly to a point 4,000 miles from its base and for the next twenty-four hours, conduct surveillance of an area the size of Illinois before returning home. Once airborne, Global Hawk flies and navigates on its own. In April 2001, it flew nonstop, un-piloted, and unrefueled, from California to a precision landing in Adelaide, Australia. The 8,600-mile trip was about two-thirds of its total range.

At the smaller and slower end of the UAV scale is the propeller-driven Predator, which the Air Force has flown with good effect on surveillance missions over Iraq, Bosnia, Kosovo, and Afghanistan. Predator weighs only 950 pounds when empty. Ground operators control it all the way to its destination and back.

Since February 2001, Predator has been exploring another role. The Air Force hung lightweight Hellfire-C laser-guided missiles under the wing of the little drone, which then made three successful attacks on a stationary tank target on the Nellis Air Force Base range in Nevada. The Air Force is exploring a turboprop version of Predator with longer endurance and greater carrying capacity.

The craft that looms large for 2020, though, is the stealthy Unmanned Combat Air Vehicle (UCAV). It is about the size of a small fighter, and carries several thousand pounds of ordnance. UCAVs will be employed initially to suppress enemy air defenses, but other missions will follow.

The concept is to preposition UCAVs in storage at various places around the world. When trouble begins, the Air Force could unpack, assemble, and unleash them. In action, the UCAVs would be under the

Depending on what other aircraft are deployed forward when a crisis begins, the pre-positioned UCAVs could be the first combat airplanes in the fight. Technology will make UCAVs increasingly better as the years go by. (Erik Simonsen)

The effectiveness of airpower derives from a combination of aircraft and weapons. Here, a test crew checks out a GBU-15 standoff weapon before a flight test. (USAF)

Above and below: *Arrayed here are several generations of stealth. The B-2 bomber (above) proved its worth in Kosovo, and the F-117A Nighthawk (left below) did so in the Gulf War. At right below is an early version of the F-22, which takes stealth technology to new levels. (USAF)*

control of an operator at a terminal back at the base. For the most part, the aircraft would fly on its own, including takeoff and landing. A human operator would control weapons release.

Over the next quarter century, engines that are more efficient will give UCAVS and UAVs the ability to endure 60 percent longer. For some systems, silent flight will become possible as fuel cells supplant combustion engines. Increased range will be especially important because world politics and the proliferation of advanced weapons have begun to pose problems of access to foreign bases.

Bombers

Increased range will also put a premium on large payload platforms that can strike from afar. In 2020, the Air Force heavy hitter will be the B-2 Spirit, although with some upgrades and enhancements. Over the years, critics have claimed that the B-2's stealthy coating would melt away in the rain or predicted that it could not sustain a combat sortie rate. B-2 procurement was cut from 132 to twenty-one. In the air war over Serbia in 1999, the B-2 made its critics eat their words.

The B-2 struck an average of fifteen separate aim points per sortie and destroyed 90 percent of its targets on the first strike. Crews regularly made the thirty-hour round trip flight from home base in Missouri to Yugoslavia. Only six B-2s were committed to the operation at any one time, but they accounted for 12.8 percent of the precision strikes. In 2001, B-2s flew sorties from Missouri to strike targets in Afghanistan.

A handful of B-2s can have an awesome effect. In World War II, it took an average of 240 tons of bombs, delivered by waves of B-17s, to drop a bridge span. Today, the B-2 can do it with four tons of modern ordnance. In 1943, the Circular Error Probable—the Air Force's standard measure of bombing accuracy—for a B-17 with iron bombs was 3,300 feet. Over Kosovo, the B-2 achieved a CEP of twenty feet, and got its target guidance from a Global Positioning System satellite in space.

By 2020, the Air Force expects to be operating a new long-range strike platform to augment the B-2. Essentially a "truck" rather than a penetrating bomber, this new aircraft will deliver 120,000 pounds of cruise missiles from standoff range. Until then, the B-52 will continue the cruise missile mission.

Top left, top right, and left: *The quest for precision weapons has been a long one. Among the earliest attempts was the VB-3 vertical bomb (above left), which had a radio set in its tail section so the bombardier could guide it. Below left, an F-16 launches a Joint Direct Attack Munition (JDAM). In Kosovo, B-2 bombers used JDAM with extraordinary effect, striking within twelve meters of the target 90 percent of the time. The F-16 on the right above carries a Joint Standoff Weapon. JSOW will be used by both Air Force and Navy aircraft, and like JDAM, will use a GPS signal from space to find its targets. (USAF)*

Weapons

Some of the big gains in long-range strike will come from new munitions. For example, hypervelocity missiles, streaking along at six times the speed of sound, will hit targets more than 500 miles away.

A new bomb rack design will soon enable the B-2 to carry up to eighty Joint Direct Attack Munitions, each of which can be independently targeted. A new type of munition, the small-diameter "smart" bomb, is on the way. A B-2 will eventually be able to carry 324 of these, with each one employed against a different target.

However, the preferred ordnance of the future is likely to be directed energy weapons. Military interest in directed energy focuses on two areas: high-energy lasers and high-power microwaves.

Laser characteristics differ from microwave characteristics. Laser weapons must be precisely aimed and they cannot operate through clouds. They heat, melt, or vaporize the target with a focused beam. Microwave weapons, on the other hand, need to be pointed only in the general direction of a target. They attack a broad area with a surge of energy that disrupts or destroys electronic circuits.

In a sense, laser-guided bombs might be considered directed energy weapons, but they represent a hybrid technology. The leading example of a true beam weapon is the Airborne Laser. Mounted in a militarized version of the Boeing 747-400, lasers will shoot down ballistic missiles in the boost phase.

The Airborne Laser will be on patrol at the edge of the battle area, flying at about 40,000 feet. Its battle laser can reach out hundreds of miles

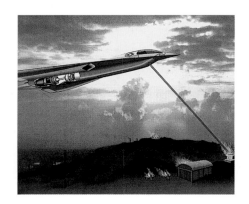

A futuristic attack aircraft zaps a ground target with a beam of directed energy. Lasers are in common use today to guide weapons to their targets, but both lasers and high-energy microwaves are likely to emerge in the years ahead as weapons in their own right. (USAF)

345

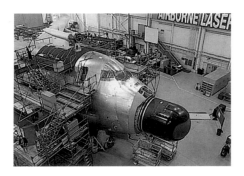

Top and above: *The Airborne Laser will be among the first systems to use directed energy weapons. In the above photos, the laser turret nose is being fitted onto a modified Boeing 747 aircraft. The Airborne Laser will shoot down ballistic missiles in the boost phase, reaching out hundreds of miles with a beam of intense heat that causes the missile components to fail within moments. (USAF)*

and hit a target a meter or so in diameter. Intense heat causes the missile components to fail within moments, and the missile falls out of the sky. The Airborne Laser will be able to destroy twenty or more ballistic missiles before landing to reload.

The next step, the Space Based Laser, is more ambitious. There are varying opinions about how soon it could be ready, but the first on-orbit test could occur around 2015, with initial systems deployed for testing about 2020. A constellation of twenty to forty laser satellites would provide continuous, overlapping global coverage in all weather conditions.

The Space-Based Laser faces political as well as technological challenges, since its primary purpose would be to shoot down Intercontinental Ballistic Missiles. There is political opposition to doing that.

A laser beam from space could also contribute to counterair missions, optical sensing, or disruption of optical systems.

Mobility

Forces from all services will need to get to the scene of future conflicts fast. Those that cannot deploy quickly are likely to be irrelevant. Consequently, the demand for air mobility is relentless. In 2020, the primary long-range airlifter will be the C-17, which began entering the fleet in 1993. It will be augmented by re-engined C-5Bs.

The standard in-theater transport will be the rugged C-130, which has now evolved into its J model, which cruises higher and faster than its predecessors, and has more range. Further into the future lies an "Advanced Tactical Transport," a medium-to-short takeoff and landing aircraft that could eventually replace the C-130 and lift about twenty tons of cargo or 130 troops into an austere landing field.

The tanker problem has been worsening in recent years. The KC-135 tankers, built long ago on Boeing 707 airframes, are wearing out and spending inordinate time in the depot for maintenance. The KC-10 tanker-transports have decades of life left in them, but they account for only about 12 percent of the total airlift capability. The near-term solution is "Tanker X," a refueling aircraft adapted from an existing aircraft, such as the Boeing 767 or the C-17.

Above and right: *The demand for airlift increases relentlessly. Over the next decade, the Air Force will need more C-17 strategic airlifters (shown at right during operations in Afghanistan) than initially thought necessary. The C-17s and C-130 theater airlifters (above) will be in service for years, but new concepts are taking shape for the future. (USAF)*

The long-term solution may be more esoteric. Ironically, large mobility platforms are generating some of the most innovative aircraft designs. One such bold idea is the blended wing tanker-transport. The wings, engines, and body of the aircraft would blend into a single lifting surface, a massive delta shape reminiscent of the B-2.

The shape would create a generous internal space for cargo and fuel, while reducing structural weight. The aircraft would be enormous, its wingspan measuring 280 feet. It could carry twice as much cargo as today's wide body aircraft. In the tanker role, it could refuel two airplanes at the same time. The design would make it fly more efficiently as well.

Similar characteristics are seen in the box wing or joined wing aircraft. Like the early biplanes, it has upper and lower wings, which are joined together. Like the blended wing, it has two tanker booms to refuel two airplanes simultaneously. Since their wing surface is distributed on two levels, five box wings can park at an airfield in the same gate space as four conventional aircraft.

A new aeronautical design closer to fruition is the CV-22 tilt rotor Osprey, which Air Force Special Operations forces want as a replacement for their aging Pave Low helicopters for clandestine insertion and exfiltration missions. The CV-22 is a variant of the Marine Corps MV-22. Its engines would face conventionally forward in flight, but rotate upward for vertical or short takeoff and landing. The V-22 Osprey has been on the drawing boards for quite a while, and was actually canceled once, but both the Marine Corps and the Air Force are among its supporters.

Where the Osprey has two tilt-rotor engines, a conceptual variant, the V-44, would have four such engines. This would allow Special Operations forces to land vertically on a site of convenience with an airplane the size of a C-130.

A Lockheed Martin "box-wing" KCX tanker refuels F-22s and Joint Strike Fighters in this artist's rendering. The big aircraft, with joined wings, is a biplane, a design that allows for shorter wingspan with greater lift. At an airfield, five boxwings could park in the same gate space as four conventional airplanes. (Lockheed Martin)

Boeing's Blended Wing Body concept envisions a huge aircraft with wings, body, and engines that converge into a single delta-shaped lifting surface. It might carry twice as much cargo as today's wide body aircraft, and it could refuel two airplanes at the same time. Compared to current aircraft, the lift-to-drag ratio would be more than 50 percent improved. (Erik Simonsen)

347

Space

As it entered the new century, the Air Force stood at the brink of fundamental redefinition. The issue is space and the Air Force role in it. Over the past twenty-five years, the military space program has moved from novelty to supporting necessity—providing air, land, and sea forces with communications, navigation, surveillance, early warning, and targeting information—toward the emerging mission of space control.

The Army and Navy also have space commands, but about 90 percent of the people and money for the entire military space program has long been provided by the Air Force. There is some opinion that the space force is ready to become a separate military service on its own. That may happen at some point in the future, but for now, the Air Force will lead the leap into space.

In recent years, the Air Force has held that the dividing line between air and space is arbitrary and that military air and space functions should be integrated into the operating regime of aerospace. While these issues percolate in public and political opinion, the armed forces continue to work on such capabilities as sensors and access to space.

Inevitably, the shooters command the spotlight, but Air Force planners believe that the linchpin of the force of 2020 will be the Space-Based Radar. Today's airborne radars can see a lot, but their view is limited by altitude and the curvature of the earth. At 30,000 feet, anything more than a few hundred miles away is beyond the horizon. They are also vulnerable to terrain masking. In Kosovo, the Serbs were able to conceal SAMs in the mountains, unseen from the slant-angle view of aerial radar surveillance.

The Space-Based Radar, consisting of several dozen satellites, could see territory—such as the interior of China—not visible to present systems,

The prime mission for a Space Based Laser would be to destroy ballistic missiles. A constellation of twenty to forty satellites could provide overlapping global coverage against ballistic missile attack and contribute to other military missions on Earth and in the atmosphere. (USAF)

and it could take in continental-sized areas at a glance. Thus, our perspective would be switched from regional to global. Unlike airborne systems, the Space Based Radar will always be on station, everywhere in the world, and surface-to-air missiles will not have the range to shoot it down.

Radar satellites could provide detailed local information on demand. They will be able to track moving targets on the ground, a job done now by the E-8 Joint STARS aircraft, but it will be too much of a technological stretch by 2020 for space radar to track aerial traffic. Thus, the E-3 AWACS or a successor to it will continue in service for some time to come.

Much of the effort for Air Force Space Command in the years ahead will be supplying essential space communications and other services. Missile warning will still be "Job One." The proposed satellite lineup includes SBIRS, the Space Based Infrared System that will replace the old Defense Support Program (DSP) satellites, in service since the 1970s and outmoded when the coalition relied on them for warning of Scud launches in the Gulf war.

SBIRS will consist of a high constellation—four satellites in geosynchronous orbit and two in highly elliptical orbit for early warning of missile attack—and a low constellation of twenty-four satellites to track missiles after they are detected.

By 2020, satellites will also be identifying what is known in Pentagon vernacular as "Things Under Trees." A hyperspectral sensor in space could read the light reflected by objects on earth and distinguish between thousands of color differences. It could tell tanks from vegetation, for example, and defeat many of the enemy's camouflage, concealment, and deception tactics.

However, the first task for a force operating in and from space is getting there.

Space Access

Twenty years from now, the Air Force expects to still be using expendable launch vehicles, affordable rockets for one-time use, to put payloads weighing up to 45,000 pounds into low Earth orbit. It is also looking ahead to a family of reusable spacecraft. This signals a return to interest in hypersonic flight and in vehicles that can reach space orbit in a single stage.

Hypersonic flight is usually defined as anything faster than Mach 5. Ballistic missiles operate in that range, of course, and forty years ago, the X-15 rocket plane achieved speeds of 4,520 mph and flew at altitudes higher than sixty-seven miles. The 1980s saw a flurry of activity on behalf of concepts known variously as the "aerospace plane" or the "transatmospheric vehicle," a craft that could take off from a runway, fly to the edge of space, and return to Earth for a conventional landing. That idea, too, faded away.

The resurgence of interest in hypersonic flight is driven by the desire for cheaper and faster access to space. Today, the time for planning a space launch is calculated in months, if not in years. Current state of the art—reaching orbit in several stages, with the launch vehicle not surviving the experience—keeps the cost high.

Today, Joint STARS aircraft are much in demand to track moving targets on the ground. Space radar satellites may replace Joint STARS mission operators (shown above) someday, but there is no space-based solution yet in sight to replace AWACS, which tracks airborne targets. (USAF)

The most fundamental issue about space is how to get there. Eventually, we will see spacecraft that can return to Earth to be used again, but the Air Force will still be using expendable launch vehicles, like this one, well into this century. (Lockheed Martin)

The 1980s saw a flurry of interest in the X-30 National Aerospace Plane. If developed, the X-30 would have taken off from a runway, flown to the edge of space, and returned to Earth for a conventional landing. The project ran into technological and financial problems and was never built. (USAF)

Air Force planners envision a family of spacecraft for the twenty-first century. The space plane shown here is one of many concepts. A Space Operating Vehicle would shuttle back and forth from Earth to space. It would carry other vehicles into space where they would perform specialized missions. (Erik Simonsen)

The Air Force will continue to work on expendable launch vehicles, better rockets that promise to reduce the cost of launch by 25 percent or more. However, the goal is routine, launch-on-demand calls for launch vehicles that can return to fly again. Thus, the Air Force is considering reusable launch systems powered by hypersonic propulsion systems that could generate speeds up to Mach 25 and reach orbit in a single stage.

Air Force planners envision a family of four kinds of spacecraft. The Space Operating Vehicle (SOV) would be a single-stage to orbit "truck," shuttling back and forth from Earth several times a day. It could perform functions in space, but its main role would be as a taxi for more specialized spacecraft and satellites.

The SOV is envisioned as a wedge-shaped lifting body, possibly a derivative of the X-33 technology demonstrator. It's possible there could be a human crew aboard, but most likely not. Revolutionary engine concepts are being explored.

The Space Maneuvering Vehicle (SMV), also reusable, would ride to space aboard the SOV. It could carry weapons, satellite replacements, or other loads, or it could act as a satellite itself. The SMV would be able to change orbits and inclinations. It would remain in space for six months to a year on each mission. It could be a variant of the X-37 experimental space vehicle, originally conceived as riding into space aboard the Space Shuttle, and sized accordingly. The X-37 is powered for maneuvering in space, and has wings so it can reenter the atmosphere and glide back to earth.

Microsats would be small, multipurpose satellites that could be used for various purposes, including jamming or disrupting enemy satellites.

The Common Aero Vehicle, also launched aboard the SOV, would be a genuine aerospace craft. It would be able to reenter the Earth's

atmosphere and put a weapon on target anywhere on Earth in less than an hour. After that, the CAV would fall to the ground. It will not be reusable.

Space has long been militarized, but putting weapons there—the Space-Based Laser, microsats, or the Common Aero Vehicle—would be a big step. Most defense experts believe it is inevitable. In any case, there are many routes to space control. An attack on or interference with assets in space would probably come from forces on the ground. Defense and counterattack would center on terrestrial forces as well.

At present, a space launch must be planned well in advance. The Air Force need for launch-on-demand pushes interest in a spacecraft that can take off promptly, achieve the necessary speeds up to Mach 25, and reach orbit in a single stage. That, in turn, has renewed interest in hypersonic flight. (Erik Simonsen)

Transformation

For several years now, the watchword for all of the armed forces has been "transformation," evolving to meet the changing needs of the 21st century. The direction was reconfirmed by President George W. Bush in May 2001, when he called for "a future force that is defined less by size and more by mobility and swiftness, one that is easier to deploy and sustain, one that relies more heavily on stealth, precision weaponry, and information technologies."

For the Air Force, transformation is not a new experience. It is the continuation of a journey begun long ago. The history of airpower has been one of constant evolution and change, as airplanes and airmen reached higher, faster, and farther.

The improvements continue across the board: in speed, range, payload, stealthiness, and accuracy. Airpower has matured into aerospace power.

In the years ahead, the Air Force will operate in and from the vast regime of aerospace, and its value to the nation promises to exceed anything that we have seen up to now.

Above: *This Lockheed Martin conceptual painting shows an Unmanned Combat Air Vehicle (UCAV) flying with an F-16CJ. UCAVs are presently planned for difficult missions such as countering enemy defenses. (Lockheed Martin)*

A Vision of the Future

General Ronald R. Fogleman, USAF (Ret)

This B-2A bomber, based at Whiteman AFB, Missouri, is on a night mission. The lights that disclose the aircraft in this photo are only used in peacetime operation. Officially called the Spirit, the Stealth Bomber is capable of delivering either nuclear or conventional weapons. Twenty-one of these stealthy bombers are expected to operate for another thirty years. (Ted Carlson)

The future of the United States Air Force will be defined by the needs of the nation, the vision of Air Force leadership, and the quality of Air Force people. As we enter the first decade of the 21st century, the United States is clearly the sole superpower in the world. Other nations generally fall into one or more of the following camps with respect to their view of the United States—we are respected, envied, or hated. In this environment, how well we define our national goals and objectives and execute our national defense strategy will determine whether we move forward in peace and prosperity or find ourselves the target of an increasingly hostile world.

The Boeing Lockheed Martin F-22 is the first production aircraft with the ability to super-cruise—fly at supersonic speed without the use of afterburners. The Raptor achieves this by combining efficient aerodynamic design with two Pratt & Whitney F119-PW-100 engines, rated in the 35,000-pound thrust range. Two F-22s are shown on test flights. (USAF)

Developing a New Vision

Since its creation, and even in the years preceding that event, the Air Force has struggled with issues of identity, promise, potential, and capability. The struggle that took place during the closing decade of the 20th century has been described as powerful stresses radiating down all axes of service posture. Geostrategically, a complex new security environment emerged. Organizationally, we experienced a wrenching downsizing and restructuring. Operationally, demand surged for air and space power in the nation's many military engagements. Technologically, we sustained revolutionary advance, especially in the fields of information and space. The Air Force reacted to these stresses by publishing a series of post–Cold

A pilot from the F-22 Test Force goes through his pre-flight routine. The Boeing F-22 Raptor is now in production. (USAF)

Lockheed Martin conceptual painting of an Unmanned Combat Air Vehicle (UCAV) firing a precision strike weapon. UCAVs are used for difficult, dangerous missions such as countering enemy defenses. (Lockheed Martin)

War vision statements during the 1990s. In June 1990, *Global Reach-Global Power* described how the Air Force would change to meet national needs in the post–Cold War security environment.

These documents stressed that airpower is national power and that the unique characteristics of the Air Force—speed, range, flexibility, precision, and lethality, are directly relevant to defense and protection of national interests. They acknowledged that space, as the ultimate high ground, will make it possible for space-based systems to provide "global knowledge and situational awareness" for the nation, and that power projection is more important as U.S. forces draw down in size and as more of the force is based in the continental United States. Capability to project power rapidly over long distances gives the Air Force a key role in the emerging security environment. Air Force leaders point to effects-based strategy as an alternative to the more conventional view of the Air Force as only "servicing targets." Effects-based strategy has begun to unlock the full potential of airpower as a supported as well as a supporting force in joint warfare. Our technology investments are denying traditional sanctuaries of night and weather to our enemies while minimizing casualties—a major issue in an era when the American people appeared to have a low tolerance for U.S. casualties.

Soon after assuming office, the administration of George W. Bush undertook a review of national defense requirements and force structure options. Throughout that review process, it became clear that air and space forces would figure prominently in the emerging strategy. The new strategy discarded the two major theaters of war planning assumption—a threat-based scenario—in favor of a more flexible capability-based strategy with military forces designed to inflict the desired effect on an enemy rather than to destroy targets. This capability-based strategy puts a premium on the core competencies of the Air Force.

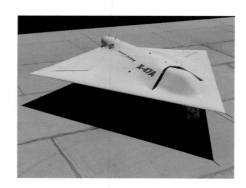

Northrop Grumman's X-47A Pegasus, a company-funded demonstrator, will be used to test the operation of an unmanned air vehicle from an aircraft carrier. The project is part of risk-reduction work for the company's Naval Unmanned Combat Air Vehicle program for DARPA and the U.S. Navy. (Northrop Grumman)

Air Force Core Competencies

Air Force core competencies are those missions that we perform best. First is air and space superiority. The Air Force has the ability to exercise dominant control over all vehicles that move through air and space, thus giving the nation and its military forces the ability to observe and deny the operations of a potential adversary. By the close of the first decade of the 21st century, we will be able to find, fix, track, target, and engage anything that moves through the air or on the surface of the earth in near real time. Second, due to speed, range, flexibility, and presence, the Air Force has the capability to strike any target anywhere in the world within hours of being ordered to do so. This characteristic makes the Air Force the weapon of choice for our national command authorities. Third, the rapid global mobility of the Air Force allows us to deploy and sustain military forces as

Bottom, left: The Boeing X-45 Unmanned Combat Air Vehicle demonstration system is designed to prove the technological feasibility of multiple UCAVs autonomously performing extremely dangerous and high-priority combat missions. The system consists of two X-45A air vehicles, a mission control station, and a variety of support elements. One task envisioned for this system is the suppression of enemy air defenses (SEAD). (Boeing)

Bottom, right: This photograph shows a Lockheed Martin Defense Meteorological Satellite atop a Titan II launch vehicle at Vandenberg Air Force Base, California. (Lockheed Martin Missiles & Space)

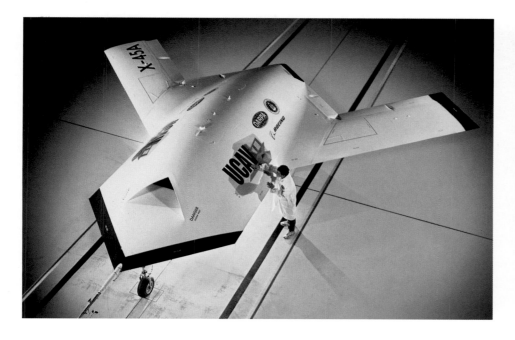

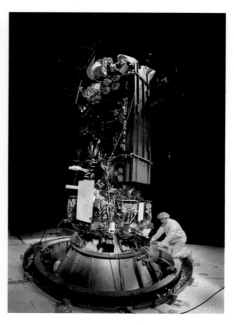

Top: *Lockheed Martin X-35 Joint Strike Fighter (JSF) program is designed to develop a family of stealthy fighter aircraft for the Air Force, Navy, and Marine Corps as well as the Royal Navy and Royal Air Force. The JSF program entered the Concept Demonstration Phase in November 1996. Lockheed Martin was selected to produce the JSF. The short-takeoff and vertical landing (STOVL) X-35B achieved the JSF program's first vertical takeoff and vertical landing on 23 June 2001. (Lockheed Martin)*

Opposite, bottom: *A mixed flight of Lockheed Martin fighters patrols the sky of the future. In this artist's concept, one variant is manned and the other is unmanned. The unmanned version would take on the most hazardous missions, while the manned fighter would be used when a human presence is important. (Lockheed Martin)*

Above: *The Boeing 767-200 tanker is a proposed replacement aircraft for the aging KC-135 and KC-10 tanker fleet. Additional capabilities could include airborne communications equipment that provides data links back and forth across the battlefield. (Boeing)*

required. We organized all of our assets into an Air Expeditionary Force tailored for operations across a broad range of missions. Fourth, the Air Force is trained and prepared to apply force precisely with minimum risk to Air Force assets, and minimum collateral damage. This capability has already begun to change the nature of warfare and the role of air and space forces. Fifth, through Air Force air and space capabilities dedicated to providing intelligence, surveillance, reconnaissance, communications, weather and navigation support, we provide dominant battlefield awareness to national command authorities and to theater commanders.

These core competencies describe not only the capabilities that air and space forces bring to the joint war fighter, but the building blocks for effects-based operations. The Air Force has the capability to apply measured force against our adversaries to achieve the desired results. We describe this as effects-based operations. With this capability, we are able to stop the functioning of an enemy's infrastructure by destroying the critical nodes within that infrastructure, thus limiting destruction and increasing operational effectiveness.

A Capability-Based Air Force

The future Air Force will need diverse capabilities because the threats of the 21st century will be many, varied, and unpredictable. Most will continue to spring from a clash of vital interests between nation states. However, many will come from non-nation actors. No matter what the origin, the Air Force of the 21st century must be prepared for everything from a nation-state armed with traditional fielded forces and nuclear, chemical, or biological weapons, to a terrorist attack.

With America's global interests and responsibility, our future Air Force will face a high operational tempo. That is why we have created the Expeditionary Aerospace Force (EAF) described in Chapter 12. The EAF of today is built around larger Air Force combat units designed to fight a more traditional regional conflict or provide presence in an area of sustained peacetime operations. As the EAF concept matures and changes in response to the changing nature of warfare, the capabilities and composition of the EAF will transform. Smaller, more powerful units tailored to individual circumstances will enable commanders rapidly to deploy task forces and engage the enemy. Specialized elements for command and control as well as integrated intelligence, surveillance, and reconnaissance (ISR) forces will decrease decision cycle times. Special operations forces

Above: *The Quiet Supersonic Platform (QSP) built by Northrop Grumman Corporation is designed to achieve supersonic flight with a less intense sonic boom. (Northrop Grumman)*

The Lockheed Martin C-130J is the newest-generation of the venerable C-130. The C-130J incorporates an integrated digital avionics suite with heads-up display, new propulsion system, and other major upgrades that reduce operating costs and crew size while offering significant performance improvements. The C-130J will be employed for combat airlift, aerial refueling, weather reconnaissance, search and rescue, and electronic combat missions. The aircraft normally has a 40-foot cargo compartment but a C-130J-30 version comes with a longer 55-foot cargo compartment with space for 30 percent more cargo or 40 percent more troop seats. (Lockheed Martin)

This Lockheed Martin F-16CJ from the 20th Fighter Wing at Shaw AFB, South Carolina, carries two AGM-154A Joint Stand-Off Weapons (JSOW). Additionally, the aircraft is configured with two AIM-120B advanced medium range air-to-air missiles and two AIM-9M Sidewinder short-range air-to-air missiles. The 20th Fighter Wing is the first Air Force unit to field the software that fully integrates the new family of smart weapons, including the JSOW. (USAF)

In a cooperative effort with NASA's Langley Research Center, the Boeing Phantom Works is studying a Blended Wing Body (BWB) aircraft concept that offers greater structural, aerodynamic, and operating efficiencies than today's more conventional tube-and-wing design. The modular design also allows for center body growth while maintaining common wings. These features translate into range, fuel economy, reliability, and life-cycle savings, as well as lower manufacturing costs. They also allow for a wide variety of potential military and commercial applications. (Boeing)

and select units from other countries, services, and agencies may be brought into these tailored packages to achieve the effects desired by the regional joint commander.

Command and control technology and procedures will continue to evolve in the next two decades. Small command and control cells in the forward headquarters will "reach back" to operations centers in the United States for most support processes, freeing forward headquarters to focus on command and execution oversight. Voice recognition technology will enable commanders to query computers verbally for essential information. Artificial intelligence tools will analyze data and offer alternative courses of action. Miniaturized devices will permit database access and update at multiple levels of operational responsibility, reducing decision cycle time.

In the closing decade of the 20th century, the Air Force envisioned the ability to find, fix, target, and engage, in real time, anything of consequence moving through the atmosphere or on the surface of the earth. We will achieve this capability in the opening decades of the 21st century. The key will be combining legacy platforms and systems with emerging technologies, rather than relying on individual platforms or systems. Persistent, broad area ISR coverage will provide the ability to detect an emerging threat or crisis and precisely engage it with the appropriate weapon. Both sensors and platforms will change over the next several decades. As the sensors improve, a combination of long endurance unmanned aerial vehicles (UCAVs) and satellites will be the platforms of choice for persistent coverage. Sensor integration will enable greater understanding of the viewed areas.

In the future, space will play a larger role in military operations. The opening decades of the 21st century will see space operations move from primarily supporting combat in other mediums to becoming the centerpiece of space superiority and counter-space activities. The Air Force will implement personnel, training and educational programs to recruit and develop space warriors who understand how to conduct both support and autonomous operations. One of the major space initiatives will be building a robust space surveillance capability with both space- and land-

based components. The Air Force will develop, field, and operate a fleet of low-earth-orbit maneuver vehicles to support national and international efforts to explore the planets. The combination of space-based mirrors and high-powered lasers will revolutionize the battlefield and concepts of missile defense, and may lead to a broader acceptance of weapons in space.

The growing importance of information warfare will lead to the activation of a new Information Warfare Command formed to provide focus within the Air Force for this vital mission.

As the Air Force develops new weapons systems, we will be challenged to balance legacy systems like fighters, bombers, tankers, airlift, and space constellations against new combinations of weapons and munitions such as high-powered microwaves, lasers, relay mirrors, small smart munitions, and both manned and unmanned advanced space and air breathing vehicles.

The single greatest breakthrough in the area of effects-based weapons will occur in the directed energy arena. Like the concept of stealth in the late 1970s, future directed energy applications will be poised to revolutionize the battlefield. The idea of precise weapons that produce minimum collateral damage will make directed energy the

The Block IIF Global Positioning System (GPS) satellite under development by Boeing will be launched into orbit as required after Block IIR vehicles have been placed into the GPS constellation. The system will include greater accuracy and improved capability against jamming. (Boeing)

Lockheed Martin Missiles and Space Defense Communication Satellite in test cell, Sunnyvale, California. (Lockheed Martin)

weapon of choice on urban battlefields. Applications in space as well as defensive and offensive capabilities on earth will become routine. Initially, advanced by the success of high-powered microwaves for force protection and the airborne laser in missile defense, directed energy weapons will become the centerpiece of America's arsenal by 2025.

Air Force People

Earlier chapters have described the history and contributions of weapons platforms and forces. Airmen have a proud record of innovation, adaptation, and exploitation of existing and emerging technologies. The key ingredient of airpower in the 20th century was the people who served in our Air Force and its predecessor organizations. As we move into the future, people will continue to be the most important factor in the success of the Air Force. Dedicated, educated, motivated, and well-led men and women, understanding our core values and focused on providing our core competencies, will carry the Air Force to new heights in the opening decades of the 21st century.

Our people will require a broad understanding of national objectives, joint and service doctrine, American culture, and Air Force competencies, and they must master their own individual specialties. Leadership must foster an environment that stimulates personal growth, innovation, and acceptance of responsibility while rewarding initiative and continuing to place the highest priority on maintaining an acceptable quality of life for Air Force members and their families. Tighter integration of the Air National Guard and Air Force Reserve forces along with greater reliance on Air Force civilians and the contractor workforce will give new meaning to the term "Total Force."

Once infrastructure is properly sized and the Air Expeditionary Force organization matures, new opportunities for enlightened assignment and basing policies will result in longer tours at one location. This will give the force and families more stability. While these and other quality of life

A crew chief gives a thumbs up to an F-117 Pilot taxiing out for another sortie. The F-117 is expected to remain in the inventory until F-22 replacements are fielded. (USAF)

A weather specialist follows evolving severe weather to warn aircrews of potentially hazardous situations. Meteorologists are essential to effective combat operations as well as to safe peacetime flights. (USAF)

Radar approach control specialists guide aircraft through departures and arrivals at Air Force bases during low ceilings and poor visibility. Skilled operators can direct an aircraft to a safe landing in very poor visibility. (USAF)

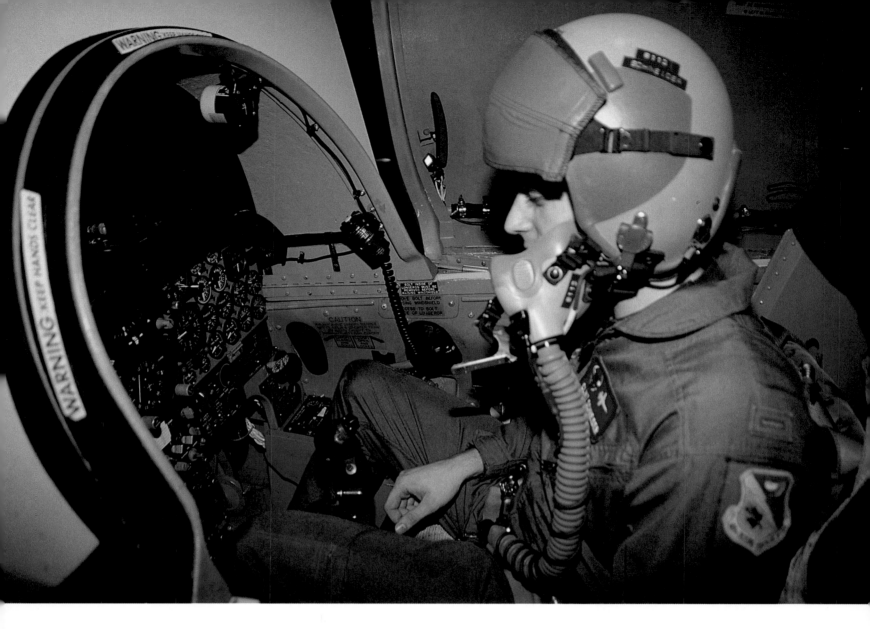

initiatives will make service in the Air Force more attractive, the leadership must make sure that Air Force people see themselves as members of the profession of arms serving the nation. From the very beginning, they must understand the contributions they are making toward the accomplishment of national goals and objectives.

The requirement to train and school our officers and enlisted force at the appropriate levels of warfare—tactical, operational, and strategic—will take on new importance. The trend of the recent past wherein air and space forces have become the force of choice for national command authorities will continue and accelerate in the opening decades of the 21st century. The Air Force will increasingly be the supported, rather than the

Above: *Student pilot in a T-38 Talon part task trainer. The instructor would stand outside the simulator giving instructions and helping him go over a "pre-flight" checklist. (Guy Aceto)*

Bottom, left: *A Non-Commissioned Officer certified air traffic controller trains young airmen in the flight tower at Randolph AFB, Texas. These important duties will probably remain unchanged for the near future. (USAF)*

Bottom, right: *A student gives a thumbs up to his flight instructor in back of theT-38 trainer before a practice flight at Laughlin AFB, Texas. (Guy Aceto)*

Above: *Northrop Grumman's Global Hawk unmanned reconnaissance system, being developed for the U.S. Air Force, provides near real-time, high-resolution imagery. Flying at extremely high altitudes, Global Hawk can survey large geographic areas with pinpoint accuracy to give military decision-makers current information about enemy resources and personnel. (Northrop Grumman)*

Opposite: *The Future Strike Aircraft (FSA) is a supersonic concept defined by Northrop Grumman for the Air Force. This aircraft could be manned or unmanned. (Northrop Grumman)*

Above: *The CRW (Carnard Rotor/Wing) X-50A. aircraft combines the vertical takeoff/landing capabilities of a rotorcraft with the high-subsonic cruise speed and agility of a fixed-wing airplane. As its name implies, its versatility is achieved by having a specially designed rotor for vertical takeoffs and landings that can be stopped in flight to serve as a fixed wing for jet cruise. Follow-on CRW versions could evolve into larger, piloted vehicles capable of conducting specialized missions, including reconnaissance, armed escort, urban operations, tactical air support, communications, data relay, and resupply. (Boeing)*

Right: *The Advanced Theater Transport (ATT) concept is currently being studied by Boeing Phantom Works. Powered by four eight-bladed turboprop engines, the aircraft features a tailless fuselage with a forward swept tilt-wing arrangement. This unique configuration provides enhanced performance capabilities for landing and takeoff within 750 feet while carrying 80,000 pounds of payload in very austere operating conditions. The tilt-wing design and computerized flight controls allow for steep ingress and egress angles, increasing flexibility in hostile areas. (Boeing)*

supporting force, in contingency operations and in conflict. It is imperative that we produce leaders who have an appreciation and understanding of the contributions of the Air Force at each level of warfare.

The Air Force of the Future

The Air Force is a dynamic, changing amalgam of ideas, technology, personalities, and discovery; of aircraft and spacecraft; of manned and unmanned weapons systems; of accomplishment and disappointment; and most importantly, of talented, dedicated men and women who volunteer to serve and defend our nation. Any attempt to forecast the Air Force of the future must acknowledge that while the hardware, the strategies, and the challenges will no doubt change, the nature and character of Air Force people will remain pretty much as today. The people of tomorrow's Air Force will come from diverse backgrounds reflective of our society. They will have talents and goals that set them apart from their peers. They will volunteer to serve their country in peace and war, and they will do so with the pride and professionalism that has characterized the Air Force from the beginning.

The Air Force of tomorrow will have an array of capabilities across the spectrum of conflict from nuclear warfare, to special operations against terrorists, to humanitarian aid in the wake of natural disaster. The Air Force will have a robust information gathering capability that keeps our national leaders informed of global threats as well as regional conflicts. Our service will be organized to conduct sustained operations with forces tailored to the assigned mission, and with command and control procedures that assure responsiveness and efficiency. The Air Force will operate in space, providing essential support to our terrestrial forces, and denying space supremacy to any potential adversary. Our service will be prepared to fight with weapons that target and destroy enemy capabilities quickly and precisely. Moreover, the Air Force of the future will continue to exploit technology, looking always for the better way to protect our nation, deter our enemies, and prevail in any conflict.

Editors and Authors

EDITOR-IN-CHIEF

GENERAL JAMES P. MCCARTHY, USAF (RET), (BS, Kent State; MA, George Washington U) is Olin Professor of National Security at the U.S. Air Force Academy. He completed thirty-five years active duty as a fighter and bomber pilot commanding at the squadron, wing, numbered air force, and combatant command levels. He chaired studies for the Secretary of Defense on lessons learned in the four most recent conflicts and on command and control for the Defense Science Board and the Air Force Scientific Advisory Board.

MANAGING EDITOR

COLONEL DRUE L. DEBERRY, USAF (RET), (BS, USAF Academy; MA, Oklahoma; MBA, Colorado) served as a long range planner on the Air Staff, an Air Force Research Associate and Senior Fellow at the Atlantic Council of the United States, and commander, 50th Technical Training Group. A navigator with 4,500 hours, he flew C-135s, C-141s, C-5s, and logged 500 hours on ninety-six combat missions in AC-130s. He taught military history and western history at the USAF Academy prior to retiring from the Air Force.

CHAPTER 1: *Army Roots*

DR. DAVID R. METS (BS, U.S. Naval Academy; MA, Columbia; PhD U. of Denver) is a professor of Air University's school of Advanced Airpower Studies. He studied naval history at the Naval Academy and taught the history of airpower at the Air Force Academy and West Point. A C-130 pilot, he flew more than 900 C-130B sorties in Vietnam and on another tour commanded an AC-130 squadron. Dr. Mets is the author of *Master of Airpower: General Carl A. Spaatz* (Presidio, 1988) and three other books.

CHAPTER 2: *Forging An Air Force*

DIK ALAN DASO (BS, USAF Academy; MA, PhD, U. of South Carolina) is curator of modern military aircraft at the Smithsonian Institution, National Air and Space Museum, Washington, D.C. A retired Air Force lieutenant colonel and command pilot, he logged over 2,700 flying hours in fighters and supersonic training aircraft. His publications include *Architects of American Air Supremacy* (Air University Press, 1997), and *Hap Arnold and the Evolution of American Airpower* (Smithsonian Institution Press, 2000).

CHAPTER 3: *Cold War Air Force*

COLONEL WALTER J. BOYNE, USAF (Ret), retired from the Air Force in 1974. Boyne received a BSBA with honors from the University of California, and MBA with honors from the University of Pittsburgh and an honorary doctorate from Salem University. He was Director of the National Air & Space Museum from 1981–1986 and has written forty books, including two *New York Times* best sellers, *The Wild Blue* (with Stephen Thompson) and *Weapons of Desert Storm*. His latest book (with Leslie Leyland Fields) is *The Two O'Clock War*.

CHAPTER 4: *United States Air Forces in Europe*

WARREN TREST was senior historian with the Air Force Historical Research Agency at Maxwell AFB, Alabama. A Korean War veteran, he was a member of the CHECO team in Vietnam (1966–1968),

headed command history programs at U.S. Air Forces in Europe and Air Training Command, and was the histories division chief with the Office of Air Force History. Author or co-author of more than fifty official histories and studies, his recent publications include, *Air Commando One* (2000), and *Wings of Denial* (2001).

CHAPTER 5: *The Air Force in the Korean War*

KENNETH P. WERRELL graduated from the USAF Academy and served five years on active duty, mostly as a WB-50 pilot. He earned his history PhD at Duke University and taught history at Radford University for twenty-six years before retiring. He has authored five books on aviation history, the most recent of which is *Blankets of Fire: U.S. Bombers Over Japan During World War II*. His book on USAF technology between the Vietnam and Gulf wars is at press and currently he is researching F-86 employment in the Korean War.

CHAPTER 6: *The Air Force in Southeast Asia*

BERNARD C. NALTY, during his career as an Air Force historian, wrote *Air Power and the Fight for Khe Sanh* and *Air War over South Vietnam, 1968–1975*. He also contributed to other official works including *With Courage: The U. S. Army Air Forces in World War II* and *Winged Shield, Winged Sword: A History of the United States Air Force*. A graduate of Creighton University, Nalty served in the Army before earning a Master's degree at the Catholic University.

CHAPTER 7: *The Air Force Renaissance*

BENJAMIN S. LAMBETH, (PhD Harvard) is an airpower specialist at RAND and served previously in the Central Intelligence Agency. A civil-rated pilot, he has flown in more than forty different combat aircraft types. In 1989, he became the first U.S. citizen to fly the Soviet MiG-29 fighter. He is the author of *Russia's Air Power in Crisis* (Smithsonian Institution Press, 1999), *The Transformation of American Air Power* (Cornell University Press, 2000), and *NATO's Air War for Kosovo* (RAND, 2001).

CHAPTER 8: *The Air Force in Space*

DR. DAVID N. SPIRES, a former career Air Force officer, holds a PhD in military history from the University of Washington and teaches history at the University of Colorado at Boulder. He is the author of *Beyond Horizons: A Half Century of Air Force Space Leadership* and *Air Power for Patton's Army: The XIX Tactical Air Command in the Second World War*. He has just completed the forthcoming *Key Documents in Air Force Space History*, a collection of documents, commentary, and historical essays.

CHAPTER 9: *From Cold War to Crisis Response*

WILLIAM THOMAS Y'BLOOD is a historian in the Air Force History Support Office. He was a B-47, RB-47, and EB-47 pilot in the Air Force from 1960 to 1966, then flew as a commercial airline pilot from 1966 to 1985, accumulating over 11,000 hours of flying time. He wrote two volumes on Air Force operations during Desert Storm, *The Eagle and the Scorpion*, and *Sharpening the Eagle's Talons* and has authored or co-authored five books on military and naval history, including *Red Sun Setting: the Battle of the Philippine Sea*.

CHAPTER 10: *Airmen*
GENERAL JOHN A. SHAUD USAF (RET) (BS U.S. Military Academy; MS George Washington U; PhD Ohio State U) served as Chief of Staff, Supreme Headquarters Allied Powers Europe. A command pilot with more than 5,600 flying hours, he has flown more than thirty-five different types of aircraft and has logged 250 combat hours in the RF-4C. He commanded an Air Force wing, two air divisions, and Air Training Command. He is known throughout the Air Force for his knowledge and concern about Air Force people.

CHAPTER 11: *Research, Development, Acquisition, and Logistics*
GENERAL RONALD W. YATES USAF (RET) (BS USAF Academy; MS University of Southern California) served as Commander, Air Force System Command, and then, Commander, Air Force Materiel Command. He served as a test pilot of modified fighter aircraft, program manager for a variety of weapons systems including the F-15, and as commander of a test wing. He is a command test pilot with more than 4,400 flying hours in more than fifty aircraft types, and flew 100 combat missions in Southeast Asia.

CHAPTER 12: *Today's Expeditionary Air Force*
GENERAL MICHAEL E. RYAN, USAF (Ret) (BS USAF Academy; MS Auburn U) served as the sixteenth Air Force Chief of Staff and as a member of the Joint Chiefs from October 1997 to September 2001. As commander of 16th Air Force and Allied Air Forces Southern Europe based in Italy, he directed NATO air combat operations in Bosnia. He then commanded U.S. Air Forces in Europe and Allied Air Forces, Central Europe. He flew 153 combat missions in Southeast Asia including 100 missions over North Vietnam.

CHAPTER 13: *Future Systems*
JOHN T. CORRELL, (BA, Lenoir-Rhyne College; MA, Michigan State U) served as Editor-in-Chief, *Air Force Magazine*, from 1984 to 2002. Correll began his career as a reporter and copy editor for the *Daily Record* in Hickory, North Carolina, before serving twenty years in the Air Force where he edited *Airman* magazine. He joined the Air Force Association staff in 1982. Respected aerospace authority, author of hundreds of articles, in 1994 he exposed Smithsonian Institution plans to display the *Enola Gay* as a prop in an anti-nuclear horror show, a plan halted by public outcry after his report.

CHAPTER 14: *A Vision of the Future*
GENERAL RONALD R. FOGLEMAN, USAF (RET) (BS USAF Academy; MA Duke U) served as the fifteenth Air Force Chief of Staff and as a member of the Joint Chiefs from October 1994 to August 1997. A command pilot and a parachutist, he logged more than 6,800 flying hours in fighter, transport, tanker, and rotary wing aircraft. He has logged 315 combat missions and more than 800 hours in fighter aircraft. He commanded an Air Force wing, an air division, a numbered air force, a major command, and a unified command.

Acknowledgments

I n this book, readers will find a number of vignettes describing the experiences of Air Force people—in most cases, the personal experiences of the vignette author. These experiences range from an astronaut's awe of the beauty and seeming infinity of space, to a nurse's compassion for the patients in her care, to the tension of being ever prepared to respond to a klaxon in the dark of night, to a chaplain explaining how flight led him to his ministry. The Air Force Historical Foundation believes these vignettes are a notable feature of this book, and we express our appreciation to the men and women of the Air Force family who contributed to telling the Air Force story in a this very special way.

Janice Feagin Britton

Charles T. Burbage

Major Dan Caine, USAF

Technical Sergeant Calvin, USAF (pseudonym)

Howard Chambers

Colonel James G. "Snake" Clark, USAF (Ret)

Colonel Drue L. DeBerry, USAF (Ret)

Colonel Frederick D. Gregory, USAF (Ret)

Colonel Alan Gropman, USAF (Ret)

Lieutenant Colonel John F. Guilmartin, USAF (Ret)

Major General Jeanne Holm, USAF (Ret)

Lieutenant General Arlen L. Jameson, USAF (Ret)

Colonel Fred Kiley, USAF (Ret)

Lieutenant Colonel Steve Kirkpatrick, USAF

Lieutenant Colonel Michael McCarthy, USAF

General James P. McCarthy, USAF (Ret)

Brigadier General James R. McCarthy, USAF (Ret)

Lieutenant General Forrest S. McCartney, USAF (Ret)

General Lloyd W. "Fig" Newton, USAF (Ret)

Lieutenant Colonel Jeffrey C. Prater, USAF (Ret)

Captain Joseph M. Rizzuto, USAF

Brigadier General Ben T. Robinson, USAF (Ret)

Major Steven A. Schaick, USAF

Second Lieutenant Scott P. Snider, USAF

Major Michael R. Terry, USAF (Ret)

Colonel Richard Uppstrom, USAF (Ret)

Colonel Robert E. Venkus, USAF (Ret)

Major General Mele Vojvodich, USAF (Ret)

Colonel Mark K. Wells, USAF

T he Air Force Historical Foundation and the editors of this book express their appreciation to the scores of historians, artists, photo archivists, photographers, and public affairs officers who assisted in locating, producing, or suggesting materials needed for this manuscript.

Index